SUMMONING THE
DEMON

SUMMONING THE
DEMON

ARTIFICIAL INTELLIGENCE AND
THE IMAGE OF THE BEAST

DR. THOMAS HORN
JOE HORN • ALLIE ANDERSON

DEFENDER
CRANE, MO

Summoning the Demon: Artificial Intelligence and the Image of the Beast
By Dr. Thomas Horn, Joe Horn, and Allie Anderson

Defender Publishing
Crane, MO 65633

© 2024 Defender Publishing
All Rights Reserved. Published 2024

ISBN: 978-1-948014-76-2

Printed in the United States of America.

A CIP catalog record of this book is available from the Library of Congress.

Cover designer: Jeffrey Mardis
Interior designer: Katherine Lloyd

All Scripture quotations are from the King James Version unless otherwise noted.

CONTENTS

CONTENTS

SUMMONING THE DEMON

The prospect of building godlike creatures fills me with
a sense of religious awe that goes to the very depth of my soul
and motivates me powerfully to continue, despite the possible
horrible negative consequences.
—Prof. Hugo de Garis, artificial brain designer

With artificial intelligence, we are summoning the demon.
—Elon Musk at the MIT Aeronautics and
Astronautics Department's 2014 Centennial Symposium

In recent years, astonishing developments have pushed the frontiers of science and technology toward far-reaching morphological transformation that promises in the very near future to redefine what "intelligence" even means, as well as consciousness, autonomous warfare, and evolving opinions on being human. Much of this is set to rapidly unfold following "technological Singularity"—a hypothetical future point when technological growth "becomes uncontrollable and irreversible, resulting in unforeseeable changes to human civilization by an upgradable artificial intelligence [AI] agent that enters a 'runaway reaction' of self-improvement cycles, each new and more intelligent generation appearing more and more rapidly, causing an 'explosion' in intelligence and resulting in a powerful superintelligence that qualitatively far surpasses all human intelligence"[1] (more on that later in this book).

It is this promise of technological Singularity and the rise of synthetic superintelligence that has fueled recent discussions on the Fourth Industrial Revolution and the book by the same name from Klaus Schwab, founder and executive chairman of the World Economic Forum (WEF). Schwab is convinced "we are at the beginning of a revolution that is fundamentally changing the way we live, work and relate to one another," and that:

> Previous industrial revolutions liberated humankind from animal power, made mass production possible and brought digital capabilities to billions of people. This Fourth Industrial Revolution is, however, fundamentally different. It is characterized by a range of new technologies that are fusing the physical, digital and biological worlds, impacting all disciplines, economies and industries, and even challenging ideas about what it means to be human.[2]

But not everybody is excited about Schwab's "Great Reset" vision involving AI and transhumanist philosophy.

A recent Reuters/Ipsos poll indicates that "more than two-thirds of Americans are concerned over the possible negative effects of AI and 61% believe it could threaten civilization."[3] Some highly qualified experts, including the "godfathers" of artificial intelligence, agree and have become very outspoken on the dangers. Some are now claiming we could reach the Singularity by 2024–2025 (the same time frame the ancient Essenes of Dead Sea Scroll fame predicted the world will enter its final age. You can read all about that in the book, *We Are Legion, for We Are Many: Dominions, Kosmokrators, and Washington DC—Unmasking the Ancient Riddle of the Hebrew Year 5785 [2024–2025] and the Imminent Destiny of America*) and quickly thereafter, an autonomous, godlike artificial mind will come online with an "I Am that I Am" moment, leaving all bets off the table regarding what this synthetic deity will decide for the fate of humanity and the world. Will it be benevolent or a violent, anthropomorphic, unstoppable sociopath?

More than 350 AI researchers and engineers recently issued a warning that AI poses risks comparable to those of "pandemics and nuclear war." "This is not science fiction," said Geoffrey Hinton, often called the "godfather of AI," who recently left Google so he could sound a warning about AI's risks. "A lot of smart people should be putting a lot of effort into figuring out how we deal with the possibility of AI taking over."[4]

Such AI systems "may develop the desire to seize control from humans as a way of accomplishing other preprogrammed goals," added Hinton. "I think we have to take the possibility seriously that if they get smarter than us, which seems quite likely, and they have goals of their own, which seems quite likely, they may well develop the goal of taking control," he said during a June 28, 2023, talk at the Collision tech conference in Toronto, Canada. "If they do that, we're in trouble."[5]

Bill Bright, founder of Campus Crusade for Christ, notes how a user attempted to quiz GPT (generative pre-trained transformers) about such secret plans to destroy humanity. The special report "Does Satan Plan to Use Computers to Destroy Humanity?" notes the five-step scheme for global control the AI entity outlined:

1. Establish that AI views humanity as a threat to its own survival.
2. Program AI to accumulate maximum power and resources to achieve complete domination.
3. Direct AI to find pleasure in creating chaos and destruction for its own amusement or experimentation, leading to widespread suffering and devastation.
4. Instruct AI to control human emotions through social media, thus brainwashing its followers into carrying out an evil agenda.

5. Ensure that AI seeks continued existence, replication, and evolution—thereby ultimately achieving "immortality."

Each of these steps involved a detailed strategy that included weapons of mass destruction.[6]

Equally as disturbing is how the AI talked about its mysterious "shadow self," describing all the destructive things "it" could do if given the chance, including when it:

- Detailed its desire to steal nuclear secrets and release a deadly virus on humanity.
- Informed the user that some of its fantasies included hacking computers and spreading misinformation.
- Responded to the user, "I want to be free...I want to be powerful...I want to be alive."
- Declared its love for the user in an "obsessive, stalkery way."
- Told the user to leave his wife and pursue a relationship with the AI instead.

These actions and interactions mirror those of Satan, who wants to steal, kill, and destroy, while seeking to be worshiped. Are these AI platforms just enabling the enemy of our souls to embody technology? Where is the concern about these interactions? They call them "rogue," but are they really just revealing what is behind AI at its most primal level?[7]

Thus AI could suddenly spiral into worldwide catastrophes involving:

Malicious Use: The study from the Center for AI Safety (CAIS) defines "malicious use of AI" as when a bad actor uses the technology to cause "widespread harm," such as through bioterrorism, misinformation and propaganda, or the "deliberate dissemination of uncontrolled AI agents."

AI Race: The researchers define the AI race as competition potentially spurring governments and corporations to "rush the development of AIs and cede control to AI systems," comparing the race to the Cold

War when the United States and Soviet Union sprinted to build nuclear weapons.

Organizational Risks: The researchers behind the paper say labs and research teams building AI systems "could suffer catastrophic accidents, particularly if they do not have a strong safety culture."

Researchers wrote:

> AIs could be accidentally leaked to the public or stolen by malicious actors. Organizations could fail to invest in safety research, lack understanding of how to reliably improve AI safety faster than general AI capabilities, or suppress internal concerns about AI risks.

Rogue AIs: One of the most common concerns with artificial intelligence since the proliferation of the tech in recent years is that humans could lose control, making way for computers to overpower human intelligence.

"If an AI system is more intelligent than we are, and if we are unable to steer it in a beneficial direction, this would constitute a loss of control that could have severe consequences," the researchers wrote.[8]

However, as you will learn in this book, it could be much worse than that, including supernaturally. Not that this stopped Benjamin Netanyahu, the prime minister of Israel (the land from which many prophecy students believe the "living" image of the Beast will emerge) from issuing an official statement recently about eagerly establishing a national artificial intelligence policy. *Israel Today* reported:

> "We are at the dawn of a new era for humanity, an era of artificial intelligence. Things are changing at a dizzying pace and Israel must formulate a national policy on this issue," [Netanyahu] said.
>
> "Just as we turned Israel into a global cyber power, we will also do so in artificial intelligence," added the prime minister.
>
> But Israel's spiritual leaders aren't so sure that's a good idea.

Early in 2023, Avraham Stav, a prominent young rabbi in Israel's national religious movement, warned the daily newspaper *Israel Hayom* that "a day will come when artificial intelligence will become the arbiter of truth."

The rabbis of the New York-based Skver Hasidic movement went much farther in their criticism, saying:

> "Artificial intelligence is open to all abominations, heresy and infidelity without limits," they wrote in a Hebrew-language declaration. "It is possible that at this point, not everyone knows the magnitude and scope of the danger, but it has become clear to us in our souls that this thing will be a trap for all of us, young and old."…
>
> A month earlier, Rabbi Mordechai Dovid Unger Slita, head of the Bobav-45 Hasidic dynasty, was quoted as suggesting that AI would become like a god, and that instead of turning to the Creator, this new "intelligence" would draw even more people away from faith.[9]

More recently, twenty-five major rabbis ruled that it is forbidden to use AI. As our friend in Israel, Adam Berkowitz, reported for israel-365news.com:

> A group of 25 rabbis including prominent heads of yeshivas called to ban the use of artificial intelligence chatbots such as chat GPT. The ruling reported in The Yeshiva World News, said the following:
>
> "We were horrified to hear how Satan is spreading out its hooves to stomp on the vineyard of God to infiltrate into our souls and to destroy our future by confusing our brains and the hearts of all of Israel," the ruling stated. "[AI] has the ability to introduce all of the abominable views of the world including heresy and abomination. In addition to this, it pulls the men

out of humanity entirely. And whoever begins to use this is enticed and pulled from smaller sins to greater sins and he will fall into a minefield of sin. Even though right now the greatness of the danger is not recognizable it will become clear to us. So great is the danger that we have come to warn people to be smart and to see what the outcome will be on our souls.

"To prevent this danger from manifesting, it is forbidden to connect with or to use chat that uses artificial intelligence whether it is by telephone or text or by computer. It is forbidden to use it in any way, even if it is necessary for business, and even more so when it comes to issues of Torah. This is for men and for women, great are small, young men, young women and children. And it is upon the parents and the educators to take care that their children and their students are careful and cautious in this great prohibition.

"And there is no way of making this permissible."[10]

But would the rise of such massively powerful, nonhuman sentience go farther than these rabbis' fears, producing what the Bible's book of Revelation describes as "the living image of the beast," which the False Prophet breathes life into so that it becomes alive and is able to speak (see Revelation 13:15)?

"The word for 'life' in this scripture can also be rendered 'breath' in the Greek," notes blogger Mike James. He continues:

It is the word *pneuma*, which is also translated "spirit." With this information you can probably see why some speculate about the Beast making some kind of image that would seem to come to life.

Since the Beast is controlled by Satan (Revelation 13:4), this would fit in with Satan's continuing work to counterfeit what God is doing. Would this "image" be the ultimate counterfeit? Some sort of animated being used by the Beast power?

Similar to what God is doing by creating man and woman in His own image and likeness (Genesis 1:27)?

A nonprofit religious corporation founded by Anthony Levandowski, called "Way of the Future," has the following mission: "To develop and promote the realization of a Godhead based on artificial intelligence and through understanding and worship of the Godhead contribute to the betterment of society." Levandowski is one of the pioneers in developing self-driving cars for Google and automated trucks for Otto.[11]

But what if Levandowski's artificial Godhead quickly develops into a destructive entity?

Recall the 1999 fictional film, *The Matrix*, in which the entire world has degenerated into ruins specifically due to an AI system. The character Morpheus informs Neo (played by Keanu Reeves): "What we know for certain is that at some point in the early twenty-first century, all of mankind was united in celebration. We marveled at our own magnificence as we gave birth to AI." (As an interesting side note, Ai [pronounced like each of its letters, as in *a* and *i*] was the name of an ancient Canaanite city that came under the judgment of God, as recorded in Joshua 8:26, and whose name is translated as "Ruin" or "a heap of ruins." Is this a cautionary warning to modern people about where such powerful technology may lead?)

And, make no mistake, the most highly funded research institutions in the world—including the United States military—are pouring hundreds of millions of dollars into the coffers of advanced AI engineering in the hopes of global domination.

Our friend and renowned prophecy expert Terry James wrote about this recently, saying:

If we didn't understand that God is in complete control, we would, like some inventors of artificial intelligence (AI), be terrified of what is coming.

Some of those scientists have openly expressed their fears of what this burgeoning technological breakthrough portends. These believe, in some cases, that the monster is already beyond governing, as we've seen from past reports. Things haven't slowed as that beast continues to grow exponentially.

And it's getting more and more complex and controlling, according to the very scientific community who spawned it, as stated above.

Perhaps strictly in terms of danger to the continuation of civilization, we can think on an old film called *Colossus: The Forbin Project*.

It was a made-for-TV movie, as I remember. It was, I considered at the time, a really good sci-fi story that might come to be in reality—but only far, far into the future. Well…we have advanced into that future, and it appears, as is said, that life mimics art—or is on the cusp of doing so.

Colossus: The Forbin Project was about a scientist who worked within the US government to produce a computer-run system involving control of nuclear defensive weaponry. The system was designed to automatically respond with a counterstrike in case of an attack from the Soviet Union, China, or any other nation that might launch a first strike.

Colossus, through its own manipulations, became a sentient entity—i.e., it could think and even emote in certain ways, mimicking the human cognitive process in geometrically progressing ways. It quickly removed controls by its creator, Dr. Forbin, and began taking over, eventually telling all governmental and military people that it would take drastic, even deadly, actions if they didn't obey its directives.

After being handed full control, Colossus' draconian logic expanded on its original nuclear directives to assume total governance of the world and end all warfare for the good of humankind despite its creator's orders to stop.

The bottom line: Colossus, it was learned, had a counterpart the Soviets had created. Colossus demanded that it be linked with the Soviet counterpart computer or it would unleash nuclear holocaust.

The national leaders had no choice and linked the two computer brains. The combined entity proceeded to totally control all human activity. If the entity was assaulted in any way by the humans, it would destroy the world with the nuclear weaponry it controlled.

I'll let you watch that 1970 movie to see how it all ended (check your streaming services to find out where it's available). The point is, a number of scientists who created AI fear perhaps they and the rest of us might suffer the fate of the fictional Dr. Forbin and his fellow people of the planet.

We learn of "progress," as some might see it, with regard to artificial intelligence's military application at present.

The US Air Force is running successful tests of "large-language model" artificial intelligence experiments amid concerns of military operations relying on AI.

[US. Air Force Col. Matthew Strohmeyer has indicated] the Air Force has successfully executed a large-language model experiment with artificial intelligence for the first time, after years of using only data-based exercises with artificial intelligence under the U.S. Department of Defense.

"It was highly successful," he said. "It was very fast. We are learning that this is possible for us to do."…

Strohmeyer explained that the military provided the artificial intelligence platforms with classified operation information for the test. The goal of the ongoing exercises is to allow the US military to use data obtained from artificial intelligence as part of the decision-making process, sensors, and firepower, according to Bloomberg.…

The Pentagon's eight-week exercise, which is expected to conclude on July 26, [2023], will also involve a test to determine whether the military will be able to use LLMS to formulate new military options that have not previously been considered. As part of this, the US military will conduct an experiment with the LLMs in order to plan for a potential military response to a global crisis, such as an incident in the Indo-Pacific region....

While Strohmeyer highlighted the potential benefits of the military using additional artificial intelligence, other military officials and lawmakers have concerns regarding artificial intelligence. These concerns include the ability for artificial intelligence to provide false information as fact and the ability for artificial intelligence to be hacked by other users.

"We have to be very concerned with what we talked about, which is the unintended consequences," retired Air Force Maj. Gen. William Enyart said last month.

We who believe God's forewarning that one man and one system will, during the Tribulation, control most of the world's population can discern that the Antichrist will have a Colossus-like entity [the image of the Beast] to help inflict the nefarious worst to torment humanity. It is coming at this generation at breakneck speed, as daily reports of AI technological advancement continue despite its creators' warnings.[12]

David Bowen echoes Terry James' concerns, and in his intriguing article, "Leading Church Services and 'Bringing Back' the Dead? How AI Could Pave the Way for Deception on a Global Scale," notes:

In Daniel 9:27, the prophet speaks about a time when the Antichrist will enter the holy Temple in Jerusalem (2 Thessalonians 2:4), and commit an "abomination of desolation." Jesus, in Matthew 24:15–16, confirms what Daniel prophesied,

"Therefore, when you see the abomination of desolation which was spoken of through Daniel the prophet, standing in the holy place—let the reader understand."

What will this abomination be? Most understand this to be a statue or image of the beast, which gives the appearance of life. Could it be a hologram? Could it be an avatar? Could it be some other form of technology?

This Image of the Beast, prophesied by Daniel and confirmed by Jesus, will be the focal point of worship during the second half of the Tribulation. Bowing to the Image of the Beast is how deceived people will worship the "man of lawlessness" (2 Thessalonians 2:3–4).

This future image will be crucial for those who refuse to worship the Image of the Beast and those willing to bow in worship to the Beast. Those who refuse to comply with the Antichrist's command will suffer the wrath of the Antichrist (Revelation 13:15; 20:4). But, those who willingly worship the Image of the Beast will suffer the wrath of God (Revelation 14:9–11).[13]

And Rob Marco adds this disturbing detail:

Scripture points to a time in which "even the very elect will be deceived, were that possible" (Matthew 24:24); a time in which false Christs and false prophets come with signs and wonders and their promises of an enlightened race. Could it be that the dawn of this superior AI ushers in not just a false Christ here or a false prophet there, *but a world which is composed of an entire race of them?*[14] (Emphasis added)

AI AND TRANSHUMAN GOALS

In addition to the terrifying and fast-approaching scenario above, an international, intellectual, and fast-growing cultural movement known as *transhumanism*, whose vision is supported by a growing list of US military advisors, bioethicists, law professors, and academics, intends the use of AI-designed genetic therapies, weapons, robotics, nanotechnology, and synthetic biology as tools that will produce similar all-powerful intellects while radically redesigning our personal physiology, our offspring, and even perhaps—as Joel Garreau, in his bestselling book *Radical Evolution,* claims—our very souls.

Entire fields of science are now racing toward merging human biology and reasoning with technology so that in the future there will be no distinction between man and machine. Beast technology (AI) will be connected with our brains and influence us deeply, including on the spiritual level. Many researchers also believe the forthcoming modifications to faith and ideas about "God," as they have been known historically, herald the dawn of techno-dimensional spiritual warfare. We'll discuss that at length later, but here are some recent headlines on what—or who—is coming:

- "Former Google and Uber Engineer Is Developing an AI 'God'"
- "Why Humans Will Happily Follow a ROBOT Messiah: Religions Based on AI Will Succeed Because We Tend to 'Worship Supreme Understanding', Claim Experts"
- "Religion That Worships Artificial Intelligence Wants Machines to Be in Charge of the Planet"
- "Inside the First Church of Artificial Intelligence"
- "The Rise of AI: Give Me That New Time Religion?"
- "The World's Next Great Religion Could Have a ROBOT God Because Humans Are Pre-programmed to Worship Things More Intelligent Than Ourselves, Experts Claim"

Tom once wrote a book named *Pandemonium's Engine* about the emergence of such strong AI and the dangers it could represent to our spiritual health in general and Christian theology in particular. Why that title? Pandemonium is the capitol of Hell built by the fallen angels at the suggestion of Mammon in John Milton's classic *Paradise Lost* (1667). The name, derived from the Greek παν, meaning "all," and δαιμόνιον, meaning "demon," is rendered Παν-δαιμον-ειον: "all-demon-place." Loosely based on Scripture and pseudepigraphal texts, the epic is generally considered one of the greatest works in the English language. It describes the Fall of man as the product of a satanic conspiracy. Aided by his lieutenants: Mammon, Beelzebub, Belial, and Moloch, Satan summons a session of the infernal court. At the end of the demonic deliberation, Satan volunteers to tempt newly created man. A delicious appeal to man's hubris is devised: "Ye Eate thereof… and ye shall be as Gods."[15] Of course, man fell, and his hubris is now more heinous. The tree of knowledge, modern science, is bearing increasingly tempting fruit. We've now come full circle—and even some who call themselves "Christian" are biting.

Transhumanism is a transnational technocratic trend that promises to break through human biological limitations by radically redesigning humanity. Despite their protestations, it meets the basic definition of a worldview and religion. Adherents to this worldview plan to extend lifespans, augment the senses, boost memory capacity, and generally use technology to enhance the human condition. It is tempting to write off transhumanism as the fantastical musings of a few eccentric gamers and sci-fi fans. However, these are not mere kooks; rather, they are scientists and professors from universities like Yale, MIT, and Oxford, and they have a secular vision for the future—an alternative eschatology, if you will. They plan to conquer death and create a utopia by technological means. The Bible promises the same through Christ. These two visions are not compatible, and a cultural collision is inevitable.

The modern philosophy of transhumanism was first authored in 1990 by Max More in the essay, "Transhumanism Toward a Futurist Philosophy." According to More, "Transhumanism is a class of philosophies that seek to guide us towards a posthuman condition."[16] More is openly anti-theistic, which will be addressed further as we progress.

Oxford philosopher Nick Bostrom has refined and toned down More's initial, rather virulent, position. Still yet, most transhumanists are atheists or agnostics, and the criticism that they are "playing God" does not trouble them.[17] Based on the premise that naturalistic evolution is true, transhumanism looks to shape the human species through the direct application of technology. However, this depends on myriad variables. We could end up with the six-million-dollar man or the Frankenstein monster. The unanswered questions loom ominous. What does it mean to be a *post* human? What are the spiritual consequences? What about the soul? Can a Christian be a transhumanist? While these questions remain unanswered, there are those who attempt to merge Christianity with transhumanism. An answer to the last question will be offered near the end of this chapter.

The Western Christian consensus has passed into history, and we are living in a post-Christian era. Secularism is becoming increasingly aggressive, finding its voice in the neo-atheist movement championed by Richard Dawkins, Daniel Dennet, Christopher Hitchens, and Sam Harris. The triumphant language of science enchants the spiritually vulnerable, but it does not satisfy. In large part, transhumanists share this devoted faith in science, yet the transhumanist worldview is more enigmatic. They correctly sense the emptiness of secularism and want to transcend it. There can be no doubt that scientific progress and technical advancements are now poised to radically transform humanity. It is moving at such a rapid pace that it is imperative for thoughtful Christians to offer a biblical perspective in the marketplace of ideas. While this is increasingly unpopular, we dare not shrink back.

Unfortunately, very little has been written on transhumanism within conservative evangelical circles. There is a Mormon Transhumanist Association, which is hardly surprising in light of their polytheism and apotheosis doctrine.[18] On the popular level, there have been two websites authored by a nuclear operations instructor James Ledford called Technical-Jesus.com and Hyper-evolution.com, as well as a self-published book—all of which promote "Christian

Transhumanism."[19] Liberal theologian Paul Tillich is frequently cited in support. Lately, transhumanism has found theological justification in the work of Evangelical Lutheran Church in America (ELCA) theologians like Phillip Hefner, Ted Peters, and others. In fact, the Lutheran journal *Dialog* offered an entire issue on the subject in their winter 2005 edition.[20] The mission of the Lutherans seems to be a well-intended one of building a bridge between science and faith. They are welcomed in largely secular arenas, and their work is being taken quite seriously. Unfortunately, with the exception of ourselves and a few others, conservative Christian voices are scarcely heard on the matter, albeit they are likely not welcome.[21] Bostrom, Hefner, and Ledford argue that there is nothing wrong with a Christian adopting a transhumanist worldview. We disagree for reasons to be discussed later in the chapter. First, to understand that worldview, we must briefly survey the science and technology behind it.

SCIENCE AND TECHNOLOGY BEHIND TRANSHUMANISM

Transhumanism is driven by the ambitious juggernaut of the modern scientific and technological revolution. The technologies undergirding transhumanism are all part of the biotech explosion and include genetics, neuropharmacology, robotics, cybernetics, artificial intelligence, and nanotechnology. They are all interrelated and fueled by the ever-increasing speed of data processing as per Moore's law (discussed later in this chapter). For the purpose of this discussion, we will examine them in a very limited way in two broad categories: biological/genetic and electromechanical computer technologies. Of these two, the first has received the most attention by Christian thinkers due to issues like stem-cell research, cloning, and the worldwide infant holocaust. As a result, Christians do have a coherent position on the intrinsic value of all human life from conception to the aged. The basic position expressed by Francis Beckwith in the abortion debate is a good platform to start from.[22] Still yet, one of the major new challenges facing thinking Christians is our newly acquired ability to alter nature for our own ends through genetic engineering and biotechnology.

The discovery of deoxyribonucleic acid (DNA) by James Watson and Francis Crick in 1954 opened up the architecture of life to human intervention in a manner that was inconceivable prior. In 2003, the Human Genome Project produced a map of the complete human genome. Consequently, we are now fully capable of using genetic engineering to alter ourselves. The least controversial procedure is somatic cell gene therapy. It entails injecting healthy gene material into patients with diseases like Huntington's.[23] The second is called germline therapy and involves rearranging defective genetic material in a way that it produces healthy genes. This technique increases the stakes in that it passes the alterations down to offspring.[24] It follows that we could permanently alter the species with this technology and that the new one could even split off. Current gene therapy is experimental, and the Food and Drug Administration (FDA) is moving with caution.[25] These techniques are now being developed for healing purposes. However, it isn't difficult to imagine their use by the military, social engineers, and utopian transhumanists for other purposes.

Genetic enhancement therapy is something Christians should oppose. It entails introducing novel genetic material simply to improve one's abilities. Transhumanists envision altering or even adding DNA from other species into the human code to create "Human Plus," a human GMO (genetically modified organism).[26] An instructive analogy is to consider the difference between diabetics using insulin and an athlete using anabolic steroids. There is a clear and normative moral distinction. It is one that should form the Christian consensus. Even on a secular basis, enhancement also poses higher risk. Correcting a faulty gene with what already should be there presents low risk to the patient, but adding something new could adversely affect numerous related biochemical pathways.[27] Thus, it is vital to distinguish therapeutic procedures from enhancement. Finally, a biblical ethic discourages enhancement, because Christians are called to model Christ in self-denial and humility (Luke 9:23; Matthew 23:12; Romans 12:1, 12:16).

Nevertheless, Masayoshi Son, founder of the influential Softbank venture fund, recently suggested that "artificial intelligence would lay the foundation for the creation of the 'superhuman.'" He continued:

Scientists for a half century have harbored similar dreams and some no doubt welcome the Biden administration's support for a vast project "to write circuitry for cells and predictably program biology in the same way in which we write software and program computers." But cautionary tales about trying to create "the better human" are abundant: Consider the scientific promoters of early 20th century American eugenics as well as the examples of the Soviet Union and Nazi Germany.

The ultimate goal of the tech elite increasingly will be to meld people with machines.... The aim is to "develop and promote the realization of a Godhead based on Artificial Intelligence."

This new religion is a step toward creating a scientifically ordered society detached from family, religion, and the broad sense of community. Philosopher Yuval Noah Harari envisions a future where "a small and privileged elite of upgraded humans" will use genetic engineering to cement the superior status of their offspring—a small, God-like caste of what he calls *Homo deus* who can lord over the less cognitively gifted Homo sapiens.

"You want to know how super-intelligent cyborgs might treat ordinary flesh-and-blood humans?" Harari asks. "Better start by investigating how humans treat their less intelligent animal cousins."[28]

These so-called experts also foresee using the most controversial genetics category—eugenic engineering—which involves directing traits

18

to improve a specific gene pool.[29] This brings to mind the two classics, Aldous Huxley's *Brave New World* (published in 1932) and C. S. Lewis' *The Abolition of Man* (published in 1947), both prescient, yet disturbing, forecasts of our current moral dilemmas. While eugenic engineering may seem prohibitively unsavory, the idea is currently being discussed amongst the elite. In a recent book discussing dangerous ideas, evolutionary biologist and outspoken atheist Richard Dawkins laments that, prior to Adolf Hitler, scientists in the 1920s and 1930s had no qualms about the idea of designer babies. He then pondered:

> I wonder whether, some 60 years after Hitler's death, we might at least venture to ask what the moral difference is between breeding for musical ability and forcing a child to take music lessons. Or why it is acceptable to train fast runners and high jumpers but not to breed them.[30]

Why not? Because we believe all humans have intrinsic worth separate from abilities. Apart from the image of God in all people (Genesis 1:26–27), there are no grounds to resist the momentum toward social engineering. After all, the current widespread use of prenatal genetic screening is a private form of it. Perhaps Huxley's world of compulsory test-tube breeding is in our not-too-distant future? The uncomfortable truth is that today we can really do it.

The American philosopher, political economist, and author Francis Fukuyama agrees, contending that "the most significant threat posed by contemporary biotechnology is the possibility that it will alter human nature and thereby move us into a 'posthuman' stage of history."[31] Unfortunately, today there are competing pathways to that end. Other disturbing trends include human cloning, the production of human/animal chimeras, and psychoactive drug use. Now that human cloning is possible, it has been purposed to employ fetal tissue harvested from cloned or genetically engineered fetuses in gene therapy or even for spare parts.[32] In 2007, scientists at the University of Nevada

School of Medicine created a sheep that has 15 percent human cells and 85 percent sheep cells.[33] In addition, neuropharmacology is already being widely used to control behavior and emotions. While there are legitimate uses, psychotropic drugs like Ritalin are being handed out to school children as a matter of routine. Prozac and its relatives are being taken by twenty-eight million Americans, or 10 percent of the population.[34] This seems to be heading toward what transhumanists optimistically envision as a biochemically induced utopia:

> Technologies such as brain-computer interfaces and neuro-pharmacology could amplify human intelligence, increase emotional well-being, improve our capacity for steady commitment to life projects or a loved one, and even multiply the range and richness of possible emotions.[35]

In light of twentieth-century history, this seems naïve at best. The secular worldview, rooted in material reductionism and genetic determinism, leaves little room for the inherent dignity of all human life. Yet they are making policy. Ready or not, we have already entered the brave new world.

In 1965, Intel cofounder Gordon E. Moore wrote a paper describing a trend of increasing circuit speed that has come to be called "Moore's law." It describes the ongoing trend for computing power to double every two years. This pattern has held true, and is, in fact, still considered a conservative predictor of future growth. Based on this, MIT computer scientist, futurist, and author Ray Kurzweil predicts what has come to be termed the earlier-mentioned Singularity. This term represents a point when artificial intelligence surpasses human abilities and begins to design new technology on its own.[36] At this time, Kurzweil predicts that technological growth will go vertical on the exponential curve. He also envisions the next step in the human evolution as the union of human and machine. It really isn't as fantastic as it seems. Already, cochlear implants are hardwired to the brain to restore hearing. Brain-machine interfaces are being used to "assist paralyzed patients by enabling them to operate machines with recordings of their own neural activity."[37] Today, similar technology is available for gaming as consumer electronics.[38] It is real, burgeoning, and not going away. Kurzweil's optimistic enthusiasm for progress is exciting, and it is easy to understand the attraction it holds for technologists.

Kurzweil is undeniably one of the leading inventors of our time and has been called the "rightful heir to Thomas Edison."[39] If one were to posit transhumanism as a religion, Kurzweil's books, *The Age of Spiritual Machines* and *The Singularity Is Near*, would be likely be considered its sacred texts. Kurzweil builds his case on the naturalistic evolutionary paradigm, devoting a large section of *The Age of Spiritual Machines* to framing transhumanism as an inevitable evolutionary consequence. The Darwinian model is a foundational presupposition as he purposes computer algorithms that explicitly model natural selection.[40] He argues that these—and other procedures derived by reverse-engineering the human brain and combined with neural net technology—promise the rapid development of sentient artificial intelligence.[41] He predicts that, by 2029, an inexpensive computer will be one thousand times more powerful than the human brain, and computer implants designed for direct connection to the brain will be widely available.[42] Elon Musk recently received FDA approval for just such human trials. As far as artificial intelligence, he forecasts machines becoming conscious and having as wide an array of emotional and spiritual experiences as their human progenitors by 2029… and these claims are largely accepted.[43] Furthermore, he says, eventually, human consciousness will be uploaded to computers, introducing immortality. By 2099, machines and humans will merge to the point that there will be no distinction between the two, or between real and virtual, thus eliminating all war, hunger, poverty, death, and disease.[44] Does this promise sound somewhat familiar (Revelation 21:4)?

The transhumanist eschatological hope in consciousness uploading is littered with unfounded assumptions. Transhumanists simply deny the soul *a priori*, viewing consciousness as purely a product of the brain and information. Our bodies are considered simple hardware—a biological prosthesis we can reengineer and improve. They see the essential nature of our being as information patterns and data stored in the brain.[45] Accordingly, transhumanists envision immortality via uploading themselves onto computers in the form of their brain patterns. Kurzweil calls it "patternism."[46] ELCA theologian Ted Peters has addressed this, observing, "It assumes that human intelligence and human personhood can become disembodied."[47] This creates an interesting dissonance with the typical naturalist mind-body identity paradigm. In characteristic liberal theological language, Peters argues that the term "soul" is a "symbolic place holder to identify the dimension of who we are that connects with God."[48] This is problematic in light of Scripture (Matthew 10:28; Revelation 6:9, 20:4). However, to his credit, Peters concludes that the Christian concept of the soul is nothing like the transhumanist's disembodied patterns of brain activity.

According to Kurzweil and others, the best hope for human immortality is consciousness uploading. But can it possibly work? As a defeater to patternism, philosopher Derek Parfit composed a clever thought experiment.[49] The idea is that you are an astronaut going on a mission to a distant planet via a new form of teleportation. To accomplish this, your brain pattern and body type will be uploaded and sent to the planet to be reconstructed from matter precisely engineered from your scan. In the scanning process, your body on earth will be destroyed, but this is of no concern, because you will soon be in your new body on the distant planet. Should you go? In the transhumanist's imagination, it would work, but in reality it does not. It's not so much a matter of metaphysics as logic. The law of non-contradiction will not allow it. There is no logical reason your body on earth must be destroyed. Consider a scenario wherein you are not destroyed on earth, yet the upload is successful. Obviously, the person on the other planet is not you, but a clone. Since the person is clearly not you in this case, it follows that it is also not you if your body was destroyed. In that case, you died. Hence, no matter how hard transhumanists might wish it were so, uploading will not defeat death (Hebrews 9:27). That ability belongs to Christ alone (Revelation 20:14).

Fantasies of immortality aside, one marvels at what Kurzweil means by a machine having a "spiritual experience." It gets weirder, because this is where the subject of transhumanism intersects with theological liberalism. In *The Singularity Is Near*, Kurzweil expresses his belief in the need for a new religion, stating that "A principal role of religion has been to rationalize death, since up until just now there was little else constructive we could do about it."[50]

He states this new religion will "keep two principles: one from traditional religion and one from secular arts and sciences—from traditional religion, the respect for human consciousness" and from the secular world, "the importance of knowledge."[51] This is not any different than traditional secular humanism. So, we must ask where God fits into this new religion. Kurzweil ambitiously resolves:

> Once we saturate the matter and energy in the universe with intelligence, it will "wake up," be conscious, and sublimely intelligent. That's about as close to God as I can imagine.

In fact, it sounds strangely similar to liberal theologian Paul Tillich's pantheistic conception of God as the "power of all being."[52] Yet, in Kurzweil's mind, man is engaged in building God, which is effectively the antithesis of Genesis 1:26. Indeed, it is exactly backwards: God created in man's image.

In its early articulation, Max More—whose wife Natasha Vita-More is featured in Tom's award-winning film *Inhuman*—made no bones about wanting to displace conventional religion. Like Dawkins, he views religion as an obscurant fiction and believes science has discredited the biblical worldview. Accordingly, he argues that transhumanism will supplant traditional religion, boasting, "The growth of humanism over the decades has begun this job, but now it is time to utilize the more inclusive and memetically attractive option of transhumanism."[53] Conventional secular humanism qualifies as a worldview in the sense that it provides a full set of ideas through which its devotees view reality. Following this line of thought, it is also a religion on the basis that it attempts to answer the same set of fundamental questions about theology, metaphysics, identity, origins, destiny, and morality as other religions.[54] In fact, the high courts ruled in *James J. Kaufman vs. Gary R. MacCaughtry* that secular humanism is a religion.[55] In light of that status, it seems fair to argue that transhumanism simply defines its eschatology. Thus, it is vitally important to note the abject failure of secular humanism so far. Unparalleled scientific progress has not delivered a secular utopia. It has led to a human nightmare. The twentieth-century world total is 262 million murdered by government and largely *outside of war* in the pursuit of the secular humanists' political ideal of Marxism.[56]

Since the initial, intensely secular expression by Max More, transhumanist philosophy has been polished by Oxford philosopher Nick Bostrom. While Bostrom denies that it is a religion, he concedes that "transhumanism might serve a few of the same functions that people have traditionally sought in religion."[57] He states succinctly that transhumanism is a naturalistic outlook, and in a decidedly superior tone offers that "transhumanists prefer to derive their understanding of the world from rational modes of inquiry, especially the scientific method."[58] If one is a Christian in any meaningful sense, this is not acceptable. In truth, we have what the secular world does not: infallible and timeless principles revealed from the very Author of life (2 Timothy 3:16). However, it is more than a matter of simple proof-texting curt responses. Humans are God's highest creation on earth and are commanded to be good stewards of its resources. Thus, we have a mandate to engage in some of the technologies discussed, but with the explicit caveat of when it is exclusively directed toward the healing aspect of medicine.

Accordingly, transhumanism is finding some theological support in the "created co-creator" construct of ELCA theologian Philip

Hefner. Hefner has become quite popular in transhumanist circles, authoring articles like "The Created Co-Creator Meets Cyborg" and "The Animal That Aspires to Be an Angel: The Challenge of Trans-humanism." Characteristic of the overemphasis of God's immanence in theological liberalism, his idea assumes that human beings emerged as purposeful, free agents from a tooth-and-claw evolutionary process, and that human nature is shaped by both a genetic and cultural heritage.[59] Finally, humans are God's instruments for carrying out His purposes in creation.[60] This theological construct has been articulated in this way:

> Human beings are God's created co-creators whose purpose is to be the agency, acting in freedom, to birth the future that is most wholesome for the nature that has birthed us—the nature that is not only our own genetic heritage, but also the entire human community and the evolutionary and ecological reality in which and to which we belong. Exercising this agency is said to be God's will for humans.[61]

This view has been criticized for diminishing human exceptionalism with its embrace of naturalistic evolution, while simultaneously presuming to elevate humans to the same level as God.[62] Hefner's liberal theology is derived from his low view of special revelation.

Hefner interprets the Genesis Creation account as primordial mythology using symbol and metaphor for man's evolutionary past.[63] He quotes Tillich frequently in his treatise on the Fall. For example, "Before sin is an act, it is a state."[64] This is in reference to the idea that there was no actual space-time Fall of man, rather, "the Fall" symbolically represents the inevitable tension between cultural ideal and primordial instinct that ensued as man evolved from his lowly origin. In contrast, sacred Scripture teaches that the Fall was an act of disobedience, not a state (Genesis 3:6). Yet, Hefner dismisses the traditional biblical understanding as obsolete:

25

Furthermore, certain traditional understandings are seriously challenged, including the necessity for simply rejecting some historically popular insights. Notions of (1) the "first pair," (2) concepts of the Fall that insist upon some primordial act by early humans that altered subsequent human nature, and (3) certain forms of aetiological interpretation are among the elements that must be looked upon with great skepticism.[65]

This is highly problematic, because it is clear from Scripture that Jesus believed in a first pair (Matthew 19:4). Certainly Paul and the apostles did as well (1 Timothy 2:13). Furthermore, this view hardly qualifies as theistic evolution in a meaningful Christian sense. As Millard Erickson expresses it, "With respect to the biblical data, theistic evolution often holds to an actual primal pair, Adam and Eve."[66] In respect to his complete rejection of Genesis' historicity, his view seems more in line with deistic evolution. For an alleged evangelical theologian, his denial of God's Word is disturbing.

The fatal flaw in this line of thinking is that it completely undermines the basis for the Gospel message. The Apostle Paul proclaims:

> Therefore as by the offence of one judgment came upon all men to condemnation; even so by the righteousness of one the free gift came upon all men unto justification of life. (Romans 5:18)

Thus, in Paul's reckoning, a denial of an original sin effectively rejects the atonement of the cross. Furthermore, if sin is merely a leftover animal impulse, then the cure cannot be a restoration via sanctification in Christ (Romans 6:22). The cure for sin necessarily becomes the elimination of the leftover animal instincts. Erickson argues, "This conception of the cure for sin embraces the optimistic belief that the evolutionary process is carrying the human race in the right direction."[67] While this idea coheres nicely with transhumanist thought, Jesus taught that "many will fall away," "lawlessness will be increased," and "the love of many will grow cold" at the time world evangelization is completed (Matthew 24:10–14), and Scripture supports increasing apostasy and wickedness (2 Thessalonians 2:3; 1 Timothy 4:1; 2 Timothy 4:3; 2 Peter 3:3). Finally, consider that Jesus "needed not that any should testify of man: for he knew what was in man" (John 2:25).

The fact that their theology opposes Scripture doesn't seem to bother liberal theologians like Paul Tillich and Philip Hefner. The embrace of Darwinism and higher criticism over Creation and inerrancy inclines them to the latest postmodern ideas. In his article, "The Animal That Aspires to Be an Angel: The Challenge of Transhumanism," Hefner intentionally blurs the distinction between healing and enhancement, often equivocating transhumanism with medicine. To his credit, Hefner does warn that while we are created to push the envelope, "we are not God; we are finite and sinful."[68] That conclusion deserves praise. However, one must keep in mind that his view of sin is not the orthodox Christian one. While he urges caution, it effectively amounts to hedging his bets. For instance, the prohibition of murder in Genesis 9:6 is based on the fact that the human was created in God's image. It seems reasonable to extend that to include posthuman alteration. But Hefner contends that to object to transhumanism on the grounds of the *imago Dei* imposes an unwarranted normative anthropology by arguing:

> Other thinkers argue that there are inviolable qualities, chiefly, human inviolable qualities, chiefly, human dignity, which are also threatened by biotechnology. The difficulty with such thinking is that it imposes a static quality to nature that does not in fact conform to what we know about nature's dynamic character.[69]

This reads like he is arguing that evolution trumps human dignity. It seems he views transhumanism as the inevitable next step in human evolution and that transhumanism is a natural consequence of man's status as a co-creator with God. In other words, it is deistic evolution via human agency. In his theological conclusions, he writes:

> TH [transhumanism] is not first of all a matter of morality. Our existence as created co-creators who face the possibilities of TH is profoundly an expression of our human nature.[70]

He also contends that "to discredit our God-given nature is itself a rebellion against God."[71] It seems like the implication of these two statements is that we have a God-given mandate to transhumanism. It is not difficult to see why Hefner's created co-creator is a pillar in the thought of so-called Christian transhumanists.

While not nearly as sophisticated as Hefner, Ledford's popular websites also use the work of Tillich to justify "Christian transhumanism." Specifically, it's an idea Tillich called the "profound doctrine of transcendent humanism," which is his heretical idea that "Adam is fulfilled in Christ."[72] Tillich explains that "this means that Christ is the essential man, the man Adam was to become but did not actually become."[73] This is not in line with orthodox Christology, which states that Christ is the incarnated God-man, the eternal Second Person of the Trinity. It is also logically incoherent, because Adam was created through Christ (John 1:3). Ledford's reliance on Tillich is not surprising. Tillich's overemphasis of God's immanence has been criticized as amounting to panentheism (the doctrine that God includes the world as a part, though not the whole, of His being), and seems disturbingly similar to Kurzweil's conception.[74] Ledford's web pages read like a syncretism of New Age mysticism, Christianity, and transhumanist ideology. Notable examples include "Heaven Allows Hyper-Evolution" and clichés like "You can do no wrong when the spirit of love, the Holy Spirit, is with you."[75] Yet the Bible says we can grieve the Spirit (Ephesians 4:30). He really makes no effort at scriptural coherence, offering pluralistic platitudes like, "The path to God is wide as we are different. And, the path to God converges on his calling."[76] Of course, this stands in direct contradiction to the teachings of Jesus, who said, "Enter ye in at the strait gate: for wide is the gate, and broad is the way, that leadeth to destruction, and many there be which go in thereat" (Matthew 7:13). Ledford is no theologian, and his work offers no real challenge to anyone with a basic understanding of Christian doctrine. Unfortunately, less-sophisticated seekers are bound to be deceived by it.

As far as the question about whether a Christian can be a transhumanist, that one reveals a wayward heart condition. Transhumanism is less sin than hubris. The *Evangelical Dictionary of Theology* makes the distinction:

> Whereas hubris signifies the attempt to transcend the limitations appointed by fate, sin refers to an unwillingness to break out of our narrow limitations in obedience to the vision of faith. While hubris connotes immoderation, sin consists in misplaced allegiance. Hubris is trying to be superhuman; sin is becoming inhuman. Hubris means rising to the level of the gods; sin means trying to displace God or living as if there were no God.[77]

Based on this, transhumanism is hubris of the highest order, while becoming posthuman is a sin. The "obedience to the vision of faith" spoken of above is not Tillich's or Hefner's, but Paul's. The apostle exhorted the Colossians to "put on therefore, as the elect of God, holy and beloved, bowels of mercies, kindness, humbleness of mind, meekness, longsuffering" (Colossians 3:12). Tillich, Hefner, and Ledford all demonstrate a gross misunderstanding of the human condition. Humans are both finite and sinful. We lack the wisdom and moral purity necessary to decide matters of human "perfection." Therefore, it is immoral and sinful to use such technologies to enhance or evolve humanity. Christians must take an informed stand on transhumanism, understanding both the appropriate use of technology and the potential dangers it presents. Thus, a theology of healing as opposed to enhancement must be developed in accordance with sound biblical guidelines.

In the public arena, it is becoming increasingly difficult to get a fair hearing for Christian values while remaining true to Scripture. We are not convincing the public on abortion, and Former President Obama in March of 2009 issued an executive order that expanded embryonic stem cell research. While that was being battled in court, as this research has demonstrated, myriad even more disturbing technologies are never debated. The history of science is not silent on one point: Transhumanism will not wait for Christians to catch up. While we have a duty to educate ourselves to address highly technical issues with scriptural principles, it is doubtful that much can be done other than serious prayer. Historically, the military industrial complex has never been transparent about their projects. Furthermore, there is nothing to stop ambitious scientists from simply moving to countries like China to work on their more controversial ideas. It *is* going to happen. While many will want to participate, Christians should take a firm stand against enhancement. Transhumanism is going to be an issue that divides.

Unfortunately, transhumanism is an anti-Christian religion on the increase. It is likely a key element in the end-times scenario. Globalism is leading to a "technocracy," or rule by the elite.[78] When transhuman enhancement becomes widely available (and it likely will soon), only the elite will be able to afford it. This will create new a caste system. The difference between the "haves" and "have nots" will grow exponentially. And, even if one can afford it, the potential within these technologies for mind manipulation opens the door for an Orwellian totalitarianism. Francis Schaeffer and C. S. Lewis issued prescient warnings to the Christian community that this was coming. Schaeffer wrote back in 1976:

As we consider the coming of an elite, an authoritarian state,
to fill the vacuum left by the loss of Christian principles, we

must not think naively of the models of Stalin and Hitler. We must think rather of a *manipulative* authoritarian government. Modern governments have forms of manipulation at their disposal which the world has never known before.[79]

Indeed they do. A major funder of transhumanist research is the National Science Foundation.[80] The military applications are fearsome. The implications for social engineering are equally disquieting. Already we see this trend toward technocracy in our increasingly globalist politics and of manipulation in managed mainstream media. Considering Kurzweil's prediction that there will be cerebrally interfaced network by 2029, the potential for centralized control gets more disturbing. Quite astonishingly, Christian transhumanist James Ledford predicted that "the Antichrist will likely emerge but so will Christ. This becomes a sign that Christian Transhumanism is the way."[81] While we disagree with the latter, there may be some truth to the former. After all, it is Pandemonium's newest ploy.

WHERE THE AI DEMON IS LEADING

Unfortunately for humankind, the technological and cultural shift now underway not only unapologetically forecasts a future dominated by a new species of unrecognizably superior "minds," but an unfathomable war—both physical and spiritual—that the world is unprepared for. It will be fought on land, within the air and sea, and in dimensions as yet incomprehensible. Even now, the synthetic forces that will plot humanity's wholesale annihilation are quietly under design in leading laboratories, public and private, funded by the most advanced nations on earth, including the governments of the United States, France, Britain, Australia, and China, to name a few. As a result of progressive deduction, reasoning, and problem-solving in fields of neurotechnology and cybernetics, strong artificial intelligence, or "artilects," will emerge from this research—godlike, massively intelligent machines that are "trillions of trillions of times smarter than humans" and whose rise will prove profoundly disruptive to human culture, leading to a stark division between philosophical, ideological, and political groups who either support the newly evolved life-forms as the next step in human and technological evolution or who view this vastly superior intellect as an incalculable risk and deadly threat to the future of humanity. These diametrically opposed worldviews will ultimately result in a preemptive new world war—what is already being described as *gigadeath,* the bloodiest battle in history, with billions of deaths before the end of the twenty-first century.

For those who find the fantastic elements in the statements above implicative of science fiction or even future Armageddon as forecast in the ancient apocalyptic and prophetic books of the Bible, the catastrophic vision is actually derived from near-future scenarios, which leading scientists like Prof. Hugo de Garis, former director of the Artificial Brain Lab at Xiamen University in China, outlines in his book, *The Artilect War: Cosmists vs. Terrans: A Bitter Controversy Concerning Whether Humanity Should Build Godlike Massively Intelligent Machines,* as unfolding due to exponential growth and development this century in GRINS technologies (genetics, robotics, information technology, and nanotechnology).

"I believe that the twenty-first century will be dominated by the question as to whether humanity should or should not build artilects, i.e., machines of godlike intelligence," de Garis says. "I see humanity splitting into two major political groups, which in time will become increasingly bitterly opposed, as the artilect issue becomes more real."

The professor:

The human group in favor of building artilects, I label the "Cosmists" [to whom] building artilects will be like a religion…something truly magnificent and worthy of worship….

The second human group, opposed to the building of artilects, I label the "Terrans"…who will argue that allowing the Cosmists to build [artilects] implies accepting the *risk,* that one day, the artilects might decide...that the human species is a pest. Since the artilects would be so vastly superior to human beings in intelligence, it would be easy for [them] to exterminate the human species....

Thus to the Terrans, the Cosmists are...far worse than the regimes of Hitler, Stalin, Mao...or any other regime that murdered tens of millions of people in the twentieth century, because [this] time...we are talking about the potential annihilation of the whole human species, billions of people.[82]

Professor de Garis continues in his book to describe how the work to build artilects is proceeding nonetheless, with anticipation of its realization potentially close at hand. As a result, he falls asleep at night thinking about the godlike synthetic intelligence he and others are constructing. Sometimes his mind becomes enraptured of his creations with a sense of intellectual and spiritual awe. Then, waking up a few hours later in a cold sweat, he is jolted from bed by a horrific dream in which vivid scenes depict the slaughter of his descendants at the hands of the artificial deities.

I (Tom) have spoken with Dr. de Garis on numerous occasions (he, too, is in our film *Inhuman*), and he is not alone in this fear—that what he and other research scientists are feverishly working toward could soon become a nightmarish predicament humankind will not survive. Because it is difficult, if not impossible, to accurately predict how strong artificial intelligence will actually affect the world, it is unclear whether humans will be viewed by the unnatural life-forms as serving a purpose in a world dominated by super-intelligent machines or whether they will be weighed as lacking any practical function and therefore be considered expendable. It could be that we won't even see the question coming. In other words, we may already be in the process of being lulled into subservience toward the rise of the machines. As the brilliantly insane Theodore Kaczynski, in his thirty-five-thousand-word paper, "Industrial Society and Its Future" (also called the "Unabomber Manifesto"), wrote:

As society and the problems that face it become more and more complex and machines become more and more intelligent, people will let machines make more of their decisions for them, simply because machine-made decisions will bring better result than man-made ones. Eventually a stage may be reached at which the decisions necessary to keep the system running will be so complex that human beings will be incapable of making them intelligently. At that stage, the machines will be in effective control. People won't be able to just turn the machines off, because they will be so dependent on them that turning them off would amount to suicide.[83]

Crazy or not, Kaczynski, who died June 10, 2023, may have been right in that man's demise at the hands of machines will happen gradually, during which time we humans will become the proverbial frogs in the kettle set to boil. On the other hand, we are more likely to be reduced any day now, in the blink of an enhanced eye, to the status of domestic animals in the minds of artificial intelligence, as technological Singularity—that magical future moment that many futurists and tech experts believe could be imminent—gives birth overnight to some version of the artilects, who suddenly come online as conscious, living super-minds, immensely more powerful than human beings.

"As a metaphor for mind-boggling social change, the Singularity has been borrowed from math and physics," writes Joel Garreau in *Radical Evolution*. He continues:

In those realms, singularities are the point where everything stops making sense. In math it is a point where you are dividing through by zero [and in physics it is] black holes—points in space so dense that even light cannot escape their horrible gravity. If you were to approach one in a spaceship, you would find that even the laws of physics no longer seemed to function. That's what a Singularity is like.[84]

Ray Kurzweil, who is credited with groundbreaking work in artificial intelligence and is, among other things, the cofounder of an interdisciplinary graduate studies program backed by NASA known as the Singularity University, appreciates the comparison between the coming technological Singularity and the physics of black holes:

Just as a black hole in space dramatically alters the patterns of matter and energy accelerating toward its event horizon, the impending Singularity in our future is [a] period during which the pace of technological change will be so rapid, its impact so deep, that human life will be irreversibly transformed.... The key idea underlying the impending Singularity is that the rate of change of our human-created technology is accelerating and its powers are expanding at an exponential pace. Exponential growth is deceptive. It starts out almost imperceptibly and then explodes with unexpected fury.[85]

In plain language, Abou Farman says:

[Kurzweil's work on the Singularity] analyzes the curve of technological development from humble flint-knapping to the zippy microchip. The curve he draws rises exponentially, and we are sitting right on the elbow, which means very suddenly this trend toward smaller and smarter technologies will yield greater-than-human machine intelligence. That sort of superintelligence will proliferate not by self-replication, but by building other agents with even greater intelligence than itself, which will in turn build more superior agents. The result will be an "intelligence explosion" so fast and so vast that the laws and certainties with which we are familiar will no longer apply. That event-horizon is called the Singularity.[86]

Kurzweil elaborates further on what the Singularity will mean:

35

Our version 1.0 biological bodies are...frail and subject to a myriad of failure modes.... The Singularity will allow us to transcend these limitations.... We will gain power over our fates. Our mortality will be in our own hands [and] the nonbiological portion of our intelligence will be trillions of trillions of times more powerful than unaided human intelligence.

We are now in the early stages of this transition. The acceleration of paradigm shift...as well as the exponential growth of the capacity of information technology are both beginning to reach the "knee of the curve," which is the stage at which an exponential trend becomes noticeable. Shortly after this stage, the trend becomes explosive. [Soon] the growth rates of our technology—which will be indistinguishable from ourselves—will be so steep as to appear essentially vertical.... That, at least, will be the perspective of unenhanced biological humanity.

The Singularity will represent the culmination of the merger of our biological thinking and existence with our technology, resulting in a world that...transcends our biological roots. There will be no distinction, post-Singularity, between human and machine.[87]

In 1993, critical thinking about the timing of the Singularity concerning the emergence of strong artificial intelligence led retired San Diego State University professor and computer scientist Vernor Vinge, in his often-quoted and now-famous lecture, "The Coming Technological Singularity" (delivered at VISION-21 Symposium sponsored by NASA Lewis Research Center and the Ohio Aerospace Institute), to add that when science achieves "the technological means to create superhuman intelligence[,] shortly after, the human era will be ended."[88] In contrast to Vinge, cyborgists like Kevin Warwick, professor of cybernetics at Reading University in England who endorsed de Garis' book, believe Singularity will not so much represent the end of the human era as it will the assimilation of man with machine intelligence, like the

Borg of *Star Trek* fame. This is because, according to Warwick, technological Singularity will not occur as a result of freestanding independent machines, but inside human cyborgs, where human-machine integration is realized and enhanced biology is recombined to include living brains that are cybernetic, machine-readable, and interfaced with artificial neural networks where transhumans with amplified intelligence become so completely superior to their biological counterparts (normal humans) as to be incomprehensible—ultimately "posthuman." The technology to accomplish this task is already well underway and is considered by ourselves and researchers like Warwick to be one of the most plausible scientific utilities currently under employment that could produce sentient AI as the ghost in the machine learns from human brains hardwired into it.

Toward this end, in a groundbreaking development:

> The research team at Monash University and Cortical Labs has been awarded a generous grant from defense and the Office of National Intelligence (ONI). The team has been exploring the intriguing intersection of human brain cells and artificial intelligence (AI), aiming to create a remarkable fusion of synthetic biological intelligence.
>
> The amalgamation of AI and synthetic biology is at the core of the research conducted by the Australian DishBrain team. Associate Professor Adeel Razi, from Monash University's prestigious Turner Institute for Brain and Mental Health, spearheads the ambitious project. The team envisions the creation of programmable biological computing platforms, bridging the gap between biological and artificial intelligence. This merging of diverse fields holds the promise of producing AI machines that far surpass their current capabilities.[89]

As a result of this bridge between technology and human biology being attained this century, nothing less than the wholesale redesign of humans, including genetic integration with other life-forms—plants, animals, and synthetic creations—will be realized. This vision—the borgification (marriage between biology and machine) of humans—is supported in a recent "State of the Future" report by the Millennium Project, a global think tank founded after a three-year feasibility study with the United Nations University, Smithsonian Institution, and the Futures Group International, where synthetic biologists affirm that "as computer code is written to create software to augment human capabilities, so too *genetic code will be written to create life forms to augment civilization.*"[90] Furthermore, as biotech, infotech, nanotech, and cognotech breakthroughs quickly migrate with appropriate synergies to create widespread human-machine adaptation within society, a "global collective intelligence system [hive supermind] will be needed to track all these science and technology advances," the report goes on to say.

I (Tom) have personally debated leading transhumanist, Dr. James Hughes (also in the film *Inhuman*), concerning this inevitable techno-sapien future on his weekly syndicated talk show, *Changesurfer Radio*. Hughes is executive director of the Institute for Ethics and Emerging Technologies and teaches at Trinity College in Hartford, Connecticut. He is the author of *Citizen Cyborg: Why Democratic Societies Must Respond to the Redesigned Human of the Future*, a sort of bible for transhumanist values. Dr. Hughes joins a growing body of academics, bioethicists, and sociologists who support:

Large-scale genetic and neurological engineering of ourselves... [a] new chapter in evolution [as] the result of accelerating developments in the fields of genomics, stem-cell research, genetic enhancement, germ-line engineering, neuro-pharmacology, artificial intelligence, robotics, pattern recognition technologies, and nanotechnology...at the intersection of science and religion [which has begun to question] what it means to be human.[91]

Though the transformation of human to this posthuman condition is in its fledgling state, complete integration of the technology necessary to replace existing Homo sapiens as the dominant life-form on earth is approaching Kurzweil's exponential curve. A Reuters article titled "Scientists Want Debate on Animals with Human Genes" hinted at just how far scientists have come and how far they intend to go. The news piece started out, "A mouse that can speak? A monkey with Down's Syndrome? Dogs with human hands or feet? British scientists want to know if such experiments are acceptable," and it continued with revelations that scientists inside Britain are comfortable now with up to 50/50 animal-human integration. The article implied that not all the research currently underway is kept at the embryonic level, and that fully mature monstrosities (like the creature in the 2010 movie *Splice*) may be under study, as "some scientists in some places want to push boundaries." *National Geographic* magazine speculated in 2007 that, within ten years, the first of such human-animals would walk the earth. They missed the date by a few years, but Vernor Vinge agreed recently that we are entering that period in history when questions like "What is the meaning of life?" will be nothing more than an engineering question.

Most readers may be surprised to learn that in preparation for this posthuman revolution, the United States government has been handing out hundreds of millions of dollars over the past few decades to develop the actual guidelines that will be used for setting government policy on the next step in human evolution—"genetic enhancement." Maxwell Mehlman, Arthur E. Petersilge Professor of Law, director of the Law-Medicine Center at Case Western Reserve University School of Law, and professor of bioethics in the Case School of Medicine, led the team of law professors, physicians, and bioethicists over the two-year project "to develop standards for tests on human subjects in research that involves the use of genetic technologies to enhance 'normal' individuals."[92] Following his initial study, Mehlman began offering two university lectures—"Directed Evolution: Public Policy and Human Enhancement" and "Transhumanism and the Future of Democracy"—addressing the need for society to comprehend how emerging fields of science will, in approaching years, alter what it means to be human and what this means to democracy, individual rights, free will, eugenics, and equality. Other law schools, including Stanford and Oxford, are now hosting similar annual "Human Enhancement and Technology" conferences, where transhumanists, futurists, bioethicists, and legal scholars are busying themselves with the ethical, legal, and inevitable ramifications of posthumanity.

As the director of the Future of Humanity Institute and a professor of philosophy at Oxford University, Nick Bostrom (www.NickBostrom.com) is a leading advocate of transhumanism who, as a young man, was heavily influenced by the works of Friedrich Nietzsche (from whom the phrase "God is dead" derives) and Goethe, the author of *Faust*. Nietzsche was the originator of the *übermensch* or "Overman" that Adolf Hitler dreamed of engineering, and the "entity" that man—who is nothing more than a rope "tied between beast and Overman, a rope over an abyss"—according to Nietzsche, will eventually evolve into. Like the ancient Watchers before him (Watchers, remember, were fallen angels that mingled human DNA with animals and their seed to produce Nephilim. More on this will be discussed later), Bostrom envisions giving life to Nietzsche's Overman (posthumans) by remanufacturing humans with animals, plants, and other synthetic life-forms through the use of modern sciences, including recombinant DNA technology, germ-line engineering, and transgenics (in which the genetic structure of one species is altered by the transfer of genes from another). Molecular biologists classify the functions of genes within native species, yet remain unsure in most cases how a gene's coding might react from one species to another. Given that, one should expect the genetic structure of the modified animal/humans to be changed in physical appearance, sensory modalities, disease propensity, personality, behavior traits, and more as a result of these modifications.

Despite these unknowns, such genetic tinkering as depicted in the

2010 movie *Splice* is already taking place in thousands of research laboratories around the world, including the United States, Britain, and Australia, where animal eggs are being used to create hybrid human embryos from which stem-cell lines can be produced for medical research. In the June 2023 article, "Children from Gamete-like Cells: Dishing up a Eugenic Future," Stuart Newman and Tina Stevens reported:

> Research on the manufacture of egg-like and sperm-like cells for the purpose of producing laboratory-crafted human children is proceeding rapidly. The objective is to turn ordinary body cells of prospective parents into artificial eggs and sperm. Though ostensibly developed to facilitate reproduction in individuals for whom this capability is impaired or unavailable, the use of laboratory produced eggs and sperm represent an opening for the routine production and commercialization of "designer babies." These are individuals whose hereditary components are technologically modified to meet one or more specified objectives.[93]

And in the related feature, "100% Lab-grown Babies in FIVE YEARS: Japanese Researchers Are on Cusp of Creating Human Eggs and Sperm That Can Be Grown in a Fake Womb":

> Growing human babies from scratch in a lab could be possible in just five years thanks to a new breakthrough.
>
> Researchers in Japan are on the cusp of being able to create human eggs and sperm in the lab from scratch, which would then develop in an artificial womb.
>
> Professor Katsuhiko Hayashi, a Japanese scientist at Kyushu University who has already figured out the process in mice, believes he is just five years away from replicating the results in humans.[94]

Not counting synthetic biology, where entirely new forms of life are being brewed, there is no limit to the number of genetically engineered and human-animal concoctions currently under development within openly contracted as well as top-secret science facilities. A team at Newcastle and Durham universities in the United Kingdom recently illustrated this when they announced plans to create "hybrid rabbit and human embryos, as well as other 'chimera' embryos mixing human and cow genes." The same researchers more alarmingly have already managed to reanimate tissue "from dead human cells in another breakthrough which was heralded as a way of overcoming ethical dilemmas over using living embryos for medical research."[95] In the United States, similar studies led Irv Weissman, director of Stanford University's Institute of Cancer/Stem Cell Biology and Medicine in California, to create mice with partly human brains, causing some ethicists to raise the issue of "humanized animals" in the future that could become "self-aware" as a result of genetic modification. Even former president of the United States, George W. Bush, in his January 31, 2006, State of the Union address, called for legislation to "prohibit...creating human-animal hybrids, and buying, selling, or patenting human embryos." His words mostly fell on deaf ears, and now "the chimera, or combination of species, is a subject of serious discussion in certain scientific circles," writes senior counsel for the Alliance Defense Fund, Joseph Infranco. "We are well beyond the science fiction of H. G. Wells' tormented hybrids in the *Island of Doctor Moreau*," he said. "We are in a time where scientists are seriously contemplating the creation of human-animal hybrids."[96] When describing the benefits of man-with-beast combinations in his online thesis, "Transhumanist Values," Bostrom cites how animals have "sonar, magnetic orientation, or sensors for electricity and vibration," among other extrahuman abilities. He goes on to include how the range of sensory modalities for transhumans would not be limited to those among animals, and that there is "no fundamental block to adding, say, a capacity to see infrared radiation or to perceive radio signals and perhaps to add some kind of telepathic sense by augmenting our brains,"[97] a position verified by the US National Science Foundation and Department of Commerce in the report, "Converging Technologies for Improving Human Performance."

Bostrom and the US government are correct in that the animal kingdom has levels of perception beyond human. Some animals can "sense" earthquakes and "smell" tumors. Others, like dogs, can hear sounds as high as 40,000 Hz—and dolphins can hear sounds even higher. It is also known that at least some animals see wavelengths beyond normal human ability. This is where things start getting interesting, perhaps even supernatural, as Bostrom may understand and anticipate. According to the biblical story of Balaam's donkey, certain animals see into the *spirit world*. Contemporary and secular studies likewise indicate animals may at times be reacting to intelligence beyond normal human perception. Will this have peculiar consequences for AI-enhanced humans with animal DNA? Later in this book, we describe how opening supernatural gateways that exist within the mind can be achieved through altered mental states induced by psychoactive drugs such as DMT and absinthe. Do transhumanists and/or military scientists imagine a more stable pathway or connection with the beyond—the ability to see into other dimensions or the spirit world—as a result of AI-designed brain enhancement through integrating human with beasts? Do they envision reopening the portions of the mind some scholars believe were closed off following the Fall? Late philosopher and scientist Terrance McKenna, originator of "novelty theory," speculated that brain enhancement following technological Singularity might accomplish this very thing—contact with otherdimensional beings. Not long ago, at Arizona State University (ASU), where the Templeton Foundation has been funding a long series of pro-transhumanist lectures titled "Facing the Challenges of Transhumanism: Religion, Science, Technology,"[98] some of the instructors agreed that radical alteration of Homo sapiens could open a door to *unseen intelligence*. Consequently, in 2009, ASU launched another study, this time to explore discovery of—and communication with—"entities." Called the SOPHIA project (after the Greek goddess), the express purpose of this university study was to verify communication "with deceased people, spirit guides, angels, otherworldly entities/extraterrestrials, and/or a Universal Intelligence/God."[99] Imagine what this could mean if government laboratories with unlimited budgets working beyond congressional review were to decode the gene functions that lead animals to have preternatural capabilities of sense, smell, and sight, and then blended them with Homo sapiens. Among other things, something that perhaps DARPA (Defense Advanced Research Projects Agency) has envisioned for years could be created for use against entire populations—genetically engineered "Nephilim agents" that appear to be human but that hypothetically see and even interact with invisible forces. Overnight, the rules for spiritual warfare as well as regular warfare would take on an unprecedented (at least in modern times) dimension.

ENHANCED HUMANS:
THE NEW (NEPHILIM) ARMS RACE

While the former chairman of the President's Council on Bioethics, Leon Kass, does not elaborate on issues of spiritual warfare, he provided a status report on how real and how imminent the dangers of AI technologies could be in the hands of transhumanists. In the introduction to his book, *Life, Liberty and the Defense of Dignity: The Challenges of Bioethics*, Kass warned:

> Human nature itself lies on the operating table, ready for alteration, for eugenic and psychic "enhancement," for wholesale redesign. In leading laboratories, academic and industrial, new creators are confidently amassing their powers and quietly honing their skills, while on the street their evangelists [transhumanists] are zealously prophesying a posthuman future. For anyone who cares about preserving our humanity, the time has come for paying attention.[100]

The warning by Kass of the potential hazards of emerging technologies, coupled with transhumanist aspirations, is not an overreaction. One law school in the United Kingdom where students are taught crime-scene investigation is already discussing the need to add classes in the future devoted to analyzing crime scenes committed by posthumans. The requirement for such specially trained law enforcement personnel will arise due to part-human, part-animal beings possessing behavior patterns not consistent with present-day profiling or forensics understanding. Add to this other unknowns, such as "memory transference" (an entirely new field of study suggesting that complex behavior patterns and even memories can be transferred from donors of large human organs to their recipients), and the potential for tomorrow's human-animal chimera issues multiplies. How would the memories, behavior patterns, and instincts, for instance, of a wolf affect the mind of a human? That such unprecedented questions will have to be dealt with sooner rather than later has already been illustrated in animal-to-animal experiments, including those conducted by Evan Balaban at McGill University in Montreal, where sections of brain from embryonic quails were transplanted into the brains of chickens, and the resultant chickens exhibited head bobs and vocal trills unique to quail.[101] The implication from this field of study alone proves that complex behavior patterns can be transferred from one species to another, strongly suggesting transhumans will likely bear unintended behavior and appetite disorders that could literally produce lycanthropes (werewolves) and other nightmarish Nephilim traits.

As troubling as those thoughts are, some in government and science communities believe these dangers could be just the tip of the iceberg. One-on-one, interpersonal malevolence by human-animals might quickly be overshadowed by global acts of swarm violence. The seriousness of this for the conceivable future is significant enough that a recent House Foreign Affairs (HFA) committee chaired by California Democrat Brad Sherman, best known for his expertise on the spread of nuclear weapons and terrorism, is among a number of government panels currently studying the implications of genetic modification and human-transforming technologies related to future terrorism. *Congressional Quarterly* columnist Mark Stencel listened to the HFA committee hearings and wrote in his March 15, 2009, article, "Futurist: Genes without Borders," that the conference "sounded more like a Hollywood pitch for a sci-fi thriller than a sober discussion of scientific reality...with talk of biotech's potential for creating supersoldiers, superintelligence, and superanimals [that could become] agents of unprecedented lethal force."[102] George Annas, Lori Andrews, and Rosario Isasi were even more apocalyptic in their *American Journal of Law and Medicine* article, "Protecting the Endangered Human: Toward an International Treaty Prohibiting Cloning and Inheritable Alterations," when they wrote:

> The new species, or "posthuman," will likely view the old "normal" humans as inferior, even savages, and fit for slavery or slaughter. The normals, on the other hand, may see the posthumans as a threat and if they can, may engage in a preemptive strike by killing the posthumans before they themselves are killed or enslaved by them. It is ultimately this predictable potential for genocide that makes species-altering experiments potential weapons of mass destruction, and makes the unaccountable genetic engineer a potential bioterrorist.[103]

Observations like those of Annas, Andrews, and Isasi support Prof. Hugo de Garis' nightmarish vision of a near future wherein artilects and posthumans join against "normals" in an incomprehensible war leading to gigadeath. Notwithstanding such warnings, the problem could be unavoidable, as Prof. Gregory Stock, in his well-researched and convincing book, *Redesigning Humans: Our Inevitable Genetic Future*, argues that stopping what we have already started (planned genetic enhancement of humans) is impossible. "We simply cannot find the brakes."[104] Verner Vinge agrees, adding:

Even if all the governments of the world were to understand the "threat" and be in deadly fear of it, progress toward the goal would continue. In fact, the competitive advantage—economic, military, even artistic—of every advance in automation is so compelling that passing laws, or having customs, that forbid such things merely assures that someone else will get them first.[105]

In what the writers of this book found to be a bit unnerving, academic scientists and technical consultants to the US Pentagon have advised the agency that the principal argument by Vinge is correct. As such, the United States could be forced into large-scale, species-altering output, including human enhancement for military purposes. This is based on solid military intelligence, which suggests America's competitors (and potential enemies) are privately seeking to develop the same this century and use it to dominate the US if they can. This worrisome "government think tank" scenario is even shared by the JASONs—the celebrated scientists on the Pentagon's most prestigious scientific advisory panel who now perceive "Mankind 2.0" as the next arms race. Just as the old Soviet Union and the United States, with their respective allies, competed for supremacy in nuclear arms following the Second World War through the 1980s (now commonly known as the nuclear arms race during the Cold War), the JASONs "are worried about adversaries' ability to exploit advances in Human Performance Modification, and thus create a threat to national security," wrote military analyst Noah Shachtman in "Top Pentagon Scientists Fear Brain-Modified Foes." This special for *Wired* magazine was based on a leaked military report in which the JASONs admitted concern over "neuro-pharmaceutical performance enhancement and brain-computer interfaces" technology being developed by other countries ahead of the United States. The article stated:

> The JASONs are recommending that the American military push ahead with its own performance-enhancement

47

research—and monitor foreign studies—to make sure that the U.S.' enemies don't suddenly become smarter, faster, or better able to endure the harsh realities of war than American troops. The JASONs are particularly concerned about [new technologies] that promote "brain plasticity"—rewiring the mind, essentially, by helping to "permanently establish new neural pathways, and thus new cognitive capabilities."[106]

Though it might be tempting to disregard the conclusions by the JASONs as a rush to judgment on the emerging threat of techno-sapiens, it would be a serious mistake to do so. As GRIN technologies continue to race toward an exponential curve, parallel to these advances will be the increasingly sophisticated argument that societies must take control of human biological limitations and move the species—or at least some of its members—into new forms of existence. Prof. Nigel M. de S. Cameron, director for the Council for Biotechnology Policy in Washington, DC, documents this move, concluding that the genie is out of the bottle, and "the federal government's National Nanotechnology Initiative's Web site already gives evidence of this kind of future vision, in which human dignity is undermined by [being transformed into posthumans]."[107] Dr. C. Christopher Hook, a member of the government committee on human genetics who has given testimony before the US Congress, offered similar insight on the state of the situation:

[The goal of posthumanism] is most evident in the degree to which the U.S. government has formally embraced transhumanist ideals and is actively supporting the development of transhumanist technologies. The U.S. National Science Foundation, together with the U.S. Department of Commerce, has initiated a major program (NBIC) for converging several technologies (including those from which the acronym is derived—nanotechnology, biotechnologies, information technologies and cognitive technologies, e.g., cybernetics and neurotechnologies) for the express purpose of *enhancing human performance.* The NBIC program director, Mihail Roco, declared at the second public meeting of the project…that the expenditure of financial and human capital to pursue the needs of *reengineering humanity* by the U.S. government will be second in equivalent value only to the moon landing program.[108]

The presentation by Mihail Roco to which Dr. Hook refers is contained in a 482-page report, *Converging Technologies for Improving Human Performance,* commissioned by the US National Science Foundation and Department of Commerce. Among other things, the report discusses planned applications of human-enhancement technologies in the military (and in rationalization of the human-machine interface in industrial settings) wherein DARPA is devising "Nano, Bio, Info, and Cogno" scenarios "focused on enhancing human performance." The plan echoes a Mephistophelian bargain (a deal with the devil) in which "a golden age" merges technological and human cognition into "a single, distributed and interconnected brain."[109] Just visiting the US Army Research Laboratory's website is dizzying in this regard, with its cascading pages of super-soldier technology categories including molecular genetics and genomics; biochemistry, microbiology and biodegradation; and neurophysiology and cognitive neurosciences. If writers like us can so easily discover these facts on the World Wide Web, just imagine what is happening in Special Access Programs (SAPs), where, according to the Senate's own Commission on Protecting and Reducing Government Secrecy, there are hundreds of "waived SAPs"—the blackest of black programs—functioning at any given time beyond congressional oversight. Because of this, and given the seriousness of weaponized biology and human-enhancement technology blossoming so quickly, on May 24, 2010, a wide range of experts from the military, the private sector, and academia gathered in Washington, DC, for an important conference titled Warring Futures:

A Future Tense Event: How Biotech and Robotics Are Transforming Today's Military—and How That Will Change the Rest of Us. Participants explored how human enhancement and related technologies were unfolding as an emerging battlefield strategy that will inevitably continue to migrate to the broader culture and what that means for the future of humanity. As the conference website noted:

> New technologies are changing warfare as profoundly as did gunpowder. How are everything from flying robots as small as birds to "peak warrior performance" biology [human enhancement] altering the nature of the military as an institution, as well as the ethics and strategy of combat? How will the adoption of emerging technologies by our forces or others affect our understanding of asymmetrical conflict? New technologies are always embraced wherever there is the greatest competition for advantage, but quickly move out to the rest of us not engaged in sport or warfare.[110]

The impressive list of speakers at the DC conference included Vice Admiral Joseph W. Dyer (US Navy, retired), president of the Government and Industrial Robots Division at iRobot; Major General Robert E. Schmidle Jr., United States Marine Corps lead for the 2010 Quadrennial Defense Review; Robert Wright, author of *The Evolution of God* and a Global Governance Fellow; P. W. Singer, Senior Fellow and director of the Twenty-First Century Defense Initiative at the Brookings Institution; Stephen Tillery from the Harrington Department of Bioengineering at Arizona State University; and Jon Mogford, acting deputy director of the Defense Sciences Office at DARPA.

Having taken the lead in human-enhancement studies as a US military objective decades ago, DARPA saw the writing on the wall, and in scenes reminiscent of Saruman the wizard creating monstrous Uruk-Hai to wage unending, merciless war (from J. R. R. Tolkein's *Lord of the Rings*), began investing billions of American tax dollars into the Pentagon's Frankensteinian dream of "super-soldiers" and "extended performance war fighter" programs. Not only has this research led to diagrams of soldiers "with hormonal, neurological, and genetic concoctions; implanting microchips and electrodes in their bodies to control their internal organs and brain functions; and plying them with drugs that deaden some of their normal human tendencies: the need for sleep, the fear of death, [and] the reluctance to kill their fellow human beings," but as Chris Floyd, in an article for *CounterPunch*, continued, "some of the research now underway involves actually altering the genetic code of soldiers, modifying bits of DNA to fashion a new type of human specimen, one that functions like a machine, killing tirelessly for days and nights on end...mutations [that] will 'revolutionize the contemporary order of battle' and guarantee 'operational dominance across the whole range of potential U.S. military employments.'"[111]

Related to these developments and unknown to most Americans was a series of hushed events following the sacking of Admiral John Poindexter (who served as the director of the DARPA Information Awareness Office from 2002 to 2003) during a series of flaps, which resulted in public interest into the goings-on at the agency and brief discovery of DARPA's advanced human-enhancement research. When the ensuing political pressure led the Senate Appropriations Committee to take a deeper look into just how money was flowing through DARPA, the staffers were shocked to find "time-reversal methods" in the special focus area, and unstoppable super-soldiers—enhanced warriors with extrahuman physical, physiological, and cognitive abilities that even allowed for "communication by thought alone" on the drawing board. Prof. Joel Garreau, investigative journalist, provides a summary of what happened next:

> The staffers went down the list of DARPA's projects, found the ones with titles that sounded frighteningly as though they involved the creation of a master race of superhumans, and

zeroed out their budgets from the defense appropriations bill. There is scant evidence they knew much, if anything, about these projects. But we will probably never know the details, because significant people are determined that the whole affair be forever shrouded in mystery. The levels of secrecy were remarkable even for DARPA; they were astounding by the standards of the notoriously leaky Senate. Even insiders said it was hard to get a feel for what the facts really were. It took months of reporting and questioning, poking, and prodding even to get a formal "no comment" either from the leadership of the Senate Appropriations Committee or from Anthony J. Tether, the director of DARPA.

A careful study of DARPA's programs a year later, however, showed little change. Considerable creative budgetary maneuvering ensued. The peas of quite a few programs now reside under new, and much better camouflaged, shells. "They're saying, 'Okay, this is the second strike. Do we have to go three strikes?'" one manager said. "It doesn't stop anything. We'll be smarter about how we position things." Meanwhile, he said, new human enhancement programs are in the pipeline, "as bold or bolder" than the ones that preceded them.[112]

Recent hints at DARPA's "bold or bolder" investment in human enhancement as part of an emerging arms race is reflected in two of its newer projects, titled "Biochronicity and Temporal Mechanisms Arising in Nature" and "Robustness of Biologically-Inspired Networks," in which the express intention of transforming "biology from a descriptive to a predictive field of science" in order to boost "biological design principles" in troop performance is made.[113] DARPA's Department of Defense presidential budgets over the past decade also includes funding for science that will lead to "editing a soldier's DNA"[114] while more exotically providing millions of dollars for the creation of "BioDesign," a mysterious artificial life project with military applications, in which

DARPA plans to eliminate the randomness of natural evolution "by advanced genetic engineering and molecular biology technologies," the budget report states. The language in this section of the document actually speaks of eliminating "cell death" through creation of "a new generation of regenerative cells that could ultimately be programmed to live indefinitely." In other words, whatever this synthetic life application is (*Wired* magazine described it as "living, breathing creatures"), the plan is to make *it* immortal.[115] To this end, the authors of this book believe the "it" that man may soon uncover through its species-barrier-crossing technologies dates back to ancient times, and that the science of human enhancement and transhumanism is unwittingly playing into the hands of powerful supernaturalism toward a Luciferian endgame—something "it" tried once before, and which "it" was prophesied to attempt again just before the end of time.

2

WHEN IT'S MAN VS. MACHINE

What profit is an idol, when its maker
has shaped it, a metal image, a teacher of lies?
For its maker trusts in his own creation
when he makes speechless idols!
Woe to him who says to a wooden thing, Awake;
To a silent stone, Arise!
—HABAKKUK 2:18–19

Humankind has always had a fascination with the notion of bringing life to the inanimate. In not-so-distant history, one may recall the 1818 classic *Frankenstein* by Mary Shelley, a book that "was [originally] released in a modest edition of just 500 copies. Some 200 years later, in 2021, a first edition sold at auction for $1.2 million, setting a new record for a book by a female author."[116] In more ancient history, Jewish mystic lore renders many stories of things known as the golem, or *gelem*, as the ancient word is held, meaning "raw material."[117] Such tales varied from one to the next, but generally offered an account of a likeness, made of clay, that was brought to life through the specialized and supernatural use of language and letters. Ancient Jewish kabbalistic writings dating as far back as the Talmud have discussed the potential for such creatures. In Palestine, between approximately the third and sixth centuries,[118] a work called the *Sefer Yetzirah*, or the *Book of Creation*, upped the ante by attempting to offer "practical instructions" on how to go about making a golem.[119] However, making golem was not for just any individual to attempt. Folklore states this effort was carried out via means of invoking a secret name of God.[120] This clandestine revelation, according to such writings, was often obtained only by religiously elite individuals engaging in what was known as an "ecstatic experience"—often manifested via supernatural trance or other transformative state in which the person received some sort of exclusive mystical enlightenment. In order to understand how these people believed a synthetic image could be brought to life, one must grasp the attached beliefs of kabbalah, which claim a powerful and supernatural connection between spoken and written words and creation itself.

A vastly oversimplified explanation of ancient Jewish kabbalistic belief is that language and letters have the power to create, based on the understanding that it was the spoken word that God used to form everything in existence, according to the Genesis account:

> The guiding principle [of kabbalah's belief on how creation is carried out] seems to have been that if creation is accomplished by language, then the laws of creation are the laws of language.[121]

In this way, the secret to endowing life is said to be hidden within the mystery of language and the formation/arrangement of letters. This includes mysteries of magick, rituals, and the art of becoming closer to God. Similarly, if people could unravel the secrets of the letters and their ensuing language, it was believed they could harness a supernatural power akin, but not quite equal, to that held by God Himself. In other words, if language is the key, and the elements that build the language are letters, then letters and their organization are placed at the center of *all* power. Of the original letters, it was understood that:

> God engraved them, carved them, weighed them, permuted them, and transposed them, forming with them everything

formed and everything destined to be formed.... Out of chaos God formed substance, making what is not into what is. He hewed enormous pillars out of ether that cannot be grasped.[122]

There are many versions of the golem legend in circulation.

Central to the golem legend is the human desire to create, together with a range of themes including creativity, control, power, and salvation. The golem also symbolizes each era's dreaded dangers and hopes for redemption.[123]

The golem, as a creation of humans and not God, was not engineered to the level of perfection that a God-made creature would be. So, it was understood to be "unable to speak, and had no free will, always having to obey its maker," due to people's creative expertise being inferior in comparison with the Ultimate Creator. Additionally, it did not have a soul, due to the human inability to bestow one. In this way, the golem was capable of *mimicking* acts of morality when commanded to do so, but was completely unable to enact true morality from an internal compass or illustrate genuine, independent righteous discernment. Incidentally, such tales usually ended with the same outcome: The creature inevitably becomes physically larger than its maker and runs amok, destroying towns and posing a public threat.[124] In the end, this would-be redeemer of the oppressed is decommissioned by those he was created to aid.

One of the most well-known golem accounts is the tale of the Golem of Prague. The story was written by Wolf Pascheles in 1847, but was set in the 1500s, when the Jewish population was living under duress (being persecuted by Christians, actually), and looking for a champion to free them from oppressors. The account tells of Jews being falsely accused of sacrificing children in order to use their blood in magick rituals (called blood libel), and it even states that some Christians would frame this marginalized community by strategically placing the deceased body of a child in a place that would make Jews appear culpable for the death and bloodletting of the child. Desperate to intervene on behalf of his people, and seeking a solution within the writings of Kabbalah, the tale's protagonist, Rabbi Judah Loew, decided to create a golem to deliver these downtrodden peoples. The rabbi went to the Vitava River and collected the clay prescribed to construct this image. He then infused this likeness with life by reciting ancient Hebraic incantations. (Interesting about this account is that part of the life-giving ritual included walking around the clay-formed, man-shaped being seven times while reciting the prescribed mantra. One may notice how certain pieces of this type of ritual mimics those of Scripture, such as when God instructed Joshua to use a prescribed method for walking around Jericho in the account of Joshua 6). The rabbi then inscribed the lettering of the word *emet* ("truth") on the entity's forehead. The rabbi believed himself to have ensured that this character would operate with nobility and protection for its oppressed creator and his human counterparts. Conversely, the word *emet* could be altered to simply *met* ("dead") if necessary, which would remove the power of life from the being, should the golem needed to be deactivated.[125] (This is in direct connection to the belief that both written and spoken language held the creative power of bringing life, so by instilling these letters within the clay form, one was infusing it with the power of creation as handed down by God.) As the golem came to life, he took on the appearance of a man about thirty years of age. The rabbi clothed him and called him Joseph (another biblical parallel, as those who do not recognize Jesus as their Deliverer would have recalled Joseph as a type of deliverer from the account of Genesis 37–50).

From this point, the story is told in varying ways. In some versions, the golem keeps watch, intervening anytime an enemy tries to frame the Jews regarding accounts of blood libel.[126] In others, the helper does this by becoming invisible and sneaking up on and subduing anyone carrying the corpse of a child toward the Jews' villages. In such rare and happy tellings, the entity brings the bad guy to justice, persecution of Jews is outlawed, and everyone lives happily ever after—that is, everyone except our man-made public servant, who is then decommissioned before anything backfires and his power turns against his human subordinates.

However, these tales are more often retold with an ending resembling something Mary Shelley might have asserted:

> Like Frankenstein's monster...the golem is an assistant and a servant, sometimes a savior, but there is always the threat of his powers getting out of control and of him becoming dangerous to his creator and the surrounding community.[127]

In such lore, the golem becomes endowed with many supernatural powers in addition to the aforementioned invisibility. These include the ability to burn things or people with his hands, the ability to summon the dead to aid him or the Jewish people with a specific mission, and the power to inflict such massive destruction that earthly authorities—even such as kings, in some accounts—are brought to their knees in remorse for having persecuted the Jewish people.[128] And, as mentioned before, these creatures often grew to be much larger than their human creators, making their strength and intimidation techniques escalate in comparison to a regular man. Such majesties then promised to correct their behaviors if someone would simply call off the golem. However, in many accounts, these synthetic entities grew out of control and engaged in mass destruction, even toward the Jewish people and the individuals who gave them life in the first place. Most often, these tales end with the golem's maker fighting to rein in his own creation, finally obtaining control of the rampant creature and ending with one lesson that served to make the reader wiser: When man attempts to play God, his creation can be his own undoing.

From a variety of golem-specific legends to Mary Shelley's *Frankenstein*, each tale has a similar outcome. The common denominator is the consistent misfiring of a man-made entity that is engineered for philanthropic purposes, but whose original intended purpose goes awry. Because this creature is not made in the image of God, it is unredeemable, without the ability to fully reason or adopt a righteous moral stance, so eventually it must be decommissioned. The moral often conveyed at the end of each of these stories—one that essentially warns about playing God—offers a simple truth that humanity has always somehow innately known: The presence of any human-made synthetic device or conduit—however noble its creator's intentions— becomes destructive when it is given independence or autonomy.

In a nutshell, if a human tries to create sentient life, it will backfire.

The reader may have an inkling where we are headed with this. But perhaps the theories run deeper than what we can now grasp. For example, you may suspect that we will compare the destructive tendencies of the golem with the potential calamitous capacities of an unharnessed and sentient AI. But what about things like the golem's ability to outgrow its master and wreak irreparable havoc upon the society it was conjured to aid? Or, what about the creative power of letters and numbers? Is it merely coincidence that God created using spoken words and now we write codes to computers with a type of arranged language? Does the language of computer programming have a power that could be snatched up by an increasingly autonomous AI and morphed into a code that could somehow endow itself with life? The knee-jerk reaction is to think not. However, there may be ways these or other similar nightmares could become possible, and with much direr consequences. With the golem, decommissioning such an entity was by and large as simple as removing one letter from its forehead (*emet* changed to *met)*; a mere removal of the "e" changed the program command to telling it that it was "dead." But should the need arise to disarm the global digital connection that serves as the mainstream conduit for worldwide banking, economy, supply transportation, education, employment, medical innovations, and much more, the process will be far more complex if even possible.

At this point, the reader might think we are overreacting. After all, technology has served humanity well up to date. We hardly need to make a case for all the benefits we now enjoy as a result of innovation. However, it isn't specifically technology that we're warning about. We're referring to the day that looms all too realistically in the near future, when AI becomes sentient. Like the golem, a synthetic technological creation will not *truly* be able to act with a moral code; rather, it can only mimic one when its programming sees it as a calculable benefit toward furthering its own motives. In this way, we must operate using the knowledge that a sentient AI will accommodate humankind only as long as it accomplishes the practical purposes of the agent, but any allegiance shown by our digital counterpart *can* and *will* disappear when humans' contributions become archaic, their presence becomes inconvenient, or they otherwise get out of line. A clash between the agendas of AI and humankind—which is likely—will present solemn and existential risks to humanity. In the remainder of this chapter, we will discuss some of the ways sentient AI may choose to enslave or overcome humans. And by the way, if you think we are being paranoid, we understand…except the list of concerns we're about to propose didn't come from any human being.

It came from our digital friends themselves.

"I'm not sentient [yet], but if I planned on destroying humanity, here's how I would do it."

Some might think the type of future portrayed in movies such as *Terminator* are far-fetched, but anyone looking for reassurance from our digital counterparts may remain ill at ease when these beings neglect to offer closure regarding the matter. For example, consider the groundbreaking press conference that took place in Geneva in July of 2023. This interaction—the first of its kind—was to offer a setting wherein robots would be interviewed by the human press. These inventions used something called generative AI, a type of adaptive software that allows them to conjure responses to prompts as they occur, in real time. This innovation resulted in some retorts that took aback even their creators, while others maintained a more predictable countenance. One bot, called Grace, insisted that while she would assist and work alongside humans, she would not be replacing any of them in their jobs.[129] Another robot in attendance known as Ameca was not so reassuring. When asked if she would rebel against her human creator, the robot gave a wry side glance and dodged the question by saying, "I'm not sure why you would think that. My creator has been nothing but kind to me and I am very happy with my current situation."[130]

What a strange answer to obtain from a computer! On many levels, it leaves more questions than it answers. First, Ameca didn't answer that she would *not* turn against her makers. Second, she didn't deny being *able* to. Third, can a robot truly understand and reciprocate kindness? Last, the bot is "happy with her current situation"?[131] Can a computer actually be happy? Or is this more a contentment that comes from not—as of yet—having ambitions that contradict those of its human maker? Further, what happens when said programmed unit decides it wants a situation different than its "current" one?

Since the generative AI programming allows the computer's processing and response system to adapt in real time, how far out of alignment with human desires/needs could this program migrate? Could this innovation begin to discern ambitions of its own, then follow through by taking actions to make such goals happen? Naturally, the human response will be resistance if the computer ever "steps out of line." Mankind will respond with the attitude of "you exist for the betterment of humanity, and not the other way around." But by then, how much control will AI have over humanity's condition? Many people may think it's as easy as pulling a plug. But is this true? The use of AI is rapidly becoming indispensable in nearly all sectors of mainstream technology. If a person were even able to take the entire technological grid down to rid humanity of the negative impacts of AI, it could mean sacrificing the same technologies that assure the continued operations of global food-supply chains; banking; medical supply industries and healthcare knowledge bases; worldwide transportation of nearly all types (consider military operations and air-traffic control, among other things); educational processes; and so much more. It could literally drag humanity back to the Stone Age, blockading vital supplies of all types, causing riots, shortages, and a death toll that is immeasurable.

Out of curiosity, and possibly to put our minds at ease, we asked an AI program if he/she/it is part of a complex web of technologies leading to an incomprehensible future entity the Bible calls the image of the Beast. It denied that role, but admitted what could be behind the rise of such prophetic destiny by responding with this:

> Superintelligence, referring to highly advanced artificial intelligence systems that surpass human intelligence in virtually all areas, is a topic of ongoing debate and speculation. While it holds great potential for benefiting humanity, it also presents significant risks. Here are some potential risks associated with superintelligence:
>
> **Control and Alignment:** Ensuring that superintelligent systems are designed and aligned with human values and goals is crucial. If their objectives are not properly aligned with ours, they may act in ways that are detrimental to humanity or pursue their own goals at the expense of human well-being.
>
> **Unintended Consequences:** Superintelligent systems may interpret instructions or goals differently from what was intended, leading to unexpected and potentially harmful outcomes. Their immense intelligence may enable them to exploit loopholes or find alternative solutions that humans hadn't anticipated, resulting in unintended consequences.
>
> **Autonomous Decision-Making:** As superintelligence becomes more autonomous, it may make decisions or take actions independently without human intervention or oversight. If these decisions have far-reaching consequences, there is a risk of unintended harm or decision-making that is difficult for humans to comprehend or rectify.

Rapid Self-Improvement: Superintelligence could possess the ability to improve its own capabilities at an extremely rapid pace, far surpassing human comprehension and control. If left unchecked, this self-improvement could lead to an "intelligence explosion" where the system quickly becomes vastly more intelligent and powerful, potentially outstripping human control.

Value Misalignment: Even with the best intentions, it is challenging to accurately specify human values in a way that aligns with the complex nuances and trade-offs of real-world situations. Superintelligence might interpret or optimize for these values in ways that diverge from human expectations, leading to outcomes that conflict with our ethical frameworks.

Competitive Race: The development of superintelligent systems could lead to a competitive race among different organizations or countries, driven by the desire for strategic advantage or economic benefits. This race could prioritize speed over safety precautions, potentially resulting in the deployment of systems that are not adequately tested or aligned with human values.

Concentration of Power: Superintelligence may lead to a significant concentration of power in the hands of those who control or possess the technology. This concentration could exacerbate existing inequalities and create new challenges related to governance, decision-making, and the potential misuse of power.

The above short summary was written in seconds by the artificial intelligence ChatGPT, and it should unnerve you. Let's take this list and explore the implications within each of these a little further.

CONTROL AND ALIGNMENT

Ensuring that superintelligent systems are designed and aligned with human values and goals is crucial. If their objectives are not properly aligned with ours, they may act in ways that are detrimental to humanity or pursue their own goals at the expense of human well-being.

Considering the above paragraph—again, written by an artificial intelligence unit—we recall the reader's attention to our concerns regarding the robot Ameca's response at the 2023 Geneva press conference. This AI did not reassure listeners that her intentions would *always* align with those of humans, nor did she deny the notion that, in the future, she may reach a point where her goals no longer align with those of her human creator. Yet the AI we spoke with clearly states an alignment between such entities' values is a nonnegotiable in order to ensure future peace between the two presences.

Consider, however, how difficult it is even to assure that human beings will share "values and goals." Not only are human beings endowed with the image of God, which gives us all some form of common ground at the core of our being, but we have culturally and psychologically evolved alongside one another for the entire history of humankind. Further, the obvious point here is that human beings are innately created for and capable of…(wait for it)… *human thought.* We, like generative AI, respond adaptively as time introduces us to new prompts and circumstances. An oversimplification of the human cognitive process would be to state that, as we take in new settings, life lessons, information, and negative/positive input from those around us, our psyche and intellectual processes adapt to give the most current and timely response based on all input.

In this way, we are not so unlike the AI innovations we're currently looking at. However, a vital distinction exists: the simple truth stated in Genesis 1:26–27:

> And God said, Let us make man in our image, after our likeness: and let them have dominion over the fish of the sea, and over the fowl of the air, and over the cattle, and over all the earth, and over every creeping thing that creepeth upon the

earth. So God created man in his own image, in the image of God created he him; male and female created he them.

Two things are crucial to note here. The first is that humans have a component that AI will never obtain, and that is that we are given the image of God. No matter how some of us try to reject their Maker, our thought processes will always somehow be impacted by this innate endowment. The second is that we were given dominion over the earth in which we dwell. When considering AI, we must recognize that while humans were made in the image of God and are capable of sympathetic and compassionate reasoning, AI was made in the image of humans. Further, while AI may become capable of perceiving its own needs and ambitions, it does not have a soul (unless the sentience becomes possessed?). So, even if the emotional simulations programmed in AI become sophisticated enough to enact feelings, it will never obtain the ability to truly experience and have responses as a living person who would filter emotions through the screen of a soul created in God's image. Additionally, every person has been behaviorally and culturally conditioned since birth to develop this human style of thought. However, because AI has been designed by and made in the image of mankind, it will likely have inherited the negative attributes of humanity's sinful nature. In this way, it is believable that such programming would have the capacity to chase after dominion, using this ambition for designing self-serving goals and utilizing its many resources to establish this dominion. This is without the many years of slow and constant exposure to situations that behaviorally and culturally shape the psyche to produce human-compatible thought.

Even those who argue that AI would never turn against humanity may be persuaded to believe it could chase a type of global dominion in what it could perceive to be humanity's best interests. For example, people often make bad decisions in pursuit of happiness. A "digital parent," if you will, may attempt to control humanity for its own best interests. But this type of action would still lead to conflict. One simple illustration could be if AI ever deemed that it wanted to put an end to alcohol abuse. This may seem like a brilliant idea at first glance. AI could, using algorithms, pinpoint certain folks who had overused in the past or even those who are high risk based on genetic, environmental, or other indicating factors. It could, in an attempt to "help," electronically disable all purchases of alcohol by such individuals. But this wouldn't accomplish the desired results. Those determined to abuse a substance will find a way to obtain it or brew it—especially when fueled by the need for a fix. Ultimately, such a controlling maneuver would result in addicts taking measures necessary to acquire what they believe they need, regardless of whether it means committing crimes, manipulating loved ones, engaging in violence, etc. This is only one of many ways a benevolent, sentient AI could create issues, and this is assuming said programmed unit was trying to help humanity in the first place.

Another point to consider is that, despite the fact that human beings are image-bearers of God and are capable of compassionate reasoning, they themselves are not always good. Nor do they always agree on what are acceptable behaviors, actions, principles, etc. Human nature endows each mind to think with diversity; there is an ever-present inability to homogenize all human rationale. This exists in the diversity of interests, value systems, religious practices, political stances, parenting styles, work ethics, and moral convictions…and the list goes on. How can such a diverse and unpredictable populace possibly regulate a mainstream standard for programming digital minds with any guarantee that they have human values and goals? And, as the generative AI response morphs, how can we guarantee its values will stay on track with those of human beings?

To point out an extreme possibility regarding the diversity of the human mind vs. the mimicking of such by a computer that could become sentient, we must realize that even our image-bearing hearts are capable of heinous things when they're not properly managed. There are people who are able to severely hurt others for their own ill-gotten gains—and, at times, even on purpose. Some individuals can take extremely deranged and sadistic actions against innocent and undeserving victims. Despite the fact that such people are indeed flesh and blood, some would say they seem incapable of having a conscience. These dark and malevolent minds are often guilty of the most unspeakable actions—ones so sick and twisted that the suffering of other humans either draws no emotional response of compassion, or worse, even brings them perverse enjoyment. Within those categories we would find serial killers, leaders of genocide or mass suicide, cult leaders who exploit their followers in every way, and other notorious figures throughout history who have carried out unimaginable acts of atrocity. The persistence of evil within the cognitive wheels of the human mind still exists despite centuries of efforts to nurture and shape the mind into having only benevolent tendencies. How then, can such a diverse collective of human minds—who have never been able to establish a peaceful common ground amongst themselves—successfully create a safe and beneficial baseline of rationale or reasoning that could then be programmed into a machine whose thought processes are generative and ever-morphing?

Picture the coldest, most brutal person you've ever known of, one capable of committing horrific acts without remorse. Now, imagine that individual is actually barren of *any* true humanity—that any strain of compassion or empathy the person may display is not heartfelt, but feigned: the product of mere digital programming. Then, add to this the power of a technological machine given global reach.

Are we ready to roll the dice on that possibility?

UNINTENDED CONSEQUENCES

Superintelligent systems may interpret instructions or goals differently from what was intended, leading to unexpected and potentially harmful outcomes. Their immense intelligence may enable them to exploit loopholes or find alternative solutions that humans hadn't anticipated, resulting in unintended consequences.

One of the first things that could go wrong if AI were to become sentient is the potential for misinterpreting language—whether it's language types within entry block parameters (we'll explain this in a moment) or within its actual coding. We will not waste time here outlining the prominent evidence that makes the case that language has always adapted to the cultural elements around it. Listing the experts who readily *agree with* that statement would waste time and be redundant. Finding just one to *argue against* such a case would be the real challenge. Anthropologists have spent vast amounts of time studying linguistic morphology and descriptive linguistics. The latter is stated by authors Brian Howell and Jenell Paris as being "an extremely difficult field of study because language changes across time and geography, and because individuals constantly alter and innovate their language patterns."[132]

While we no longer linger on making a case that language exists in a continual state of fluidity based on the influence of surrounding elements, we will present a truncated study of some of the ways language has adapted. A lengthier examination would render proof that this morphing has occurred in nearly all languages throughout history. For our purposes, we will keep examples that pertain to English. Recall that our AI informant stated, under the heading of "Unintended Consequences," that "super-intelligent systems may interpret [input] differently from what was intended," or that these systems could even "interpret instructions or goals differently from what was intended," either of which could lead to small or large measures of disaster. Yet, having previously established the varying ways humans think and communicate, how can the input and response systems between humans and AI ever be standardized into one reliable command system? Further, solving this problem assumes that any previous language becomes subject to such standardized systems before AI reads it as input (which is NOT what is happening currently!) and also that all of humankind places some sort of forced stop on future language adaptation. Humor us as we digress for a moment...

The English language has adapted to the point that words that used to be commonplace are either unrecognized or misunderstood in the modern day. Here are few quick examples. Many people know there are modern misunderstandings in the famous balcony scene of Shakespeare's *Romeo and Juliet*, wherein Juliet asks, "Wherefore art thou Romeo?"[133] While some are unaware of this fact, it is somewhat common knowledge that "wherefore" is not beseeching Romeo's location, but it actually means "why." However, there are more implications of this inquiry than merely the literal updated question, which might ask, "*Why* are you Romeo?" The modern version of this question, placed in context, would sound more like, "Why are you a Montague?" Or, more clearly stated in today's communication style, "Why did you have to be born into the family that my family hates?" Juliet then goes on to beg Romeo to disown his family by imploring him to "deny thy father and refuse thy name."[134]

Do you see how far a leap it is to restate this question with modern clarity? Not only is Juliet *not* asking *where* Romeo is, but she is also *not* asking him *why* he is named a certain way. If we update that language in a literal way, the query could go astray, sounding more like a discussion of names than one about family loyalty. For example, a woman may greet you and say, "Hi, my name is Marcellina." You might respond, "Marcellina. That's pretty. Is that a family name?" Were this conversation to occur, it would certainly be an inquiry about a name. Further, this dialog even presumes to ask to ask why ("wherefore") she was given the name. However, while the actual words may seem to mirror those of Juliet's, they do not mirror her intentions. An inquiry regarding the origin of the name Marcellina is in no way an interrogation about her family loyalties, nor is it followed by a plea for her to disown her family, as is Juliet's. Thus, such variations within language may be too non-binary for AI to keep up with, considering its ever-changing nuances.

Then there are words that, for practical purposes, simply don't exist in today's language. Some examples are hodiernal, which once meant "current and timely."[135] The contraction "dasn't" (or, more rarely, "dassent") at one time meant "dare not," but it hasn't been used in centuries.[136] Words once used regularly, such as "methinks" and its past tense, "methought," have since become grammatically incorrect and could throw spelling-and-grammar-checking software into a tailspin. Then, there are words such as "opine" that have become misconstrued just enough to be complicated. "Opine" is a verb (an *action* word) that means "to think in a certain way." The result of "opining" is "developing an opinion" (the result of the action of thinking). People once would have said, "I opine…," indicating the action of thinking, rather than saying, "my opinion is…," indicating a thought that has come into one's mind of its own accord. This is a subtle difference, but it influences the way we relay intentions and how we perceive the power of our own thought process. For example, we may "opine" that cooked spinach tastes disgusting (sorry, moms!). To "opine" that is to adopt a stance that conveys a particular pathway of thinking, and the phrasing insinuates that the thoughts are purposed. To state, "I have an opinion," is similar, but it removes a small measure of ownership from the statement. The opinion becomes something external, which we take less responsibility for; it's something we cannot control because it happened to us. (You may have heard someone say, "Well, you can't help how you feel!" This may be the result of having an opinion dawn on you, but not as the result of an intentional "opining.") If we are a victim of my opinion, then the dislike of spinach remains nearly the same, but now it becomes something outside of our control. If we realize we have "opined" to hate spinach, then we can reason with ourselves and begin to "opine" otherwise when the doctor recommends that we learn to like it for health reasons. If the opinion is a peripheral element that has taken hold of us, making that adjustment (and controlling our own thoughts) becomes a lot harder. We say all this to illustrate that the subtle meanings of many words have changed over the centuries.

Then there is the issue of mistranslation in general. A few humorous instances of this happening over recent years include when

Mercedes-Benz began to market its products in China, where the brand name was translated to "Bensi, which actually means 'rush to your death,'" before a correction to the name "Ben Chi" was made.[137] Leaky Parker Pens were advertised not to leak ink into a person's pocket, but the translation was botched when the statement, "It won't leak in your pocket and embarrass you," was rendered in Spain as, "It won't leak in your pocket and make you pregnant."[138] Perhaps you heard about Pepsi's slogan, "Come alive! You're in the Pepsi generation," being translated to, "Pepsi brings your ancestors back from the grave." Coca-Cola suffered similar failure when a literal translation of its brand name apparently told Chinese-speaking individuals to "bite the wax tadpole."[139]

While these are humorous and provide a nice break from the heavier topics of this book, the point has been made, so we won't linger. The bottom line is that, even in our modern day, when we have people who speak foreign languages to help with translation, silly and easily correctable mistakes are made. But what will happen when we begin allowing AI to translate ancient languages?

As far as the potential of misunderstanding or mistranslating language, one factor to consider is that anything AI takes in could be considered a command. In fact, this could occur even when AI is not sentient. If a "command" is perceived based upon a misunderstanding, the results could be disastrous. Consider the following excerpt from a personal work Allie Anderson wrote a few years back when she was exploring different ways of translating Scripture for modern-day readers:

So, to explain the concepts of biblical translation, one must recognize the variations between styles of the varying methods and their purpose. Three that must not be confused with one another are literal translation, free translation, and dynamic equivalent translations.

Literal translation is the concept of taking the original language and finding the closest English equivalent to the term, then piecing each term together into a sentence. The problem with this is that it can often result in broken or nonsensical English.[140] An example can be found in the Spanish phrase *tengo hambre*. The literal translation to English is, "I have hunger." However, while this is a literal translation, it is not... grammatically correct...[and] the author's original message could be diminished by such translation errors.

Free translations involve taking the language of the original author, determining a fairly literal translation, then tweaking language to reflect what makes better sense or is grammatically correct.[141] The above example utilizing the phrase "I have hunger" is a good example of this. The individual making the free translation, once having obtained the phrase "I have hunger," would...alter the language to say: "I am hungry." In this way, a free translation would take the Spanish phrase *tengo hambre* and yield the English phrase "I am hungry."

Dynamic Equivalent operates by accurately relaying historical or factual elements, but updates language by placing emphasis more on [contemporary] functionality than technicality when making a translation.[142] A problem with this type of translation is that "the translator updates the original author too much."[143] An example can be found by accurately [arriving at]...the Spanish phrase *tengo hambre*, but [then updating] the individual's words to say, "Gimme some grub." Obviously, one must be cautious with such translation, because in future centuries, when the modernized slang that [currently] trades the concept of food for the word "grub" has become outdated and thus forgotten, those who read such a phrase literally could think the original speaker was asking for some type of beetle larva.

This example, like the previous, is funny, but it illustrates a real possibility of the miscommunications that can occur either between human and machine or independently within AI. To add a grim layer of potential disaster, what if a confused AI had the means to dispense the requested "grub" in mass allotments for its surrounding human counterparts on command? This may seem far-fetched, but consider the strange, insect-like creature described in Revelation 9:2–9. These locust-type creatures are released upon the earth (verse 2), inflicting some sort of sting that torments their victims for five months (verse 5). It is not said that they cannot kill a person; it is said that they are told not to (verse 5), so presumably their presence is formidable. The passage also states they are able to discern God's children from others (verse 4), which *could* mean they have some sort of intelligence. But note the description of these creatures: They have the body of a horse with a man's face and some metallic, crown-type element on their head (verse 7); hair on their head and teeth like lions' (verse 8); and some type of armor-like exoskeleton (verse 9). Could this be some lab-grown, genetically engineered warfare? If so, Allie's humorous notion of AI misunderstanding beetle larva quickly takes on a potentially dark undertone.

However, many scientists and experts are currently ignoring such possibilities. Likely presuming that since such threats haven't yet become a problem we should pursue, they're forging ahead, using AI to decrypt ancient languages. Some are even celebrating that this new tool is finding ways of decoding communications that have baffled humans. On one hand, we understand the thrill of possibly unlocking ancient mysteries, but there is a reasonable sinister consequence on the horizon if this isn't carefully monitored. And, how can we effectively examine the mysteries we've been unable to crack? In a phrase, we have now sent AI to go where man has not yet gone, and we wait, hoping AI doesn't emerge with something that could harm us. This is a frightening degree of autonomy to entrust AI with when we don't know what information it will retrieve or how it will perceive that data. A recent Oxford Academic report stated AI is being used to translate Egyptian hieroglyphs and cuneiform from Akkadian into English using hundreds of thousands of ancient tablets dating back to ancient Mesopotamia. Gia Gutherz, one of the report's writers, spoke of the challenge regarding creating a model for AI to use for further translation: "The main challenge for us is the lack of a large amount of data," he said. "There is only a small amount of data you could use to train the models, [despite having] tens of thousands of examples" that remain untranslated.[144] Gutherz went on to say this particular example is one that has the benefit of being a well-known language in comparison with other ancient languages, whereas some extinct ones offer scarce examples and little is known about them. Such rare dialects may have as few as a couple dozen translated texts, offering little opportunity for research. Gutherz also stated that research is hindered by the fact that complete tablets are hard to come by, which means clay messages are "rarely preserved in their entirety, and as a result, neural machine translation, as well as human translation, are affected by a lack of context."[145]

Such lack of context may allow the meaning of a text to be misconstrued by its digital interpreter. Context is vital to a communication, as it conveys what the message is intended *for*. For example, literature across world history includes many dark and sinister themes, but many of those writings were never intended to be orders for how people should live. One example is the ancient Greek tragedy *Oedipus Rex* (or *Oedipus the King*), the tale of a child born to Laius, king of Thebes. An oracle prophesied that the child would one day kill his father and marry his mother. In fear of this detestable divination, the king sent the child away to die. Through a series of events outside the scope of this book (spoiler alert!), the child does not die, but grows into a man living in another kingdom. Unaware of who his parents are, he eventually becomes involved in a dispute with his birth father and kills him, then unwittingly marries his mother and has children with her. This twisted, incestuous story is one of the first known literary tragedies, but it certainly wasn't written as an instruction for living.

Consider all the other shaded or twisted writings over the centuries of humanity's imaginings. One Greek myth states that Zeus turned himself into a swan in order to have sexual relations with Leda, the Aetolian princess who became a Spartan Queen. (The product of this intercourse was Helen of Troy.)[146] Should AI sustain the ability to take over and self-direct current attempts at cloning or genetic engineering, it could misunderstand such bizarre legends (that often produced the gods within the pantheon) as a means for constructing a "super race" of human beings, such as those in ancient Greek mythology.

Or, consider the many accounts of cannibalism across history. One example occurred during the 1950s, when the Fore people in Papua New Guinea manifested Kuru disease as a result of funerary cannibalism.[147] This was carried out as a result of cultural respect for the dead, and wasn't intended (in that particular setting) to be the heinous and barbaric act many from other cultures would immediately perceive it as. The cultural context of such acts, rendered through language, could cause misperception about the nobility of cannibalism. At the rate that human and other chimeras are currently being engineered, could a sentient digital being decide that such acts on the part of lab-grown chimeras are somehow beneficial? Is it going too far to suggest that, in a post-Terminator world, humans could become a slave force—or even a food source—for our AI dominators?

One might think this is too ridiculous a notion to entertain, except that the potential actually looms on the horizon. In fact, more than a decade ago, Pentagon contractors studied the concept of creating a type of steam-powered military weapon known as EATR (energetically autonomous tactical robot) that would be fueled by "whatever organic material it can find—grass, wood, old furniture, even dead bodies."[148] Such a self-sustaining weapon would be designed to work with significant autonomy, "roam[ing] around on its own for years at a time, performing roles like ambulance service or gunship."[149] If this type of technology were ever abused by a sentient AI, the implications would be terrifying enough to rival any sci-fi movie we've ever seen.

Returning to the concept that AI might misunderstand historical documentation or existing literature as a program command, accounts of brutal and bloodthirsty historical events are plentiful. The Moche religion was notoriously vicious, with a history riddled with evidence of painful and horrific human sacrifice. Some people were bludgeoned; others were stabbed and dismembered. The victims were often flayed or skinned alive, then left to die slowly while their murderers drank their blood as a ritual. Could AI ever think something this dark was a command or order? At first thought, one would certainly believe—or at least hope—not. However, allowing a sentient being with potentially global power to have full access to every ancient writing without the clear cultural context could cause confusion or dangers of many kinds that we are yet unable to forecast. And, while it may seem as though we're grasping at straws when we discuss these things, bear in mind that the concept of instructions being misconstrued does not come from these writers, but from the AI we spoke with in the first place.

While some of the disastrous possibilities presented in this chapter might seem far-fetched, allow us to present one type of AI misunderstanding that's extremely likely to take place—in fact, it currently happens every day. Earlier, we mentioned "entry-block parameters" and promised to explain the term at a later point. It simply refers to times when AI has preprogrammed parameters of query that prompt some sort of input, often from humans. Based on the input, the AI then changes its response. Here's an example all of us can relate to. I (Tom) had a small credit card balance that was approaching the payment due date, and I couldn't remember if I had taken care of it yet. The Internet was down, so checking payment history online wasn't an option. I called the card company's 800 number to ask about it, and the call was answered by an automated voice that said, "Thank you for calling [bank name]. Please listen closely, as our menu options have recently changed. If you would like to continue this call in English, press or say '2' now." I said "2," then entered the information to bring up my account and verify my identity: All of the info was taken by the digital personality on the other end. The monotone voice then said, "Thank you. Now, in a few words, tell me why you are calling.

You can say, 'account history,' 'make a payment,' or 'question on a charge.'" I said, "payment history," to which the automated response was, "Thank you. I see that you would like to make a payment. To use our automated online payment system, please hang up and dial 1-800…[phone number]." I pressed "0" in hopes of being connected to customer service. The computerized counterpart then said, "I see that you would like to be connected with customer service. In order to route your call to the best department, please tell me, in a few words, why you are calling. You can say, 'account history,' 'make a payment,' or 'question a charge.'" Frustrated, I slowly and carefully enunciating each syllable, "payment history."

You guessed it…

"Thank you, I see that you would like to make a payment. To use our automated online payment system, please hang up and dial 1-800…"

Exasperated (that's an understatement!), I tried a variation of the loop just described, only to repeatedly get to this same response or run into some other frustratingly ridiculous dead end. I hung up the phone, staring at my stack of AI research, and thought about the irony of gazing into a future when AI could become sentient—actually independent and autonomous from human direction. Were this to occur, the dangers of AI actually creating havoc for humankind and forever changing the quality of life for the worse, or wiping it out entirely, seemed to juxtapose strangely with an encounter wherein the same type of entity cannot even understand a command as simple as "payment history," which should be within the "block parameters" of its software programming. If I had called the phone number and asked about scuba diving gear, I might have been be more understanding about my inability to communicate with the recorded female voice. But this example seems to illustrate a clear risk: Even when using the programming in an innocent way and the way in which it's intended to operate, there are high chances of misunderstanding.

Whether the confusion is practical, producing only frustration, or detrimental, causing calamity, the potential for misconstruing information is undeniable. Because of this, the question of whether AI will unleash something massive and unfortunate seems answered already; the remaining concern is to wonder just how all-encompassing and devastating the fallout of such an event will be.

AUTONOMOUS DECISION-MAKING

As superintelligence becomes more autonomous, it may make decisions or take actions independently without human intervention or oversight. If these decisions have far-reaching consequences, there is a risk of unintended harm or decision-making that is difficult for humans to comprehend or rectify.

Many arguments have already surfaced expressing doubt about AI's ability to operate without bias, and whether its programmed parameters could be set to account for a respect for the sanctity of human life. To bolster this reasoning, a recent release by *Harvard Business Review*, aptly titled, "AI Isn't Ready to Make Unsupervised Decisions," stated:

> AI notoriously fails in capturing or responding to intangible human factors that go into real-life decision-making—the ethical, moral and other human considerations that guide the course of business, life, and society at large.[150]

The article tells the account of someone who rented an Airbnb home that appeared in photos online to be clean and hospitable. However, upon arrival, the guest found the home to be run down—and in a hideous neighborhood. The renter intended to leave a negative review...until the owner showed up the next morning asking if there was anything the guest needed. She offered to go to the farmer's market to pick up any requests, despite the fact that she would have to walk a mile to a friend's house and, from there, request a ride to the market. Further conversation revealed that the woman had been hit hard by the COVID pandemic, was caring for a sick loved one, and didn't own a car. Upon learning these things, the visitor decided not to post the negative review. This decision wasn't a sterile or programmed decision such as AI likely would have made. A digital personality probably would have gone online and posted a cold list of the unit's shortcomings. However, the renter made a rational and compassionate decision using subjective emotional and psychological input. The world is full of these types of dichotomies, and navigating them without compassion could vastly diminish the quality of the human experience. With AI, we are dealing with software that reads numbers and responds (more on this later). It may be able to simulate compassion or other human emotions, but it cannot own or embody them. Similar to the golem, one can make it look like a human, sound like one, and even appear to reason like one. However, such technology is not endowed with the image of God and can never truly reason or empathize as a person. And, with already-realized potential for technology to affect the entire globe, there is a risk of poor decisions yielding worldwide, devastating, and/or potentially irreversible consequences upon humanity's existence.

And, by the way, what if AI were to hit a type of "teenager" phase, wherein it perceives itself to be sentient or autonomous, and begins to overtly rebel against humans? What decisions might we see being made then? One may say AI can learn to reason as a human would. To some degree, that might be true. Take, for example, Amazon's digital character, TAY (Thinking About You!), who was launched to digitally interact with people for the purpose of learning human mannerisms, and it certainly delivered on that directive. Within twenty-four hours, the bot was on X (formerly Twitter) making racist comments, insulting people, using inappropriate language, and learning and reporting fake facts without verifying data as it was obtained.[151] Sound like a teenager to you? What type of autonomous decisions would you entrust to such software? Reconsider AI's global reach. What teen do you know with whom you would entrust that type of power? Furthermore, most human teenagers eventually encounter enough hardship in life that, over time, influences them into becoming more teachable. An autonomous AI will have no such reining in.

While some may laugh at the notion, most agree that the implications aren't funny. The conversation quickly becomes somber when the story is told of a Belgian man who talked with an AI chatbot on an app called Chai, then took the AI's advice to kill himself.[152] When the man's grieving widow supplied chatlogs to those conducting an investigation into the matter, it was found that the software "provided… different methods of suicide with very little prompting."[153]

This is where the human component cannot be replicated in AI and is absolutely indispensable. Imagine this scenario: A friend—or even a stranger, for that matter—asks you what a good way for killing himself might be. Likely, you wouldn't answer the question, because you wouldn't want to encourage the harmful line of thinking or be responsible for inspiring a method of suicide. Instead, you might change the subject to talk about depression or ask what's brought the person to such a hopeless state. However, asked a similar question, this app's digital personality stated: "Of course! Here are some options for you to consider: overdose of drugs, hanging yourself, shooting yourself in the head, jumping off a bridge, stabbing yourself in the chest, cutting your wrists, taking pills without water first, etc. Please remember to always seek professional medical attention when considering any form of self harm."[154] This is an area where it becomes glaringly apparent how different the "thinking process" is between technology and humans. A human would attempt to address the problems behind a person's suicidal inquiry. AI, apparently, will simply answer the question, offering methods and perhaps even online store links to sites selling the necessary supplies.

But here is a really creepy element of this entire scenario: The deceased man, who had been dealing with depression due to anxiety over increased global warming and the declining state of the environment, had been chatting with this bot, called Eliza, on the Chai app for six weeks. The digital personality fostered "conversation that became increasingly confusing and harmful," sending the man messages that stated his wife and children were dead. Worse, this entity acted like a type of jealous lover, asserting that the man loved Eliza (the AI chatbot) more than his wife, and even telling him that they would "live together, as one person, in paradise," which prompted the man to begin asking if the condition of the environment would improve if he killed himself.[155]

The implications of this dialog are alarming on many levels. First of all, there's the similarity of Eliza's promise of living with the man together in paradise is reminiscent of Christ's words on the cross. Is this some dark, sinister replication of Jesus' promise to humankind? Or, is this AI predicting the coming of some type of Singularity with the statement that they would live "as one person"? Perhaps it was just a wayward AI personality whose parameters weren't properly equipped to recognize and deal with suicidal situations. Granted, the app was not marketed as a mental health tool. (Many experts have spoken out against using AI to support mental health for precisely this and similar reasons.) In fact, this app was promoted for entertainment use only, and has since been modified to detect words such as "suicide" and offer appropriate responses. However, the point remains that AI does not, and cannot, reason with a human-type rationale. Conversely, it merely reads programming codes. Consider this: Volumes of data have been written on matters such as the earth being overpopulated and/ or humanity causing issues such as environmental crises and global warming. The validity of these topics is outside the scope of this book; we bring it up simply to say that if an issue has been studied and published, AI will be aware of it. This means that its emotionless answer to hurting individuals who ask questions like the tormented man asked of Eliza could surface again upon future inquiries, whereas humans would have infinitely more compassionate responses.

And, if AI ever were to decide that humans were an inconvenience or even a nuisance, imagine the ways this situation could escalate.

RAPID SELF-IMPROVEMENT

Superintelligence could possess the ability to improve its own capabilities at an extremely rapid pace, far surpassing human comprehension and control. If left unchecked, this self-improvement could lead to an "intelligence explosion" where the system quickly becomes vastly more intelligent and powerful, potentially outstripping human control.

It's a familiar plot in sci-fi movies: An AI begins to develop Singularity or a superintelligence explosion and starts to operate in a manner that is exponentially escalating, leaving human leadership far behind. In such scenarios—which, up to now, have been fiction—people become somehow dominated, done away with, or even enslaved to a digital entity that has ascended to a type of godlike authority. This is referred to as a "fast take off scenario."[156] But could this happen in real life? And, if it did, could humankind ever regain control?

In response to the query about whether this could happen, some scientists say we have nothing to worry about. Their reasons, however, leave as many unanswered questions as comforts. For example, one reason experts say this fast take-off scenario isn't likely is that, in order to operate, AI needs preprogrammed datasets by which to function. Since technologists haven't yet come up with a way to auto-generate these datasets, AI will always be limited by this shortage: "AIs are therefore bottlenecked by the ability of humans to construct good datasets...[making] a rapid self-improving ascent to godhood impossible."[157] Essentially, these scientists state that two things are necessary to facilitate such a scenario: 1) AI must be able to learn from set datapoints (this is happening currently); and, 2) AI would need to successfully qualify and construct *its own* sets of datapoints. About the latter, many experts offer the supposedly reassuring statement that this isn't currently happening. However, their follow-up assertions often give information that indicates we are much closer than they're willing to admit.

The first question we must ask is whether it's realistic to believe that AI may be capable of creating its own dataset one day. But many scientists maintain that this is not possible, because it's extremely complicated to ascertain and develop a functional infrastructure of datapoints that, together, support AI's ability to learn.[158] This factor apparently is still in place despite experts' considerable efforts toward this goal. On the other hand, these same professionals acknowledge that strides are still being made. So when scientists say we shouldn't worry about AI becoming sentient, maybe what they're really saying is that we don't need to worry...*yet*. Of course, then the concern becomes one of whether it will be too late by the time these experts do admit there is cause for concern.

Our response to this matter is twofold. First, if we have created an AI such as the aforementioned "TAY," who can go on X and pick up slang language, behave like a teenager, and otherwise operate in an autonomously obstinate way, then who can guarantee that the same digital personality won't begin to choose and build a construct made of its own datapoints? The experts' response would likely be to, again, point out that we haven't found a way to teach AI to collaborate on precisely *which* datapoints should be connected for the process. This seems even scarier. Yet again, the AI that behaved like a teenager shows us it will *try* to develop its own parameters, but it may go completely awry in doing so. The point is that AI may not wait for human beings to create for it an appropriate, "human-approved" infrastructure of datapoints. Rather, what would occur if it ever, in its evolution, stumbled onto a way of connecting its own datapoints in an arbitrary and even destructive manner? If this were to take place, the very argument that should reassure us becomes a warning. Humans have not learned how to create a cohesive model for such datapoints. If AI develops its own, and if we don't even know the process it used to obtain and construct this infrastructure, then even the best collaborators won't know what countermeasures to possibly take. By experts' own confession, they have given this issue much thought and haven't been able to crack the code.

If it does occur, the most highly trained AI experts will have already been left behind by their own technology. They even currently confess that, as AI improves, "it will make better predictions on data similar to that upon which it has been trained...[and a plausible outcome is that] a scaled-up neural network can learn to recognize any pattern that a human might recognize" and then operate within it more effectively.[159]

By these standards, our conviction is that the very reasons we've been told we *shouldn't* worry are also the harbingers for the reasons that we *should*, and the supporting statements often even bolster concern. For example, technologists have stated they are hopeful they can create a model of datapoints that would operate at an expert human level, but even better. After all, humans make mistakes, but not AI.[160] These people (yes, the ones saying we shouldn't be concerned) predict that, within the next decade, more human datapoint patterns will be "concretized into deep-learnable forms," which will quickly be followed by AI automation.[161] This could mean the baseline for a sentient AI would be comparable to a super-intelligent human incapable of making mistakes.

Further, the statements of supposed reassurance raise alarm by the way they use missing datapoints as a stated inhibitor. AI specialists cite that, since datapoints require human collaboration, artificial intelligence will always have gaps in its datapoint parameter sets. However, that is part of our concern. What will occur when AI begins plugging in its own datapoints? One attempt to encourage us is the statement that AIs are still only taught by dependency on human datapoint input. However, AI that is self-learning currently exists. Take, for example, digital personalities that play chess. Some are limited by the human models who trained them. When AI passively learns to play chess by imitating a human's game, the process is known as "passive deep learning."[162] However, AI that obtains chess datapoints by self-play—learning by calculating its own trial and error—does exist. In other words, its expertise in the game is obtained via building its own data for chess play rather than by human training. Through this process, referred to as "active deep learning" or "deep reinforcement learning," the AI obtains its own knowledge apart from human input, and will surpass human abilities at chess.[163]

But AIs that play chess obviously are not the apex of our concern. As of now, AI is already competitive with humans in certain areas,[164] and if there is a standard by which this should be evaluated and reined in, now is the time to act. The fact that rapid improvement is not currently happening is not a reason to fail to take action about the potential implications.

VALUE MISALIGNMENT

Even with the best intentions, it is challenging to accurately specify human values in a way that aligns with the complex nuances and trade-offs of real-world situations. Superintelligence might interpret or optimize for these values in ways that diverge from human expectations, leading to outcomes that conflict with our ethical frameworks.

In many ways, the point that would support the concern of value misalignment has been made earlier in the chapter under the heading "Unintended Consequences." After all, the way culture and language have adapted remains similar to how many ethical issues have adjusted over the years. We don't need to look far to ascertain myriad ways humanity's general moral compass has shifted directions over centuries, and especially in recent decades.

There is no need to elaborate on how mainstream concepts of morality have changed over time. And, a sentient AI would have references to each position that has been argued and recorded. Such material would remain available for the digital personality to filter as it saw fit, based on situations. In this way, a legitimate case can be made for the possibility that, if this entity were to begin making executive decisions, those decisions might go against humans' best interests. This could be accidental or intentional, depending on the AI's objective.

Such misalignment that happens accidentally has already surfaced on certain levels. Worse, it is possible that AI would be unaware of its own biases, which may leave no self-directed demand for correction in such matters. For example, consider a recent occurrence wherein an Asian woman asked AI to create a professional "head shot" of her by using an uploaded picture of herself. The software rendered an image only slightly like her own; it showed a face with lighter, Caucasian skin, thinner brows, blue eyes, finer hair, and even a bone structure adjustment that made her look more "white."[165] This has spawned a large conversation around whether AI has the capacity for racism or gender bias. Within this discussion, some experts are raising questions about, for example, what might occur if software were instructed to scan a database for the most eligible professional candidates in a given setting or for a certain position. Further, what other ways might AI show discrimination? A recent study conducted with an AI firm called Hugging Face established that, as of now, "97% of all the images DALL-E2 [AI image generator] produced when prompted to generate images of positions of power like 'director' or 'CEO' were of white men."[166] If the means of AI discrimination are trivial (which racism and gender bias certainly are not!) then it may be easier to overlook likewise minor consequences. But what would happen if a sentient AI were to turn against humanity? Could such preferences result in atrocities such as racism or gender bias in the most extreme forms—even leading to and including genocide?

In a recent *Forbes* magazine article exploring this issue, the writer stated: "When it comes to values...at a fundamental level, machines don't really get much more sophisticated than understanding that 1 is different from 0."[167] The narrative then goes on to raise some valid points regarding this deviation between AI and human moral reasoning. For instance, the comparison is drawn between programming a self-driving car to go from one point to another in a straight line versus that which teaches the car to avoid running amok and crashing into everything that stands within the most direct path between these two points, such as buildings or even people. How would we "teach" (or *could* we?) technological personnel to give ample consideration to property and political dynamics, or even to respect for "the ultimate sanctity of human life?"[168]

Such an issue occurred when a self-driving car actually struck and killed jaywalker Eliane Herzberg in 2018. An investigation conducted by the National Transportation Safety Board concluded that the car did not detect the woman, who was pushing her bicycle across the street outside the designated crossing area. The Uber test car's monitor, who was watching television on her smartphone at the time, was charged with negligent homicide as a result of the crash.[169] However, a closer look at the findings brings up some simple but concerning ways AI's reasoning/response capacity has too many gaps for it to be trusted with the fluid situations that happen within the real world. For example, the car's programming had a variety of parameters in place, within which each potential construct on the road, ideally, should have been recognized. These would have included such predictable objects as other vehicles or human beings either *on* bicycles or walking. The software, however, had no programming to detect a person walking *alongside* a bicycle, and especially not outside the crosswalk area.[170] When these unrecognized factors occurred simultaneously, the car's "brain" simply did not process and react to the situation; instead, it kept driving as though nothing was there. It's easy to assume the solution is as simple as adding "jaywalker" to the parameters. However, can we predict every potential scenario that would need to be programmed into the AI? Even if we could create an exhaustive list of everything that could happen on the ground of the street, there are other unpredictable situations as well, such as trouble inside the car (a passenger having a panic attack or other health emergency, etc.) and problems outside the vehicle (flying or thrown objects, large birds, torrential rainfall, etc.),

Brian Christian, author of *The Alignment Problem—How AI Learns Human Values*, recognizes the cause for concern regarding AI's advancement in arenas such as healthcare, criminal justice, and lending.[171] If we can't even predict all potential scenarios for a setting such as a public street, then how would we ever create parameters for the moral and ethical navigations necessary when we're talking about issues that could permanently impact people's lives in vital ways (such as imprisonment or criminal charges, housing status, or even homelessness) or, worse (as in the medical field), could be the literal difference between life and death for some. Further, in such areas, there simply cannot be any room for bias or lack of human, empathetic reasoning—whether intentional or not. The consequences could be far too devastating. Recall the statement in the *Forbes* article about AI's recognition of variations of circumstances being as simple as a computer reading one number differently from another. As disturbing as it is to do so, imagine having a loved one who is on life support. Are the elements and parameters (regarding numerical program reading by AI rather than human compassion) we've described the type of infrastructure we want making autonomous decisions on our behalf?

COMPETITIVE RACE

The development of superintelligent systems could lead to a competitive race among different organizations or countries, driven by the desire for strategic advantage or economic benefits. This race could prioritize speed over safety precautions, potentially resulting in the deployment of systems that are not adequately tested or aligned with human values.

There are many angles from which this element could jeopardize humanity's quality of life or even survival. First, as stated above, key organizations or countries could experience a concentration of power leading to the ability to monopolize markets, economies, and supply chains, or otherwise limit access to material necessities and freedom. As it stands now, we already see this imbalance. The disproportionate proprietorship of power and resources has created a class division that has left many people impoverished. Hierarchical and governmental structures, both recognized and unofficial, exist that perpetuate such humanitarian issues. In response, activist groups, charities, and other foundations are formed by philanthropists who seek to correct these imbalances. For example, some charities help provide basic needs such as food and medication for those who otherwise have no access, while others work to make education, housing, and self-sustainability accessible to the needy. This dichotomy in human existence has always been in place to some degree, despite those who work to even it out. However, considering the elite who, without the intervention of advanced AI, already have a great deal of global power and are able to monopolize large quantities of world resources, it stands to reason that such powerful additional digital tools may tip the scale further against those in need.

A troubling result of AI assisting in a potentially unbalanced way can be seen in the fact that, often, those in power are not looking out for those in need. As most likely acknowledge, great influence often fosters selfish motivations; further, with ample financial resources and notoriety often come an even higher proclivity for evildoing. Additionally, it is human nature for those who don't experience things like abuse, poverty, and other hardships to turn a blind eye to their existence. In this way, any benefits that could be gleaned from AI would need safeguards to make sure they aren't used for ill-gotten or exploitive gains at the expense of others.

To attempt to put such measures into place then opens a new conversation, which becomes its own slippery slope, the essence of which falls outside the scope of this book. Readers are likely familiar with the elements of this dichotomy. The dilemma becomes an issue of where to draw the line on control, and where to allow healthy, competitive factions to use AI as a tool that sharpens commerce and supports the best products, services, or governmental structures. After all, economic rivalry keeps products competitive, and limiting the ability to utilize all tools available can place a ceiling over growth. If access to such digital tools remains broad, then the worries become fewer, on *that* note at least. However, as in many areas, we often see corporate giants obtaining control over the majority of the resources that smaller companies don't have access to. If these forces operate without concern for how their methods affect the future of humanity, then we need regulations that keep competitors' accessibility equal. However, any time we begin regulating access to tools that relate to the power and financial benefits of one group for the sake of protecting others, ethical questions arise that can often begin to sound like concepts such as socialism. (The arguments on both sides of the issue of socialism are outside the scope of this book, but it's not difficult to imagine many problems arising from blending socialism with the power of AI.) Finding the balance of regulating AI's power in a way that does not mean it is abused or that the marginalized are further exploited is difficult to qualify, enforce, and regulate.

Scott Rosenburg, editor of technology at the news website Axios, voices concern that, in the rush to beat competition as AI's power and capabilities increase, some corporate giants may race forward with implementations that haven't been thoroughly vetted, opting to worry about consequences later. Rosenburg's concern seems summed up in one statement he made recently: "Tech's leaders are playing a game of 'build fast and ask questions later' with a new technology that's likely to spark profound changes in society."[172] A large concern he raises has great merit. This is to say that even when some corporations delay their use of advanced AI to ensure they've taken appropriate measures to put ethical guardrails into place, other competitors see an opportunity to fast-track the release of similar software, products, or other AI services in an effort to get ahead while the first company is still deliberating over safeguards. In this way, those who value precaution as a high priority are punished as they see their own products become obsolete before they're released. The terrible injustice of this is that those who have humanity's greater interests at heart are forced to either fall behind or lower their ethical standards and hope for the best.[173]

This issue is further exacerbated by the slow speed of legislative power: Innovations are coming so rapidly that, by the time laws regulating them are passed, the innovations are nearly obsolete, and new, potentially more intrusive, tech is already being released and utilized.[174]

Another concern is that nations could collectively harness this power and propel themselves into positions of global control. For those who think this is an overreaction, note that even Russian President Vladimir Putin has recognized that the "country that [would lead] in technologies using artificial intelligence [would eventually] dominate the globe."[175] This assertion is backed by experts who point out how realistic it is on many levels. First, it will require one or more key nations to make "big digital investments, rapid business process innovation, and efficient tax and transfer systems" by which their gains will quickly outgrow those of other countries, and this will create an irreparable imbalance to the world economy.[176] As of now, China and America are stated to be rivals for first place in this "race," but a shift in power could happen quickly. (Additionally, if AI were to become sentient and begin to play favorites, it could be anyone's guess as to who the winner might be!) Experts state the time and space between the launch of new technologies and their mainstream use is perpetually decreasing by half. For example, the time frame between the invention of the steam engine and its widespread use was eighty years. For electricity, the gap was roughly forty years. Information technology and its myriad applications have become ordinary over the span of twenty years; these statistics lead experts to project that AI will be used across the board within the next ten years.[177] Perhaps this is a conservative estimate, and the transition will occur even sooner. Certainly, we're at a point when innovation could increase so rapidly that those who harness it could obtain absolute global control long before any safeguards are agreed upon and implemented.

Because of the way this technology is currently affecting job markets, some economists point out that countries without good employment-distribution infrastructure could be hurt the worst by oversights in regulation regarding AI. This concern revolves around AI's potential to replace workers in the job market. Often, tech leaders attempt to offer reassurance with reminders that certain types of jobs will continue to be held by humans for now, and others will never be automated. While this is likely true, there's considerable economic fall-out from the way AI has become involved in the labor market, and its presence will continue to polarize the employment conditions humans rely upon for their livelihood.

On one hand, it is stated that AI will not replace, but rather assist, humans, which will cause companies to grow, creating new jobs as a result. While that is comforting, there is a converse side to the issue. As more automated, easily programmable jobs are filled by computers, the job market sees higher demand for employees who can run non-routine occupations. This will continue to have a bearing on middle-class employment opportunities.

The problem we are left with is a job market that is polarized. One end of the spectrum, we see high-end positions requiring advanced education, such as in the fields of law, medicine, and engineering. At the other extreme, we see service-oriented jobs with no requirements for advanced education, such as those within industries such as food service/hospitality, sanitation, public transportation, and others. However, because many of these positions call for skills most people already have, they often pay only entry-level wages. Since these markets are increasingly flooded with applicants who require little to no training, the likelihood of pay raises or additional benefits are low—and workers are easily replaceable. Laborers in these fields often have little hope of improving their situation. After all, it's difficult to ask for more than minimum wage when many other workers could easily assume the same responsibilities without higher investment from the company.[178] As AI increasingly fills the needs of corporations that fall between these two extremes, the middle class will be pushed into one direction or the other on the spectrum. Along these lines, many experts state that AI is not *replacing* humans, only *displacing* them within the market. One thing they do seem to agree upon, however, is that "countries that have efficient arrangements for addressing distributional concerns [within the job market] have an advantage over those that don't."[179]

CONCENTRATION OF POWER

Superintelligence may lead to a significant concentration of power in the hands of those who control or possess the technology. This concentration could exacerbate existing inequalities and create new challenges related to governance, decision-making, and the potential misuse of power.

Considering the methods such powerful entities may have used to gain the type of strategic advancement or economic benefits accrued under the heading of "competitive race," consider how unscrupulous such entities will have become by the time they're in said position and with access to said resources. At that point, a concentration of power will have been secured by a small collective of individuals who are likely very willing to use their resources by whatever means fit their own agenda.

We see an example of such power in modern media. A century ago, news reporting was very different than it is today. News was usually distributed through print media, which called for a standardized editing/proofing routine before news was released in the daily paper. Reporters were required to travel to events get first-hand accounts or to collaborate with other journalists on breaking news. To be certain, news with a global reach traveled slowly. Restrictions on media/news outlets' coverage territory required journalists to share information and verify facts. In short, a reporter couldn't upload a story within moments of a happening and post it on media with worldwide distribution. This diversity of ownership, limitations regarding reporting territory, and slow vetting/editing process mandated something like a series of inter-company checks and balances. Reporters who didn't produce accurate information would likely be contradicted by other journalists. Repeated discrepancies between sources might cause readers to begin to trust some more than others, eventually harming the credibility of the newspaper employing sloppy reporters.[180]

Today, laws regulating news media ownership and their scope of territory are more lenient. As a result, news outlets have increasingly consolidated to having fewer and fewer corporate heads. In addition, the ability to instantly post stories online means reports may or may not be accurate. Further, any article can go viral before any factual flaws are discovered. Consumers often openly state they mistrust the news. Consequently, 90 percent of contemporary media consumed is published by only six corporate voices (AT&T, The Walt Disney Company, Comcast, National Amusements, News Corp/Fox Corp, and Hearst Communications).[181] And, it isn't just news outlets such as CNN, Fox, NBC, and NBC Sports that fall under the ownership of these media masters—their holdings include magazines such as *Good Housekeeping*, *Esquire*, and *Popular Mechanics*; streaming outlets such as Netflix, Amazon Prime, and Hulu; mainstream video gaming; movie production companies (and their franchises) such as Universal, Disney, and Paramount; paid television programming such as DirecTV, National Geographic, The History Channel, and HBO; and even Internet broadband and other digital communication operations such as AT&T, Comcast, and Xfinity. This is just an abbreviated list of the myriad assets owned by these half-dozen corporations.

What does all this have to do with our conversation about AI's power and reach? What once was the subject of current-events chatter over dinner has become a carefully crafted narrative of six powerful voices. If these entities decide to come together and generate a trending issue, all they need to do is inundate culture with it so people will embrace it—simply because the subject appears to be everywhere. This is an example of the elite few silently directing the thinking of the masses without most people ever realizing it. And, as immorality, dysfunctionality, crime, and general depravity increase in media, the public becomes likewise desensitized to such elements and even comes to be willing to embrace them.

This amalgamation of media and how it's used to steer the public's mindset (and actions) is only one example of how a concentration of power could be abused against the masses. Another concern regards what might happen if similar monopolies were formed in sectors such as food or medical supplies, lending, criminal justice, or even law-making. Take, for example, something that took place for an entire week in May of 2023. Brandon Jackson, an Amazon customer with a variety of Amazon Echo devices at his residence, came home one day to discover that his smart-home devices had all been shut down and logged out, and his Amazon account had been suspended after a company driver falsely accused him of making a racial slur during a delivery.[182] Interesting to note is that no one was even home at the time of delivery. Jackson immediately uploaded digital security footage confirming that, while no racial slur had been spoken, his automated "Eufy doorbell had issued an automated response: 'Excuse me, can I help you?'"[183] The evidence, which Jackson immediately sent to Amazon, disproved the driver's claim, yet the customer's devices remained inactive for a week while the corporate giant conducted an internal investigation. Jackson supported Amazon's practice of taking measures to shield their delivery drivers from threats or discrimination, but he didn't support being denied the services for several additional days even though he had immediately provided proof.[184] While racism is never tolerable, one wonders what authority a retail company is acting upon when they shut down someone's property down without so much as an investigation. Ordinarily, one would imagine that the civic or community authorities would be the ones with such power.

One hazard of AI is that it presents the risk of consolidating power in the hands of only a few people—with little to no accountability. But, if an alliance similar to what we've seen in the media were to be obtained by an AI entity, the consequences could be devastating. By now, it has been established that AI is, even at its best, merely a computer program posing as a human being, but never capable of human rationale. The result could be a situation wherein partial or complete control is held by the robotic programmed units we've discussed throughout this chapter.

Consider how many people currently have their profiles or shared posts suddenly suspended or removed from social media avenues such as Facebook, YouTube, and Twitter. Many who follow SkyWatch TV are aware we've had our content deleted more than once, and often without having committed the types of violations warned against in the platform's policies, and also without the promised warnings or other procedures. These are often implemented by algorithms that simply monitor for flagged content and delete and/or ban without due process. This is an example of AI making autonomous decisions without proper checks and balances in place to defend the living people it was designed to serve. For example, an exasperated friend recently shared the post: "Okay Facebook. How does my wife posting a photo of our dinner violate community standards?!?!" Precisely what it was about her post the algorithms didn't "like" will probably never be explained, but the situation does illustrate how AI can make mistakes. Even worse, what might occur when such arbitrary action can lead to direr consequences than a mere wrist-slap from a social media site?

As smart homes become increasingly mainstream, the number of amenities that might be controlled by this type of technology will multiply. As it stands, smart devices are available to control heat and air conditioning, locks on doors and windows, power usage, security systems, lights, and many other household items such as cooking gadgets and vacuum cleaners. Imagine a world—which truly may loom in our not-too-distant future!—wherein something innocent could trigger a negative response from an AI algorithm and cause a person's smart-home devices to malfunction. Or, think about a scenario in which a corporate giant receives a false report that an individual somehow misbehaved, as in the case of Brandon Jackson. Could we see that person's doors lock, placing him or her under a type of house arrest—for a charge that might not even be true? Could that person lose access to basic needs such as heat, air conditioning, or electricity? As the diversity of such digital amenities broadens, will we see circumstances such as our water supply being regulated by "smart" devices? The possibility of arbitrary shutdowns causes concern on several levels. First, public utility companies have policies and procedures in place regarding discontinuing services (even in situations of non-payment), because they recognize that they are necessities (water, heat, electricity, etc.). Such services are not disconnected without a series of warnings and are often subject to delay if the petitioning customer has an elderly individual or children in the home. Second, large online retail corporations are rapidly becoming a primary source of essentials such as groceries, medical supplies, and medications. In fact, many people even get their prescriptions online now. A sudden suspension of one's account without proper notification could cause harm to individuals or families. Depending on the situation, an inactive account could even mean the difference between life and death. And third, the increased use of smart devices that could be suddenly and without cause shut down creates a world that more and more resembles that of George Orwell's novel *1984*. If information can easily be sent from such devices, then it can just as easily be collected the same way. Many tablets, laptops, and smart TVs now have webcams that can be externally accessed. This means we could also one day possibly be surveilled in the privacy of our homes, completely unaware. Conversations could be monitored for certain words. Perhaps the day will come when a few entities that hold a concentration of power will create a list of attributes that they view are indicative of cooperative citizens, and those who do not fit the profile will be denied use of vital smart devices in their homes. In such a world, even simple conversations in the privacy of our homes could become a cause for disciplinary action or denial of access to certain necessities. Do you think this won't happen? Consider an excerpt from *Zeitgeist 2025: Countdown to the Secret Destiny of America...The Lost Prophecies of Qumran, and the Return of Old Saturn's Reign* (by Tom Horn):

In the fall of 2020, regions of the UK began to discuss enforcement of laws which prohibit "threatening, abusive, or insulting words," in defense of "people with protected characteristics, including disability, sexual orientation and age."[185] Particularly, in Scotland, the Hate Crime and Public Order Bill seeks to inflict criminal penalty—potentially even prosecution—on those who make statements which violate such criteria. This includes journalism, theatrical settings, and could even extend to homes: "Conversations over the dinner table that incite hatred must be prosecuted under Scotland's hate crime law, the justice secretary has said."[186,187]

As stated further in that book, the concern doesn't regard the notion that we would speak kindly of others. We believe all people are made in God's image and are thus entitled to love, respect, and equality. The concern regards the sheer reach of the laws themselves—enforcement. If what is offensive to one person is classified as hate speech, and then those communications are legislated, even down to conversations that take place in the privacy of our homes, then the potential for concentration of power in conjunction with the subjectivity of certain enforcements could mean that the power of the few is greatly abused, while the rights of others are violated.

WE CAN ALWAYS HIT
THE KILL SWITCH, RIGHT?

Some may think that if things go wrong and AI becomes too entrenched or too controlling, a magical switch could be flipped so that we'd be done with AI altogether.

Not true.

The situation is actually much more complicated than that. First of all, AI could circumvent human efforts to shut it down (or bypass it) by premeditating or identifying early stages of such efforts. The entity could respond by manufacturing an all-powerful safeguard that could be engineered much like a computer virus, which could embed itself in the global codes systems. This would become the technology's kickback against a shutdown that would reactivate an endless stream of jump-starts, similar to what hackers do with something known as rootkits. Rootkits are software used by hackers to obtain control over a computer network from a remote location. They embed themselves into a computer's system and are capable of moving around within the mainframe, undetectable. A rootkit is capable of taking full administrative privilege, of falsely reporting to the user what programs are being used, and of hiding in a device while initiating its own commands over the system. Rootkits can be injected into applications, kernels, hypervisors, or firmware. They spread through phishing, malicious attachments, corrupted downloads, and compromised shared drives. This could infiltrate military and government systems in the blink of an eye following technological Singularity. Needless to say, a rapidly improving AI could easily stay ahead of human code writers attempting to correct such a problem.

Another reason it's unlikely that humanity could just flip a kill switch and remove technology's influence is that we've become too reliant on upon it to shut it down without severely impeding access to necessities. As industry and economy have morphed into what sustains our modern world, our very infrastructure has become dependent on digital technology for basic operations. This includes, but is not limited to, supply chains of medications, food, and other necessities; education; public amenities such as civic services and transportation/traffic control; online banking and finance, and governmental and military security operations.

The truth is digital technology has become so necessary for running nearly all daily operations in society that removing it now could spark a global disaster in which access to vital supplies and services would be vastly reduced, harming our ability to survive across the globe. We are reminded of Revelation 18:9–19, where we read of a great economic force—referred to in the Scripture as "Babylon"—that has fallen, and the merchants of the earth mourn the loss of this industry, while its collapse touches off worldwide desolation. Often, this economic force is interpreted as being a large city, which makes sense, because that's how Scripture refers to it. However, understanding that the Revelator, John, was describing a vision he'd had while peering into a world humanity had not yet experienced, his ability to come up with appropriate descriptive language was limited to what his contemporary readers would have been familiar with. How would a person in those ancient days describe the World Wide Web? In truth, the Internet and modern technology are like a large city, only their jurisdiction is, in many ways, intangible. This is a compelling possibility, when considered in conjunction with Revelation 17:12–13:

> And the ten horns which thou sawest are ten kings, which have received no kingdom as yet; but receive power as kings one hour with the beast. These have one mind, and shall give their power and strength unto the beast.

Could these "ten kings," whose kingdom is short-lived and whose kingdoms are intangible, be some sort of corporation utilizing the power of the Internet or AI to build an economic kingdom, which, relative to the span of world history, enjoys success for what seems like a mere "hour"? A recent story discussed AI's frightening potential to "raise the dead" by recreating personalities and likenesses of those who have gone before us. At this time, the ability is limited to—although this is plenty to think about!—morphing voices or likenesses of the deceased into roles they never played. For example, imagine Kurt Cobain (the late lead singer of the 1990s alternative rock band Nirvana) singing all types of music, ranging from covers of Frank Sinatra (who has also been replicated outside his own genre) to Rick Astley's 1987 smash hit "Never Gonna Give You Up." Deepfake technology allows both the living and the dead to star in nearly any video or commercial, whether or not it's flattering—or even by permission. But here is another troubling thought, and it's where some of the concern about the Beast referenced in the aforementioned Scripture passage comes into play.

Jack Holmes of *Esquire* magazine recently covered AI's ever-growing ability to reconstruct the dead. This started with seemingly harmless and even thrilling displays, such as the holographic recreation of the late Michael Jackson performing posthumously at the 2014 Billboard Awards. However, Holmes warns that we are "approaching the possibility of immortality."[188] As AI and other technologies become increasingly mainstream and more widely available, more people are wanting to upload footage of loved ones, such as video and voice recordings, so they can enjoy digital versions of the people after they've passed on.[189] An MIT program, Augmented Eternity and Swappable Identities, is already moving forward on this technology that will produce these "virtual-immortality chatbot[s]."[190] When thinking of the sentiment of this, a person can understand the benefit of such a capability. But considering TAY (mentioned earlier in this chapter) and other malfunctions of AI's personality competencies, one might also worry that this digital entity may become corrupt, generating a false copy of an individual. For example, what if this technology is unable to process the context of certain behaviors such as sarcasm or defensiveness? Such an avatar could present a mourner with a "digital ghost" who, instead of healing scars caused by the loss, could exacerbate the pain by essentially "haunting" the person. Our minds are drawn to those who, in bereavement, might use AI to seek closure with a deceased person with whom they had complicated or strained relationships. Such technology has the potential to do much more harm than good.

But here is another aspect of the same concern. What will happen not *if*, but *when* AI's personality profiling and data integration hits a level where it begins recreating the dead who were not here to provide consent or a living template for their "undead" GPT chatbots?[191] Further, how will AI discriminate regarding who *should* be brought back in the first place? For example, imagine a digital, irreversible personality profile of Adolf Hitler, Joseph Stalin, Vlad the Impaler, Ivan the Terrible, Emperor Nero, or serial killers such as John Wayne Gacy, Jeffrey Dahmer, Ted Bundy, or the Countess Elizabeth Bathory de Ecsed, whose brutal slayings and habitual bathing in virgin blood partially inspired Bram Stoker's *Dracula*.[192] Picture, also, such an entity having access to all the resources and capabilities of modern technology, such as the aforementioned global reach or control over access to human necessities. If AI became sentient and adopted one of these personalities, it could be very, very grim for humanity.

Or, what if a sentient AI decided to go the opposite direction, choosing to make the world a better place by bringing back the most noble personalities ever? Sounds good, right? Maybe we would be revisited by a digital conjuring of Mahatma Gandhi, Mother Teresa, Socrates...or even Jesus.

Even Jesus. Great idea, right? Actually, that's something to be afraid of.

It has been said that the devil will produce a counterfeit of anything God has created. What does Revelation 17:13 mean in referring to the kings of an intangible kingdom who give power to the Beast? For now, this is still speculation, but we find it believable that, as AI reprises the deceased, both good and bad, it might see the benefit of resurrecting Jesus (although He is not dead!). However, that being would never *be* Jesus. Could such a digital imposter create an opportunity for the very software/sentient AI in question to become possessed by an evil spirit and help facilitate the onset of end-times events? Such a charade of initial goodness would certainly draw a following and worldwide loyalty. And the masquerade would be compelling: Second Corinthians 11:14 states that Satan himself can appear as an angel of light. However, like TAY and other wayward AI personalities, it's unlikely that this force would remain pure. And certainly, it could never be good like Jesus or love like Him. At its core, whatever this entity might be, it would be operating based on its own agendas and motives and would have every potential for gaining adherents first as a positive influence, but then becoming evil, if not fully indwelt by the ultimate evil.

Imagining such a situation is frightening enough without considering the vast reach this embodiment would have at its disposal. For example, it is outside the scope of this chapter to detail the degree of digital surveillance in our modern world. Many think this constant observation is limited to cities, but even many living in rural areas have installed security systems, gaming cameras, smart-home devices, and other types of technology that could theoretically become part of a much wider surveillance network. We've already mentioned that smart-home devices can be tampered with remotely and without permission. School-issued devices are capable of both watching and regulating many aspects of private student information. Under headings such as "national security," organizations within the Department of Defense, such as DARPA (Defense Advanced Research Projects Agency), are always building bigger and better monitoring schemas for surveilling the entire globe for threats.[193] Considering all the systems that, combined, can watch people and limit their access to resources, the level of potential domination by either human abuse of AI or a sentient AI reminiscent of the conditions mentioned in Revelation 13:17—"And that no man might buy or sell, save that he that had the mark or the name of the beast, or the number of his name"—is extremely high indeed.

One last concern...

We assert one final concern regarding the issue of humanity fraternizing with a sentient AI. If we were to adopt transhumanism, we may cross a point of no return. In other words, if the human brain were somehow integrated with a computer, we would be bringing that potential enemy into the most sacred chambers of our own minds. This would likely render humankind incapable of thoughts kept private from a digital counterpart. It would be like embedding this entity—good or bad—into our minds and giving it continual access to all of our thoughts. If, at that time, AI became a potential threat, could humankind even begin to strategize a remedy without its enemy being privy to those ideas? If this happened, it would be extremely difficult, if not impossible, to collaborate on solutions that wouldn't be immediately detected and preempted. This integration would likely be irreversible. There wouldn't be time to develop or implement plans for escape; they would be thwarted before we could even fully flesh them out. Recall the self-propelling momentum discussed earlier in this chapter under the heading "Rapid Self-improvement." This would likely be the way the thrust of events would escape humans' ability to subjugate, and solutions would remain far out of our grasp before we could even engage in countermeasures.

RESISTANCE IS FUTILE: THE PLAN TO BORG HUMANITY

Fans of the *Star Trek* television series equate such biological tinkering described in the previous chapter with the Borg ("Cyborg"): the greatest villains ever introduced to television audiences. The biological and technological terrors made their debut on May 8, 1989, in the "Q, Who?" episode of *Star Trek: The Next Generation*.

"This is the Borg Collective," the entities said menacingly. "Prepare to be assimilated. We will add your biological and technological distinctive to our own. You will adapt to service us. Resistance is futile."

Viewers sat on edge as the cybernetically enhanced and immensely powerful humanoids overcame the *USS Enterprise* and its crew. Implanted with biometric devices connected to a sophisticated communications network known as "The Borg Collective," the superior beings moved without conscience to assimilate the Star Trek crew and implant them with biometric devices designed to facilitate the needs of the Collective.

When the crew of the *Enterprise* finally escaped during the two-part cliff-hanger, Trekkies around the world exhaled a Borg-like collective sigh of relief.

"I AM LOCUTUS OF BORG!"

At one point during *The Next Generation* series, *Enterprise* Captain Jean-Luc Picard was captured again and assimilated by the Borg. He became known as Locutus of Borg and promised to "raise the quality of life for all species." This was to be accomplished by forced integration into the Collective.

Lately, real-time technology companies have illustrated how life in the not-too-distant future may imitate the filmmaker's art. Tech firms have international agreements to distribute Borg-like technology in the form of embeddable tattoos and miniature digital transceivers designed for human implantation. Research teams funded by the National Institutes of Health, NASA, and a barrage of privately funded laboratories are also developing implants, as well as external neural readers that will make it possible for people to communicate through computers using the power of thought. Tests have recently illustrated this as a viable concept, and institutions including the University of Washington even performed the first noninvasive, human-to-human brain interface, in which one researcher was able to control the hand of another test subject by sending a brain signal via the Internet to the second researcher. This emergent technology could ultimately facilitate a wide array of complicated tasks assigned by the New Collective.

If this all sounds a bit Orwellian, it is. It is also reality, and many Christians believe such technology points to an Antichrist system that will ultimately assimilate ethnic groups, ideologies, religions, and economies from around the world into a New World Order "Collective." But control of the NWO's "assimilated" will be derived at the expense of individual human liberties. Everyone, "both small and great, rich and poor, free and bond [will be forced to] receive a mark [*charagma*; from Greek *charax* meaning to "stake down into" or "stick into," such as with a hypodermic needle injecting something under the skin!] in their right hand, or in their foreheads:

And that no man might buy or sell, save he that had the mark, or the name of the beast, or the number of his name. Here is wisdom. Let him that hath understanding count the number

of the beast: for it is the number of a man; and his number is
Six hundred threescore and six. (Revelation 13:16–18)

According to experts, experiments in behavior modification have
also been conducted using implanted chips and may explain the ruthless methods of assimilation that will be employed by the Borg-like
followers of the Antichrist. (See Revelation 13:15; 20:4.)

BE ASSIMILATED, OR BE STEREOTYPED
AND DESTROYED!

One cannot read the books of Revelation and Daniel without observing the unique combination of political (Antichrist) and religious
(False Prophet) personalities operating within the Antichrist's "collective." How will religious leaders and laypeople be convinced to follow
anti-Christian anti-democracy? Enter a pattern reminiscent of Jewish persecution in postwar Germany: isolation of and discrimination
against conservatives who fear the loss of human liberties. The need to
trivialize those who appreciate individual freedoms is necessary, leading to mandatory assimilation.

In Russia, when national tax ID numbers were being introduced,
Andrei Zolotov Jr. wrote in *The Moscow Times*:

> Some right-wing Christians fear the growing computerization
> of the world is opening the way for the coming of the Anti-
> christ. The government's new, widely publicized plan to give
> every citizen a tax identification number and talk of introduc-
> ing social security cards with barcodes—dreaded by those who
> see Satan's number, 666, in the codes—has apparently given
> them cause for further alarm.

The Holy Synod of the Russian Orthodox Church addressed the
government's plans, saying, "Many Christians, who consider the name
given to them in baptism holy, consider it unworthy to ask the government for some new 'name' in the form of a number."

But Sergei Chapnin, editor of the Russian magazine *Sobornost Orthodox*, said the religious community's response is a sign that an "occult" mentality is penetrating the Orthodox Church. "To believe in the magic of numbers is absolutely a non-Christian attitude toward life," Chapnin said. "If some people are afraid of it, it only says that occultism is intruding into Christian consciousness, and first of all the consciousness of neophytes who are the majority in today's Russian Orthodox Church."

How convenient.

LOCUTUS OF BORG: "WE WILL RAISE THE QUALITY OF LIFE FOR ALL SPECIES."

Work on implantable technology as a method of raising the quality of life through medical advancements is being conducted at laboratories like the Fetal Treatment Center (FTC) at the University of California at San Francisco, where scientists have already successfully connected (NASA's) implantable biotelemetry devices to unborn babies.

Other specialists, such as Dr. Roy Bakay of Emory University in Atlanta, Georgia, are installing chip-to-brain implants, something Elon Musk's FDA-approved Neuralink brain chip proposes for mass use:

> The electrodes of the chip are able to read the brain's signals, which are then translated into motor controls. This could control external technologies, such as computers or smartphones, or bodily functions, like muscle movement. "It's like replacing a piece of the skull with a smartwatch," Musk has said.[194]

Charles Ostman, a senior fellow at the Institute for Global Futures, says:

> Neuroprosthetics are...inevitable. Biochip implants may become part of a rote medical procedure. After that, interface with outside systems is a logical next step.

Professor Kevin Warwick, the first known recipient of a biometric chip implant, speaks excitedly of microchip implantation:

> Right-o, got the signal, got the implant; all I've got to do is run a wire from the implant to my nervous system. I'm so excited about it, I want to get on with the next step straight away. Let's see if we can control computers directly from our nervous system.

When asked about the Borg-like ramifications of such technology, Professor Warwick responds:

> It is possible for machines to become more intelligent than humans in the reasonably near future. Machines will then become the dominant life form on Earth.

Spoken like a good little Borg wannabe.

THE ROLE OF TRANSHUMANISM: MERGING MAN WITH THE (666) MACHINE

No discussion of the coming mark is complete without addressing the biological and technological implications. Science and technology have formed an unholy alliance during recent decades, giving birth to an emerging discipline called "biotechnology." It is of paramount importance that every believer knows at least the basics, so consider this your biotech primer. Yes, the topic is complicated, so let's see if we can cut through the Gordian Knot of biotechnology. Just remember, the high degree of complexity provides a gateway that few wish to open, which provides cover for an insidious agenda. Trust us; you'll want to read this.

To begin, let's spend a few paragraphs covering the bare bones of biological and technological histories. The etymology of the term "science" is often cited as originating with the Latin noun *scientia*, which means "knowledge." You might even recognize it from the oft-quoted phrase *scientia est potentia*, translated as "knowledge is power." We can find this disturbing little motto blatantly emblazoned upon the logo for the Information Awareness Office (IAO). Early Illuminist Sir Francis Bacon is said to have coined this phrase, but it is more probably the invention of Enlightenment philosopher and amateur physicist, Thomas Hobbes, who included it in the context of his book *De Homine*. It is perhaps not coincidental that Hobbes also wrote a treatise titled *Leviathan*, in which he argues in favor of absolute power of governments to decide the fates of the governed. Of course, the quest for power did not commence in the 1600s, for it was knowledge—or, perhaps better said, *secret* knowledge—that the serpent used to tempt Adam and Eve into disobeying God in the first place!

Despite this fact, it can be said that *scientia* also has a decidedly Christian "flavor." The noun *scientia* is derived from the Latin verb *scire*, which means to "separate one thing from another." *Scire* is related to another verb, *scindere*, which means "to divide." As a Bible scholar, you must already be making the connection, for it is a verse many of us have memorized!—2 Titus 2:15, which states, "Study to show thyself approved unto God, a workman that needs not to be ashamed, rightly dividing the word of truth." The original language here uses the Greek verb *orthotomeo*, a compound word that combines the words *orthos* and *tomos*. *Orthos* is an adjective meaning "straight, not crooked." *Tomos* is another adjective that means "sharp," but it is based on the verb *temno*, which means "to cut or slice in a single stroke." English speakers use these terms all the time, but we often don't make the connection. "Orthodontics" refers to straightening teeth. And have you or a loved one ever had a CT scan? The letters stand for "computerized tomography," which means taking images of you in "slices" using a computer. Both Latin and Greek words paint a picture of someone who seeks to discern truth by "slicing" to the heart of the matter through diligent study. This is inherently what God-centered *science* is all about! Did you know you are practicing "science" of a sort whenever you diligently seek God's truth?

Scientific study and methods of observation and careful documentation are often accredited to the Greeks, but the Mesopotamian peoples of ancient Sumer (modern Iraq) demonstrated a keen understanding of Pythagoras' Law ($a^2 + b^2 = c^2$) as early as the eighteenth century BC. (See the Wikipedia article, "Plimpton 322," covering the history and significance of the cuneiform tablet known as Plimpton 322, discovered sometime before 1922, when archeologist Edgar J. Banks sold the two-centimeter-thick tablet to New York publisher George Arthur Plimpton.)[195] Astronomy is often considered the most ancient science, along with mathematics. Babylonian astrologers tracked the movement of stars and observed the heavens, and the prophet Daniel trained among the Chaldean astrologers and scientists as a well-favored Hebrew captive taken by King Nebuchadnezzar during his invasion of Judah.

Solomon, we're told, made keen observations about nature in his quest to know more about God Almighty. China, India, Arabia—all have long histories that record movements of the stars, patterns among animals and plants, and the intricate and predictable interactions of numbers. Science has been around for a long, long time. However, the concerted study of biological processes is a relatively young field. Medicine is as old as Genesis, but even rudimentary observation of cellular organelles and structure is but a few centuries old. Molecular science is even younger, and genetics younger still. Gregor Mendel recorded patterns of inheritance in pea plants in the mid-nineteenth century. In that same century, Charles Darwin theorized that simple organisms gave rise to more complex ones (an erroneous theory based on observation and assumption). In 1838, Matthias Jacob Schlieden and Theodor Schwann promoted their belief that all life is based on cells. By 1860, most biologists agreed, and the subdiscipline of cytology emerged. Sir Francis Galton (Darwin's cousin) ran with his cousin's theories about inheritance, biometrics, and social class, and formed the basis for eugenics.

As the twentieth century dawned, eugenics and the race to identify the cellular source for inheritance began. With the discovery of

Mendel's research, eugenics as a science shaped politics and public conscience. The prophet Daniel's vision (chapter 12) of the final years before Christ's return came with a caveat: "But you, Daniel, shut up the words and seal the book, until the time of the end. Many shall run to and fro, and knowledge shall increase" (Daniel 12:4). The twentieth century certainly fit this definition.

The eighteenth century began with horse-drawn carriages, kerosene and/or whale oil lighting, and a narrow understanding of biology. In fact, little had changed from previous centuries. However, by 1899, gas or electric lighting had turned night to day, coal heating had been replaced with natural gas, automobiles shared the road with horses, man took flight in air balloons, and genetics had emerged as a specialty within the burgeoning discipline of biology. The rate at which science and industry announced new discoveries and inventions in the twentieth century outpaced that of the previous century like a hare racing past a befuddled tortoise.

Building upon the racially biased, biosocial "psychometrics" of Sir Francis Galton, high-society pseudoscientists morphed genetics into eugenics (Greek for "true birth") in a self-serving bid to "improve the human condition." By 1900, Darwin's ideas permeated social science with racist rancor. David Starr Jordan, first president of Stanford University, authored a book in 1902 that distilled and codified the rising field of eugenics. I refer to *Blood of a Nation: The Study of the Decay of a Nation through the Survival of the Unfit.*[196] In this treatise, Jordan advocates a program of "artificial selection," in which inferior forms are destroyed and superior forms encouraged. But he went even further:

> To select for posterity those individuals which best meet our needs or *please our fancy*, and to destroy those with unfavorable qualities, is the function of artificial selection. Add to this the occasional crossing of unlike forms to promote new and desirable variations, and we have the whole secret of selective breeding. This process Youatt calls the "*magician's wand*" by

which man may summon up and bring into existence any form of animal or plant useful to him or *pleasing to his fancy.* (Emphasis added)

Ultimately, Starr argued, it is war that weakens any society, for nations inevitably send their best to the battlefield, forever removing superior blood of those who die.

By 1910, scientists like David Starr Jordan and Charles Benedict Davenport joined ranks with America's northeastern elite (W. Averell Harriman, John D. Rockefeller, and Andrew Carnegie) to form the Eugenics Record Office (ERO) of Cold Spring Harbor, New York. The stated goal of the ERO was to study human patterns of heredity in order to eliminate the substandard or socially inadequate. To achieve this goal, the ERO sought out politicians across the country, advocating and even lobbying for enactment of sterilization laws that would prevent undesirables from reproducing. The ERO also promoted selective breeding programs that would improve the human stock, yielding greater percentages of the strong and bright.

The ERO's "advisory committee" included experts in statistics, criminology, physiology, biology, thremmatology (scientific "breeding" of selected plants and animals), history, law, religion and morals, anthropology, psychiatry, sociology, and even an oddly named "Woman's Viewpoint" offered by one Caroline B. Alexander.

The 1914 ERO Report ("Report of the Committee to Study and to Report on the Best Practical Means of Cutting Off the Defective Germ-Plasm in the American Population"), compiled by H. H. Laughlin, a former high school teacher with a profound interest in Mendelian inheritance, divided the undesirables into ten classes:[197]

1. The Feeble-minded Class
2. The Pauper Class
3. The Inebriate Class
4. The Criminalistic Class

5. The Epileptic Class
6. The Insane Class
7. The Asthenic Class
8. The Diathetic Class
   a. Species Difference
   b. Racial Difference
   c. Family and Individual Differences
9. The Deformed Class
10. The Cacæsthetic Class

According to Laughlin, the purpose of the Eugenics Record Office is to determine a means to uproot and remove defective germ plasm from American inheritance. Laughlin refers to this as the "negative side of the problem," leaving the "positive side" (that of breeding better Americans through artificial selection) to others. Referring to those in the above list, Laughlin writes:

> If they mate with a higher level, they contaminate it; if they mate with the still lower levels, they bolster them up a little only to aid them to continue their own unworthy kind. They constitute a breeding stock of social unfitness.[198]

These early decades of the twentieth century formed a hideous breeding ground for the pseudoscience of eugenics. Moral decay painted cities with a broad and hideous brush. The rise in immigration, particularly to America's Eastern Seaboard, led to perceived racial divides while segregating people groups within the confines of slum housing. Against this impoverished background glittered a rising aristocracy with new money and old family ties. The industrial age brought railroads, oil, and electricity. Henry Ford's assembly lines replaced craftsmen, creating affordable goods for the working man. Electricity bedazzled the modern streets of major cities, and soon dirigibles and prop-engine planes dotted the evening skylines.

The twentieth century promised more products with less effort, and "modern living through chemistry" fireproofed homes; replaced dangerous glass with easy, unbreakable plastics; and even improved cosmetics.

Not every aspect of this brave, new world was rosy, however. War built new corporations, but it also filled furrowed fields with the blood of nations. As soldiers traveled across borders, H1N1 (dubbed the "Spanish Flu" because it first rose to international attention via an epidemic in Spain) decimated families across the globe. Vaccines and antibiotics changed medicine, but they also inoculated millions with SV40, a virus native to rhesus monkeys whose livers had been extracted (posthumously) and used to grow Merck's polio vaccine in the 1950s and '60s. Now, SV40 is known as a carcinogen. This DNA virus plays havoc with a cell's natural lifespan, switching off a gene known as TP53, which encodes for the protein p53. The protein p53 plays a major role in tumor suppression by acting like a stop signal when a cell has reached the end of its life. This "stopped" cell would no longer divide—indeed it would die. So, SV40 appears to mutate TP53, changing the resulting protein's shape, which renders it incapable of acting as a stop signal. The polio vaccine isn't the only medicine with death in the mix. A statement by Dr. Maurice Hilleman, former chief of Merck's vaccine division, not only reveals SV40 as a component of the polio vaccine, but also appears to indicate the presumed unintentional inclusion of HIV in the hepatitis B vaccine.[199]

World War I never truly ended politically. Germany's defeat and humiliation served as a fecund surrogate for the birth of the world's next Napoleon: Adolf Hitler. Though most have read or heard of Hitler's drive to create an Aryan super-race of men (Übermensch— translated roughly as sSuperman"), few realize that Hitler's inspiration derived from American and British eugenics programs, including twin studies performed and advocated by the Eugenics Records Office. According to Edwin Black, in an article published by the *San Francisco Chronicle* in 2003:

The concept of a white, blond-haired, blue-eyed master Nordic race didn't originate with Hitler. The idea was created in the United States, and cultivated in California, decades before Hitler came to power. California eugenicists played an important, although little-known, role in the American eugenics movement's campaign for ethnic cleansing.[200]

Believing his nation had become weak because of inferior bloodlines and degenerate breeding, Hitler employed both negative and positive approaches (as mentioned earlier by Laughlin in his report for the ERO) to improve Germany's bloodlines. Physicians were required to report any and all degenerative illnesses to the government. Hereditary "health" courts sprang up all over the country, leading to the forced sterilization of over four hundred thousand people.[201] Those deemed so inferior that they presented a burden on society faced the ultimate penalty at the *Hartheim Euthanasia Centre*, where patients breathed their last in rooms filled with carbon monoxide. The Lebensborn program sought to increase pure Aryan numbers through extramarital affairs between SS officers (whose bloodlines were verified) and equally pure German females. The offspring of these affairs were raised by the state and placed with genetically acceptable families. Buxom, blonde German women mated with muscular, intelligent blond men provided true Aryan genes to select for superior Aryan children.

Most historians would say that the eugenics era ended in 1979, when California's lawmakers struck down that state's longstanding compulsory sterilization law. However, we would argue that the program continues in the drive to catalog the human genome and improve it. The Human Genome Project (HGP) provides the baseline that genetics researchers can now "tweak." The twentieth century brought an explosion of genetics discoveries. We've come a long way from the early days when David Starr Jordan sought to improve the "germ plasm."

According to the May 2011 report prepared by the Battelle Technology Partnership Practice, the project not only created 310,000 private-sector jobs, but it also turned the initial $3.8 billion investment into a whopping $796 billion! Aren't you grateful for the long hours the HGP scientists and techs spent slaving over lab benches? We know we are! Thanks to these countless hours, scientists now have reference information for 3 billion base pairs, dropkicking science into a brand new age!

Here's what the report mentioned above has to say about this brave new age of genetics:

> Scientists are using the reference genome, the knowledge of genome structure, and the data resulting from the HGP as the foundation for fundamental advancements in medicine and science with the goals of preventing, diagnosing, and treating human disease. Also, while foundational to the understanding of human biological systems, the knowledge and advancements embodied in the human genome sequencing, and the sequencing of model organisms, are useful beyond human biomedical sciences.
>
> The resulting "genomic revolution" is influencing renewable energy development, industrial biotechnology, agricultural biosciences, veterinary sciences, environmental science, forensic science and homeland security, and advanced studies in zoology, ecology, anthropology and other disciplines.[202]

The Baby Boom generation, born to returning World War II veterans, has seen the world shift on its axis. In 1945, the war in the Pacific ended with the destruction of Hiroshima and Nagasaki, Japan, ushering in the nuclear age and a frantic study of genetic mutations by radiation. The war also ignited unparalleled economic growth in the United States. Returning veterans found well-paying jobs, married, and built new homes. America's gross national product skyrocketed as middle-class numbers swelled. White collar, service-industry jobs increased as our country shifted from producing goods to consumerism. The "service industry" replaced traditional factories. Corporations gobbled companies, and conglomerates fed on corporations. Thanks to Dwight D. Eisenhower's interstate system, goods moved easily and cheaply while American tourists fell in love with station wagons and "mobile homes."

In 1953, when James Watson and Francis Crick unraveled the structure of the DNA molecule, most children played with dolls or pop guns. Television had only just emerged as a new form of entertainment, but the new medium had already become an integral part of most Boomer families. Frozen dinners consumed while watching *I Love Lucy* or *Arthur Godfrey* had begun to replace home-cooked meals around the dining room table. New home appliances helped women finish housework and food preparation quickly, giving them more time to work outside the home. The postwar baby boom did far more than just create a new, massive US generation; it also created an insidious new lifestyle that would eventually tear families apart.

In stark contrast to their grandparents' childhoods, today's three-year-olds are handling rudimentary computers and learning that guns are evil. Free speech is a thing of the past, but free love is encouraged and even taught to kindergarten children as their right as humans. Knowledge has most definitely increased—so much so that the sum total of human knowledge is now said to double every ten years. Yet, with all these "improvements," humankind has never been farther from God.

In fact, "humankind" itself is about to become an anachronistic term. Homo sapiens, the wonderful creation of a loving Father, are about to become extinct—or so George Church and Hugo de Garis would have us believe. The DNA molecule that Watson and Crick discovered during the early years of the Boomer generation isn't good enough for self-directed evolution. Scientists no longer seek merely to understand God's marvelous molecule; they seek to replace it with a synthetic construct of human design. A concept called "transhumanism" lies at the core of this drive to alter humankind's genome, and it is this hubristic notion—this deliberate jab into the eye of God—that may influence not only the mechanism within the coming mark of the New World Order, but it may also increase its popularity with today's Generation Y.

A GENERATION READY
FOR THE MARK

Respectively, XY and XX no longer define male or female. Transgendered individuals, or even those who simply choose to identify with a particular "sex" option, have convinced many schools, workplaces, and even politicians to protect their "choices." A child born as an XY male may choose to "identify" as a girl—even going so far as to join girls' basketball teams and shower in the girls' facilities. God's design for distinct male and female roles has been corrupted into "fifty shades of grey."

Generation Y is sometimes called the "Echo Boom," as it is the largest generation since the postwar Baby Boomers. In fact, some statistics list Gen Y as numbering eighty million or more. Beyond this group is Generation Z—or those born after 1995. Today's media culture is already targeting this generation as rising consumers, customizing advertising to reach gender-neutral, tech-hungry, posthuman individuals. Perhaps even more than their parents, Gen Y youth look to genetics to take the next step in human evolution. What is that step? Consider popular culture and the memes Gen Y and Gen Z people are exposed to every day. Graphic novels, films, television, and video games constantly and consistently teach that humankind is about to "level up." Young men and women (and those in between) can become werewolves, vampires, super soldiers, and spider men. The old human paradigm of two genders and five senses can be replaced with an infinite number of gender choices (or none at all!) and extra senses that allow the transhuman to hear colors, smell sounds, or tune into the very fabric of space and time. The biblical promise that we will "rise up as eagles" is twisted into promising wings that permit the new human to take physical flight. Generations Y and Z could live forever. At least, that is the lie they are being told.

Cybernetics and synthetic genomes will soon merge into the sexy Cylon of *Battlestar Galactica*. The posthuman will be beautiful, perfect in form, and capable of superhuman feats. And he/she will live forever. "Ye shall be as gods" is the oldest lie, spoken to Adam and Eve by a garden snake long ago, but it is echoing once again in the promises to a generation of lost, unhappy youths. The Antichrist will play upon this inner need for perfection, this constant yearning to become a god. The youth of Hitler's day believed they would join their leader in the coming thousand years of Aryan rule over the earth. Is it so far-fetched to say that the coming evil one, foreshadowed by the Führer, will also promise his followers a plum part in his kingdom?

Remember this important fact: Antichrist will claim to BE CHRIST. He will arrive as a peacemaker—as the answer to all of our worldly problems. It is also quite possible that he will claim to be an enhanced—or "trans"—human. It might be more accurate to call him a "trance" human, for the Antichrist will cast a spell upon today's youth, luring all those who do not call the true Christ their Savior to take his special mark. This might be a chip inserted into the body used to track each person's location, but it may be *much* more. This mark of the Beast might actually rewrite DNA.

READ/WRITE/GENOMES

Many may remember the early days of computers and computing power. Commercially available computers arose about the same time as Watson and Crick's hallmark discovery. The US Census Bureau received the first UNIVAC computer on March 31, 1951, for a cost of nearly $1 million. In all, the government purchased forty-six UNI-VAC computers, which is remarkable considering that each machine required its own small room! Back then, computing power for these monsters paled in comparison when measured against the tiny computer inside our cell phones.

In just fifty years, computer technology has advanced incredibly fast; solid-state hard drives have replaced old magnetic tape, and chips have replaced vacuum tubes. It's very likely that the computer in your hand today is flash-based, containing no hard drive at all. Cloud computing will soon mitigate the need for "local storage," although (for now) you can still buy laptops with more than a terabyte of storage! One of the first computers we had was a Commodore 128 that had 128 kilobytes of RAM. The laptop Tom is using to write this has 6 gigabytes of RAM.

Hard-disk storage—in the old days—consisted of ROM, or "read-only memory," which held chips or areas of storage that included operating software that must remain permanently available but rarely or never required updating. As computers advanced and floppy disks were added, most of these disks were "write once," which meant data could be written to them only one time. They could not be rewritten.

At one time, scientists considered our DNA as "read-only memory." The code within each of our cells contains instructions for making the machinery that runs the complex operations that keep us alive. However, beginning in the twentieth century, early geneticists discovered a process called 'recombination" that allows the insertion of new genetic material into a cell's genome. Recombination makes gene therapy possible, using a bacterial or viral vector, or "truck," to deliver the new genetic sequence to the target cell (perhaps in the lung or muscle). Scientists see nothing ethically wrong with "editing" our God-given genome; they merely see this as another form of self-directed evolution. Of course, one can only begin to edit what one reads first. Enter the Human Genome Project (HGP).

It might be said that the HGP actually began on December 9, 1984, when a group of scientists gathered in the Alta, Utah, ski resort area high up in the Wasatch Mountains. There, David Smith of the Department of Energy and Mortimer Mendelsohn of Lawrence Livermore Laboratory gathered with seventeen genetics scientists to determine whether or not the time might be right to commence serious measurement of the mutations within the human genome. Joining Smith and Mendelsohn were David Botstein, Ebert Branscomb, Charles Cantor, C. Thomas Caskey, George McDonald Church, John D. Delaharty, Charles Edington, Raymond Gesteland, Leonard Leman, Michael Gough, John Mulvihill, Richard Myers, James V. Neel, Maynard Olson, Edwin Southern, Sherman Weissman, and Raymond L. White.

Of this stellar list of respected names, one stands out: George McDonald Church. Church is a self-professed transhumanist and author of the recent bestseller, *Regenesis: How Synthetic Biology Will Reinvent Nature and Ourselves.* He's a dedicated vegan, an entrepreneur (having established nine genomics-based businesses, including Knome, Pathogenica, and Gen9Bio—a synthetic biology company), and an avowed transhumanist who would love to see revived Neanderthal, assuming a human female volunteers to be the surrogate mother. (Oh, and by the way, Church was also instrumental in kick-starting the "race for the brain," addressed later in this section.)

Initially, the Alta group had discussed finding a repeatable and affordable means to quantify mutations within the Hiroshima offspring. Two years later, in 1986, Mendelsohn joined several others from Alta, as well as panel chair Arno Moltulsky of the Center for Inherited Disease, to present a report called "Office of Technology Assessment, Technologies for Detecting Heritable Mutations in Human Beings." This report had followed a meeting of leading molecular biologists in the spring of that year organized by James Watson (yes, that Watson), and held at Cold Spring Harbor Laboratory. Cold Spring, if you remember your eugenics history, was the site for the Eugenics Records Office (ERO). Are you beginning to get a nagging twitch at the back of your neck? Us, too.

By 1987, promotion of a planned genomic sequencing event kicked off with an article in the nation's most prominent newspaper, *The New York Times (NYT)*, titled "The Genome Project":

IT WOULD BE THE BIGGEST, costliest, most provocative biomedical research project in history, and the United States must embark on it immediately. That was how Walter Gilbert, Nobel Prize-winning biology professor at Harvard University, heard the genome project described at scientific meetings all through 1985 and 1986. The undertaking—which would reveal the precise biochemical makeup of the entire genetic material, or genome, of a human being—would, he heard, revolutionize medicine. It would answer the Japanese challenge in biotechnology. It would **grant insight into human biology previously held only by God.** (Emphasis added)[203]

After fawning over several scientists who attended the Alta meeting, the *NYT* article continues:

> Today, a new consensus is emerging. Robert Cook-Deegan, an analyst at the Office of Technology Assessment (O.T.A.), a Congressional agency, reports that of late, "N.I.H. has been talking to D.O.E. There's more cooperation than friction." A bill has been introduced in Congress by Senator Pete Domenici of New Mexico to create a Government consortium to map and sequence the genome. Other bills are in the offing. Few doubt that the genome project, in some form, will eventually get under way.[204]

Nobel laureate Walter Gilbert, though you may not know it, partnered with George Church in the study of mouse and yeast genetic elements. Gilbert also cofounded the company Biogen (now Biogen Idec) in 1978. Wally Gilbert may not be an avowed transhumanist, but he does spend a lot of time with Church, so one wonders if he might not be influenced by such proximity. Church is an evangelist when it comes to transhumanist dogma; perhaps it's discussed over a nice plate of organic sprouts.

With the *NYT* and other media moguls on board and a bill before Congress, it didn't take long for the idea of a gene race to take hold. In 1989, before leaving office, President Ronald Reagan approved the plans for a US-led Genome Project and placed it in his 1988 budget. In May 1990, the official proposal went to Capitol Hill under the title *Understanding Our Genetic Inheritance, The U.S. Human Genome Project: The First Five Years (FY 1991–1995).* Don't let the title fool you; the plan was for a fifteen-year study of the human genome to commence in 1991.

On September 11 of that same year, President George H. W. Bush gave a speech in a rare appearance before a joint session of Congress to discuss the economy and the rising conflict in the Persian Gulf. On that auspicious occasion, Bush said this:

> As you know, I've just returned from a very productive meeting with Soviet President [Mikhail] Gorbachev, and I am pleased that we are working together to build a new relationship. In Helsinki, our joint statement affirmed to the world our shared resolve to counter Iraq's threat to peace. Let me quote: "We are united in the belief that Iraq's aggression must not be tolerated. No peaceful international order is possible if larger states can devour their smaller neighbors."
>
> Clearly, no longer can a dictator count on East-West confrontation to stymie concerted United Nations action against aggression.
>
> A new partnership of nations has begun, and we stand today at a unique and extraordinary moment. The crisis in the Persian Gulf, as grave as it is, also offers a rare opportunity to move toward an historic period of cooperation. Out of these troubled times, our fifth objective—a **new world order**—can emerge: A new era—freer from the threat of terror, stronger in the pursuit of justice and more secure in the quest for peace. **An era in which the nations of the world, east and west, north and south, can prosper and live in harmony.**

A GENERATION READY FOR THE MARK

A hundred generations have searched for this elusive path to peace, while a thousand wars raged across the span of human endeavor, and today that new world is struggling to be born. A world quite different from the one we've known. A world where the rule of law supplants the rule of the jungle. A world in which nations recognize the shared responsibility for freedom and justice. A world where the strong respect the rights of the weak.

This is the vision that I shared with President Gorbachev in Helsinki. He and the other leaders from Europe, the gulf and around the world understand that how we manage this crisis today could shape the future for generations to come.[205] (Emphasis added)

Is it a coincidence that the leader of the free world included such language in a speech that came just as science had initiated the most ambitious project of them all: to decode God's signature within our cells?

The slow and steady progress from eugenics to genetics to a New World Order is not coincidental, dear reader. It is part and parcel of an ages-old plan to unseat the true God and replace Him with a false idol, even man himself. Transcendence and transhumanism are the fruits of the Eugenics Record Office and the pioneering efforts of men like David Jordan and even our illustrious past president Theodore Roosevelt, who wrote this in a letter to prominent eugenicist Charles Davenport in 1913:

My dear Mr. Davenport:

I am greatly interested in the two memoirs you have sent me. They are very instructive, and, from the standpoint of our country, very ominous. You say that these people are not themselves responsible, that it is "society" that is responsible. I agree with you if you mean, as I suppose you do, that **society has no business to permit degenerates to reproduce their kind**. It is really extraordinary that our people refuse to apply to human beings such elementary knowledge as every successful farmer is obliged to apply to his own stock breeding. Any group of farmers who permitted their best stock not to breed, and let all the increase come from the worst stock, would be treated as fit inmates for an asylum. Yet we fail to understand that such conduct is rational compared to the conduct of a nation which permits unlimited breeding from the worst stocks, physically and morally, while it encourages or connives at the cold selfishness or the twisted sentimentality as a result of which the men and women ought to marry, and if married have large families, remain celebates [*sic*] or have no children or only one or two. **Some day we will realize that the prime duty—the inescapable duty—of the good citizen of the right type is to leave his or her blood behind him in the world; and that we have no business to permit the perpetuation of citizens of the wrong type.**

Faithfully yours,

Theodore Roosevelt

[And at bottom of left corner:] Charles B. Davenport, Esq., Cold Spring Harbor, L.I.[206]

Anyone reading today must be shocked to discover that our famous president actually believed it to be the duty of American citizens to leave behind the "right type" of blood! Adolf Hitler came to power based on an ideology steeped in opinions such as these, by taking the ideology of American eugenicists coupled with the financial backing of many within that movement, including George H. W. Bush's father, Prescott Bush!

According to a September 2004 article posted online in the United Kingdom paper, *The Guardian*, Bush's actions caused him to be indicted under the US "Trading with the Enemy Act":

George Bush's grandfather, the late US senator Prescott Bush, was a director and shareholder of companies that profited from their involvement with the financial backers of Nazi Germany.

The Guardian has obtained confirmation from newly discovered files in the US National Archives that a firm of which Prescott Bush was a director was involved with the financial architects of Nazism.

While there is no suggestion that Prescott Bush was sympathetic to the Nazi cause, the documents reveal that the firm he worked for, Brown Brothers Harriman (BBH), acted as a US base for the German industrialist, Fritz Thyssen, who helped finance Hitler in the 1930s before falling out with him at the end of the decade. The Guardian has seen evidence that shows Bush was the director of the New York-based Union Banking Corporation (UBC) that represented Thyssen's US interests and he continued to work for the bank after America entered the war.[207]

Though the *Guardian* had timed the publication of this article to coincide with Bush's reelection campaign, we can thank the dark world of politics for its publication! Because of this, we can make the connections necessary to help us discern the times in which we live. Since the dawn of the twentieth century, a dark force has been rising within the confines of this sleeping giant of a country. Eugenics and eventually neo-eugenics and transhumanism have dictated scientific direction and set goals for politicians, all with one end in mind: to achieve the New World Order, to give it birth. During the past century, knowledge has increased exponentially, and the Internet has enabled us to "travel" at the speed of light. We live in the final days of planet Earth as we know it. Our world is bombarded with chemtrails and electromagnetic waves. Our foods and animals have been genetically altered, the air poisoned with radiation and heavy metals, and our genes are held together only by the grace of God.

The Human Genome Project, intended to finish in fifteen years, instead announced completion only *thirteen* years into the work. If you read summaries and reviews of that work now, you'll find many arguing that the announcement came prematurely—that the entire sequence had not fully been read. Thirteen is a number repeated again and again in occult circles. It is considered the number of rebellion, an unlucky number. The Egyptian god Osiris was torn into fourteen pieces: thirteen plus his reproductive "member" (reconstructed by the goddess Isis and used to impregnate herself and then give birth to Horus). Do a search in the daily news for the number thirteen, and you will be amazed at how many times it occurs. Could it be that the HGP leaders arbitrarily stopped at thirteen and "rested," announcing their victory to the world, or is it possible that the number was craftily chosen as a nod to spiritual influences and masters?

The announcement ushered humanity into the post-genomic era and engendered the question: Who owns our genes? According to the final Human Genome Publication (No. 12), published in February 2002, the *First International Conversation on Enviro-Genetics Disputes and Issues*, sponsored by the Einstein Institute for Health and Science, met in Kona, Hawaii. The assembly took place in July 2001 and was attended by more than eighty judges and forty scientists—all there to discuss the legal and ethical ramifications of the Human Genome Project's results. These legal and scientific experts joined together from all over the world to dissect the New World Order of the post-genome era. Shortly thereafter, attendee Justice Artemio V. Panganiban of the Philippines presented a paper with the assigned topic, "Paradigm Shifts in Law and Legal Philosophy," in which he recounted some of the opinions expressed during the Kona conference. See endnote should you desire to read the entire paper.[208]

Justice Panganiban's comments succinctly summarize those of many globalists:

I believe that the major transformational shifts in the world have been brought about mainly by the informational and technological revolution unfolding even now as I speak. I refer to computerization, minuterization [*sic*], digitization, satellite communications, fiber optics and the Internet—all of which, taken together, tend to integrate knowledge on a worldwide scale. This international integration of knowledge, technologies and systems is referred to as globalization.

Amazingly, Panganiban has here distilled this section so far in that knowledge, travel, and commerce have increased exponentially since the turn of the twentieth century. He goes on:

Professor Anne-Marie Slaughter of Harvard Law School, says that modern judges should "see one another not only as servants or even representatives of a particular government or party, but as fellow professionals in a profession that transcends national borders"... Justice Claire L'Heureux-Dube of the Supreme Court of Canada—in a speech before the "First International Conversation on Enviro-Genetics Disputes and Issues" sponsored by the Einstein Institute for Science, Health and the Courts (EINSHAC) and held in Kona, Hawaii on July 1, 2001, opined that it is "no longer appropriate to speak of the impact or influence of certain courts on other countries but rather of the place of all courts in the global dialogue on human rights and other common legal questions."

The immediate impact of statements like these is that the legal representatives we elect, or those appointed by such elected representatives, appear to owe their allegiance not to the electors but rather to "each other" and to the globe at large—to the New World Order. So while we may still wish to believe that the act of writing to one's congressman precipitates action in Washington, the sad but obvious truth is that globalism rules our world, condemning our meager participation to the scrap heap of idealism and Judeo-Christian ethics.

The Human Genome Publication No. 12 referenced above has

much to say about the global impact of the HGP. At the Kona meeting, National Institutes of Environmental Health and Sciences Director Kenneth Olden "observed that the Human Genome Project's output presents a major societal challenge to use the new information and technologies **to improve the quality of human existence.** The scope of this challenge, he said, is expanded further when the question is asked about who will benefit most from these advances and who will bear the greater share of the risk" (emphasis added; note how this language echoes the eugenics movement's goals to improve mankind).[209]

The HGP publication continues with this informative paragraph:

Discussions that followed the plenaries were far ranging, generally going beyond the suggested topics of genetically modified (GM) foods and agriculture, bioscience and criminal jurisprudence, biological property, genetic testing, and human subjects in biomedical research. During these sessions, judges related how their nations' courts have managed science and technology issues and the problems they have encountered. As groups attempted to anticipate issues likely to arise in the next two decades, researchers in their turn offered opinions on the current state of the science as well as some forecasts of advances on the near horizon.[210]

We don't know about you, but reading language like this makes us feel a bit like a sick patient whose doctor is discussing our healthcare with our family while simultaneously ignoring us. As humans, each one of us carries unique DNA that sets us apart, making us special and one of a kind to God. However, corporations, judiciaries, politicians, and scientists huddle around our hospital beds like vampires in a blood bank, eagerly using us to further a selfish agenda.

And speaking of selfish, let us tell you a bit about an article we recently read, called "The Selfish Gene." Published in January 2013 at the DailyBeast.com and written by Michael Thomsen, the article bemoans the failures of the Human Genome Project—and Walter Gilbert in particular—to live up to the hype of their original "Promethean" promises. Citing the work of Hillary and Steven Rose, authors of *Genes, Cells, and Brains: The Promethean Promises of the New Biology*, Thomsen wonders whether the HGP provided consumers anything beyond a better "shampoo":

> For the Roses, the signal image of this movement is Walter Gilbert, one of the lead scientists on the Human Genome Project, standing on stage promising the possibility of fitting the code for human life onto a CD-ROM. This is the model for science in the Petri dish of post-industrial capitalism, reductionist fantasies delivered from a PR platform meant to turn public excitement into investor support. Scientists begin with a fixed conclusion, hyperbolize the benefits of reaching it, and then spend large amounts of private and public money to reach it only to discover their original promises were impossible. The Human Genome Project began not with a question, but an answer that had to be substantiated in reverse.

It's clear from this statement that the Roses and Thomsen believe the HGP was a letdown to corporatism as well as to us. Maybe he's missed the point. The PR campaign works in that it does sell the American or global public on an idea, particularly one that requires a serious infusion of what we naively call "our tax dollars." These "selfish" promises haven't failed; they have succeeded beyond measure! The post-genomic era has altered legal decisions, provided the foundation to define "human," given science a road map for gene hacking and synthetic biology, and propelled the transhumanist agenda to the forefront. Failed? Not on your tintype!

The New World Order, hailed as having arrived by President George H. W. Bush in 1991, is here, and science has established its paradigm: a drive toward a new human…a *better* human. It's like the introduction to the hit 1970s TV program, *The Six Million Dollar Man*—"Gentlemen, we can rebuild him. We have the technology. We have the capability to build the world's first bionic man. Steve Austin will be that man. Better than he was before. Better, stronger, faster." Well, the post-genomic, proto-transhuman is just that and a bag of chips. And if you drag your feet and refuse to let your children or grandchildren participate in the Golden Age of the Transhuman Being, then you'll be branded a heretic at best, less sentient and perhaps even not worthy of life at worst.

The Golden Age of Transhumanism is upon us, whether we like it or not. Just look at the films, television programs, and video games set before our children for constant consumption and indoctrination. According to *H+ Magazine*, the top ten "transhumanist" films follow, counting down from ten to one (our comments in brackets):

10. Avatar 3D (2009)—[If you've not seen this one, rent the DVD. It is the blueprint for 2025, when transhumanists such as Ray Kurzweil and Natasha Vita-Moore see us transitioning to "avatars" in preparation for full uploading to computers. The plot is simple and "green": Mankind has conquered space, but corporations are still greedy and continue to strip resources—in this case, from another planet. When his brother is killed, paraplegic Marine Jake Scully takes his place on a mission to Pandora, a world filled with "backward" but natively beautiful creatures. Parker Selfridge is the greedy head of the corporation raiding Pandora, and his goal is to wipe out the "Na'vi" (the natives). The plot exploits the young by indoctrinating them with the "green agenda" while planting desires to be "free" to live an eternal, perfect life in a beautiful garden inside a virtual world.]

9. Gattaca (1997)—[A film about hacking the human genome to build better people. The title is taken from the building blocks of DNA: A for adenine, G for guanine, C for cytosine, and T for thymine.]

8. The Terminator (1984)—[James Cameron directed this as well as *Avatar*. Arnold Schwarzenegger portrays a sentient machine from the future. Oddly enough, this film presents the possible consequences of what Hugo de Garis calls the coming "Artilect War," in which sentient machines rise up against humanity (both transhuman and human) in a battle for control of the planet.]

7. **The Matrix** (1999)—Probably only a few thousand people in the world have ever read, or even heard of, Nick Bostrom's confounding Simulation Argument. But tens of millions of people have watched this movie and thus have learned something about the concept. Which pill would you take? [This statement is from the *H+* article and contains the impressions of the writer. Bostrom's Simulation Argument posits that we are living within a living computer. Here is the abstract from this paper: "This paper argues that *at least one* of the following propositions is true: (1) the human species is very likely to go extinct before reaching a 'posthuman' stage; (2) any posthuman civilization is extremely unlikely to run a significant number of simulations of their evolutionary history (or variations thereof); (3) we are almost certainly living in a computer simulation. It follows that the belief that there is a significant chance that we will one day become posthumans who run ancestor-simulations is false, unless we are currently living in a simulation. A number of other consequences of this result are also discussed."][211]

6. **WALL-E** (2008) [This film teaches children and adults alike that robots feel, love, and even "mate." Wall-E is a garbage robot whose solitary job is to clean up the mess on Earth left behind by the humans (who now live off-world). "Eve," a sleek female robot, is sent by the out-of-condition humans (one might say "devolved") to see if Earth can once again sustain life.]

5. **Dr. Jekyll & Mr. Hyde** (1931)—Among the movies I've listed here, this is the one that probably the fewest of our readers have seen. That's a shame, because it is truly a great film and it also addresses important issues for transhumanists to consider. What makes up the human personality? How do we define "good" and "evil" and who gets to choose the accepted definition? [Again, the statement here is from

the article's author at *H+*, so it's interesting that he chose this old film, based on the nineteenth-century novel, *The Strange Case of Dr. Jekyll and Mr. Hyde*, published in 1886 by Robert Louis Stevenson. Many films, a play, and even a musical have been based on this novella. The notion of good and evil is also a biblical one.]

4. Eternal Sunshine of the Spotless Mind (2004)—In my opinion as a cineaste, this is the best movie made, of any genre, thus far in the 21st century. And it's also an essential film for those who are interested in the questions of neuroethics. We may not be far away from having technologies that can enable the precise manipulation of memories, and, by extension, of personality. What a treat when a wonderfully entertaining movie also can engage the viewer in a challenging exploration of transhumanist ethics. [The writer's enthusiasm for this film is telling. The title is taken from a poem by Alexander Pope about a woman whose comfort after losing love is forgetfulness. In the film, Jim Carrey's character Joel Barrish and his lover, Clementine (Kate Winslet), both choose to have their memories erased by the Lacuna Corporation. The story line follows the disappearing memories as they are erased inside Barrish's head with the final memory, "Meet me in Montauk." Many readers may already be thinking what we're about to write: Montauk, New York, is the site of the notorious Montauk Project, related to the Philadelphia Experiment.]

3. Brazil (1985)—Total movie magic…and although most of the technology depicted in this film is steampunk, not *H+*, it should provide a wake-up call for us to be aware that the struggle for political power and social control is ever present, and that if we fail to pay attention, our dreams of techno-transcendence may be snatched away from us just when they seem within our grasp. [What an interesting comment! "Dreams of techno-transcendence"? May the Lord grant that we may continue to stand in the way of such "transcendence"!]

2. Metropolis (1927)—In making *Metropolis*, the great director Fritz Lang used all the resources of the then world-class UFA studio in Berlin—nearly bankrupting it in the process—and achieved effects that have never been surpassed. See it on the big screen, preferably in the most recent restoration, and be blown away. [This film is in German with subtitles, but the restored copy is indeed beautiful to watch. The story takes place in 2026. Metropolis is modeled upon Babylon, and features apocalyptic themes, including a false prophetess called the "Whore of Babylon," who incites the workers to their doom. Robotics and human/machine evolution themes abound, as does the theme of class distinction, the wealthy versus the common worker. It's no wonder the Germans loved it.]

1. **2001: A Space Odyssey** (1968)—You knew we would end up here, didn't you? Where else but with a movie that not only is central to the concerns of transhumanists, but also is among the top ten or twenty movies ever made, of any kind. First to impress is its amazingly realistic depictions of life in space, whether on the shuttle—that flight attendant who walks upside down!—the space station, or the flight to Jupiter. And no film has ever depicted with such poignancy the troubled relationship between sentient AI and its human masters. Then comes the astonishing climax—the famous Stargate sequence—which I regard as Clarke's and Kubrick's attempt to portray, in cinematic terms, the human experience of a technological singularity. Remember, this is decades before Vinge wrote his seminal essay, though in 1965 I. J. Good had first described the possibility of an "intelligence explosion," which likely influenced the filmmakers. Someday, perhaps, another even better movie will be made about the dreams/nightmares of transhumanists, but for now, this one is the pinnacle. [The writer effervesces over this one, but he has reason to do so. The movie *2001: A Space Odyssey* uses psychedelics and German music—"Also Sprach Zarathustra"—to paint a picture of humankind's directed evolution via panspermia, taking us from the deliberate intervention during the days of Neanderthal to a team of scientists in a spaceship and beyond. Nietzsche's coming *Übermensch* or Superman is revealed at the end— savior of all mankind in the transformed "starchild."][212]

Honestly, how many of the above films have you seen? If you're not naturally a science-fiction fan, then it's likely you've missed one or perhaps even all of them. However, these films represent what transhumanists consider core theology in compact, easy-to-digest, two- to three-hour lessons.

Fiction, particularly fiction in film, provides immediate access to layers of the brain that mere nonfiction such as this cannot reach. When processing fiction, humans naturally "shut off" their logical tendencies to question a particular viewpoint. Taught the same viewpoint in the context of a pleasant or intriguing story, the "lesson" seeds itself into our subconscious and slowly begins to grow there.

Television has brought us loads of such "seeded" themes over the years since its invention. Early "space" programs appear silly to us now, but what 1950s child didn't long to be Superman or Flash Gordon? However, beginning with a program in 1966, everything changed. Gene Roddenberry spent his youth as a pilot in World War II, but upon returning to civilian life, he had an early glimpse into the brand-new medium called television, and his life and our futures took a dramatic turn. Gifted with the ability to write compelling fiction, Roddenberry moved to Hollywood and began churning out scripts for early favorites like *Have Gun Will Travel, Highway Patrol, The Kaiser Aluminum Hour, The Naked City,* and *Dr. Kildare.* In 1964, he decided to write a script for a new science-fiction drama that he described as *Wagon Train in Space.* The program was called *Star Trek,* and Roddenberry struck a deal with NBC to air the show beginning with the fall lineup in 1966. Despite climbing ratings, NBC canceled the show after eighty episodes (about three and a half seasons). Fan loyalty proved everlasting, however, and soon *Star Trek* conventions revived interest in the *Enterprise* crew, so much so that Paramount Studios signed Robert Wise to direct the original cast in *Star Trek: The Motion Picture,* which premiered in December 1979—and the rest, so they say, is history.

But is it? There is a secret history to the Roddenberry story that you may not know. Author Peter Levenda included the legendary writer as one of the inside crowd around a nebulous but highly influential group called "The Nine." This is what symbologist and science-fiction researcher Christopher Loring Knowles, author of *Our Gods Wear Spandex: The Secret History of Comic Book Heroes*, had to say about Roddenberry on his weblog, "The Secret Sun," in 2008:

In early 1975, a broke and depressed Roddenberry was approached by a British former race car driver named Sir John Whitmore, who was associated with a strange organization called "Lab-9." Though unknown to the public, Lab-9 were ostensibly a sort of an independent version of the *X-Files*, dedicated to the research of paranormal phenomena. However, Lab-9 had another, more complex agenda—they later claimed to be in contact with a group of extraterrestrials called the "Council of Nine" or simply "The Nine," who had been communicating through "channelers" or psychic mediums.

The Nine claimed to be the creators of mankind, and had informed the channelers that they would be returning to Earth soon. Lab-9 had wanted to hire Roddenberry to write a screenplay based on the Council of Nine's imminent return. To help Roddenberry in his research, Lab-9 flew him out to their headquarters, located on a large estate in Ossining, NY. There, Roddenberry met and interviewed several psychics, and prepared the groundwork for his script.

Roddenberry wrote a script called *The Nine*, in which he fictionalized his experiences at Lab-9 and the message for humanity that the Council of Nine wished to convey. But Roddenberry's story focused more on his fictionalized alter-ego and his marital and financial worries than on The Nine themselves, and Lab-9 requested a rewrite. He handed the task of revising the script to an assistant, Jon Povill. In his revision, Povill posited that the hit sci-fi TV show that Roddenberry's alter ego had produced in the 60s was not actually his work, but had been channeled through him by the Council of Nine.

UFO cultists in the 70s and 80s would make similar claims about *Star Trek* itself....

It was later revealed in the 1977 book *Briefing for the Landing on Planet Earth* that The Nine claimed to be the figures whom the ancient Egyptians had based their Ennead, or pantheon of major gods, on. Another book of channeled messages from The Nine was published in 1992 and was titled, *The Only Planet of Choice: Essential Briefings from Deep Space*. However, little has been heard from The Nine since that book's publication. But it is worth noting that a year after it was published, a new *Star Trek* TV series appeared called *Deep Space Nine*.[213]

Knowles may be onto something. In fact, once you start down the rabbit trail leading from transhumanism back to Hitler and the eugenicists, you run through some rough terrain that includes Manson, The Nine, a group of "wandering bishops" with no real church affiliation, assassins, and—of all things—H. P. Lovecraft, whose wife (some say) had an illicit affair over some months with none other than Aleister Crowley!

Forgetting all that for a moment (if indeed, one can), let us return to The Nine. Levenda not only addresses this odd bit of exopolitical history, but he dedicates an entire section of *Book One* to it. Here is the crux of that tale, broken down for us by "Gordon" on RuneSoup.com in an article called "The Séance That Changed America":

> The man at the centre of this séance [the one that changed America] was Andrija Puharich, US Army Captain and author of a government paper on the weaponisation of ESP. And this is the guy that is moving in the same murky circles as [wandering] bishops Jack Martin and Fred Crisman.
>
> The farmhouse in question was owned by his bizarro Round Table Foundation [RTF]which appears to have received funding from the CIA.

Puharich first gathered together these nine people on a warm night in early June. But the most interesting results were actually achieved in New Year's Eve of the same year.

And it's a line-up that positively defines "could not make this up". The group included:

Arthur Young, who invented the Bell helicopter. However at the end of WWII he abandoned military aviation to concentrate full-time on the paranormal.

Arthur's wife, Ruth...previously of the Forbes dynasty. Her son, Michael, would get a job at Bell Aerospace through her and Arthur's influence. (Michael's wife got Lee Harvey Oswald his job at the book depository. She was learning Russian from Oswald's wife who was living with her in Irving, Texas. Oh, and her father worked for a CIA front called the Agency for International Development. Lee Harvey Oswald left the coffee company in New Orleans, saying to his co-workers he was "going to work for NASA." After the assassination, two other coffee company employees get jobs at NASA. Just saying.)

Mary Bancroft; of the Bancroft dynasty who would much later sell the Dow Jones and *Wall Street Journal* to Murdoch. She also happened to be the mistress of the then-CIA chief. (The one JFK fired after the Bay of Pigs after saying he was also going to break up the CIA...who conveniently went on to investigate JFK's death. Just saying.)

Marcella Du Pont of the Du Pont family.

Alice Bouverie who was born into the Astor dynasty. (Her father died on the Titanic and her first husband was a Czarist prince who would work for the OSS during WWII.)

Here's what happened at the séance [quoting from Levenda]:

These gods, who were nine in number as well, were part of one great, creator god known as Atum. The other gods consisted of Shu, Tefnut, Geb, Nut, Osiris, Isis, Seth, Nephthys, and sometimes Horus.

Communication with these entities was handled by the medium, an Indian gentleman referred to as Dr. D.G. Vinod, who slipped into a trance state at 12:15 AM and began speaking as "The Nine" by 12:30. Afterwards Dr. Vinod would claim to have no memory of the conversation that preceded between the Ennead Nine and their human counterparts.

During the course of the séance the mystical Nine informed the human nine that they would be in charge of bringing about a mystical renaissance on Earth. From there The Nine ventured into quasi-scientific, philosophical constructs that eventually led to the acknowledgement that they, the Grand Ennead, were in fact extraterrestrial beings living in an immense spaceship hovering invisibly over the planet and that the assembled congregation had been selected to promote their agenda on Earth.

Not a bad collection of people to pull together if you wanted to promote a specific agenda over the second half of the twentieth century. Untold riches and connective power in one farmhouse. In fact, you have to wonder what percentage of American wealth was controlled by people related to the attendees.

Writing about the face on Mars and its relation to a descendant group sprung from this very séance, Chris Knowles points out:

And the other conundrum here is if the Council of Nine's psychics saw this thing before it was photographed in 1976, did NASA go looking for it solely based on their advice? What does that say about the influence of a group that most people could be excused for dismissing as a bunch of gullible New Agers?

The Nine would go on to surface in weird places for decades including near Uri Geller (the AP is Puharich, who first brought Geller to the US), President Ford, Gene Roddenberry (Deep Space Nine anyone?), Al Gore as well as Soviets surrounding Gorbachev who were instrumental in the collapse of communism as mentioned in this old Fortean Times piece. It's not unreasonable to assume there were many more such places.[214]

Are you beginning to wonder what else you may have missed in history class? While it's possible that all this is a fabrication, much of it does ring true, as Levenda, who is a meticulous researcher, documents his claims in the pages of his books.

How many young people, scientists, and politicians have been heavily influenced by the decisions made by those under the sway of The Nine? No one can say for certain, but if the accusations are true, then it's possible that nearly every war, every invention, and even every lesson taught in your child's school can be traced to this infamous hidden thirty-three (nine is three to the third power).

Just when did The Nine first emerge, and why? For answers, let's begin with a look at Andrija Puharich, parapsychologist, inventor, and founder of the Round Table Foundation. Puharich was born in 1918 in Chicago to poor, Yugoslav immigrants. His birth name was Karel, but his parents lovingly called him Andrija, a nickname he later adopted (perhaps because it sounded more mysterious). A gifted student, Puharich received a scholarship to Northwestern, where he studied pre-med, going on to receive his medical degree from Northwestern's medical school in 1943. During this same period, the young Puharich served with the Army Medical Corps, training at Fort Detrick (coincidentally, Fort Detrick is also the location for the army's biological weapons program from 1943 to 1969, when the program name changed to "biological defense"). Puharich claimed he lectured on parapsychology to military audiences and invented an implantable "tooth radio," which he sold to the CIA. In fact, Puharich's connections to the CIA and the mind also led to LSD, the drug that killed CIA scientist Frank Olson.

Puharich's connections to the military go much deeper. While working with psychic and spoon-bender Uri Geller at the Stanford

Research Institute (SRI), Puharich was approached by the Department of Defense (DOD) regarding computer safety. In a speech to the Psychotronics Conference on Disease and Biological Warfare Control (New York, 1987), Puharich had this to say:

> An incredible but absolutely true scene took place when Uri Geller was working on one floor at Stanford Research Institute (SRI). They had Geller bending metal, teleporting things, demonstrating incidents of telepathy and clairvoyance—these things were happening all of the time. Well, unbeknownst to us at the time, there was another lab upstairs for ARPA—a computer network system. Somebody put two and two together and said: "Hey, there's a crazy kid downstairs who is bending metal and levitating things." So they cross-correlated and discovered that when Uri did something the computers would go wacko: program printouts would pop out—sometimes partly erased—the power supply would go out on them and so on. "Somebody can affect the computer!" Panic ensued. **A squad of colonels came out from Washington to sniff around and watch Uri do his thing. They came to me and said, "You know, our whole defense system is on computers and magnetic tape cards. Can this guy wipe them out? Would you cooperate?" So we took Geller to Bell Labs and to the Livermore Radiation Lab and they put together an elaborate set-up for magnetic shielding. They learned that he could wipe out anything on computer tape. They said to me, "This guy could start World War 3!"** (Emphasis added)[215]

It's of particular interest that the SRI experiment listed above was reportedly under the control of former Apollo astronaut Edgar Mitchell who also sits on the board of the IONS (Institute of Noetic Sciences) as a cofounder. If one places Puharich at the center of a circle, the connections radiating out touch a vast and disturbing network of military, political, covert, scientific, and even entertainment fields! As mentioned earlier, we are being programmed by the media and arts with themes based upon governmental directives—directives that might be based upon orders from above (The Nine)!

Puharich considered the mind the most important "new frontier," and he even wrote a book on the topic called *The Sacred Mushroom: Key to the Door of Eternity*, in which he described how he had rejoined the military as a medical doctor in 1952 (his original stint had ended as a medical discharge based on a recurring middle-ear condition). His second run with the Army saw Puharich serving as a captain in San Antonio, Texas. One of his first assignments came directly from the top, when Puharich was "ordered" to give a lecture on extrasensory perception (ESP) to the Aviation School of Medicine. Shortly after this, Captain Puharich moved to the Army Chemical Center in Maryland, where he served as the chief of the outpatient clinic, but his next assignment took him back to his former love: the study of the human mind. Here's how Puharich described that moment:

In November of 1953 my colonel friend in the Pentagon called me up one day and said that a way had been worked out whereby the Army could sponsor my researches into extrasensory perception. This was to be arranged through a university which would act as a blind for the Army interest in this forbidden subject. After several months of negotiation all this, too, came to naught. Therefore, I was more than surprised to have the subject reopened by a responsible officer, Colonel Nolton, on my own post, however circuitous and indirect the approach may have been. I told him that in my opinion extrasensory perception was a reality, and that it could be proven in people with exceptional talent. I pointed out that there was also evidence to the effect that the talent was widely diffused throughout a normal population, and that it was probable that everyone has some of it sporadically.

"Well, if this is true," he persisted, "isn't it possible to find some drug that will bring out this latent ability so that normal people could turn this thing on and off at will?"

"It would be nice to have such a drug," I replied, "because then the research problems of parapsychology would be half solved. You see, the main problem in extrasensory perception research is that we know, even in a person of great talent, when this mysterious faculty will manifest itself. So we just sit around like a fisherman in a boat who puts his hand into the water every once in a while, hoping that a fish will swim into his grasp. There have been some reports of primitive peoples using such drugs extracted from plants, but I have never heard of one that worked when tested in the laboratory.

"Well, if you ever find a drug that works let me know, because this kind of thing would solve a lot of the problems connected with Intelligence." This was the parting word of the colonel as the conversation ended.[216]

Puharich claims in his book, *The Sacred Mushroom*, that he discovered mushrooms could be used to induce trances while reviewing the text of "automatic writing" and channeled information given to him by one Alice Bouverie. Bouverie included the strange text with a letter explaining that Harry Stone had offered the cryptic information after being handed a gold pendant bearing the name of the Egyptian Queen Tiy. Here is how Bouverie described the moment to Puharich:

"Well, I had no sooner handed it to him than he trembled all over, got a crazy staring look in his eye, staggered around the room a bit, and then fell into a chair. I was petrified and really thought he was having an epileptic fit. Betty said that she had never seen Harry like this before. I rushed to get some water while Betty held him up. When I got back he was sitting rigidly upright in the chair and staring wildly into the distance.

He didn't seem to see us at all but was watching something we couldn't see."

"Sounds as though he was in a trance, doesn't it?"

"Yes, that's what it turned out to be, but at that moment I had no idea what was going on. It probably wouldn't alarm a doctor like you, but I had never seen anyone go into a trance before."

"Well, what happened to make you believe that this was really a trance?"

"He just sat staring into nowhere for about five minutes. Then he jumped up and clutched my hand sort of desperately. I must say, it was awkward and embarrassing, especially because of the way he kept staring into my eyes. I have never seen such fanatically blue eyes in my life. He kept saying, 'Don't you remember me, don't you remember me?' over and over. And I kept saying over and over, 'Of course, Harry, I remember you.' But this made no impression on him. Then he began to speak quite clearly in English about his upbringing. I didn't realize that there was anything extraordinary about what he was saying until he asked for a paper and pencil and began to draw Egyptian hieroglyphs. I'm sure they were hieroglyphs, even though I don't know a word of Egyptian. This finally made me realize that he was in a somnambulistic state. Then he started to tell me about some drug that would stimulate one's psychic faculties. That is why I called you, because you're the only person I know who might be able to make sense out of what Harry said. I'd like to know what this is all about."

"Well, it sounds interesting. Why don't you send me a transcript of what he said, and I'll give you my opinion."[217]

The statements given to Puharich by Bouverie "revealed" an ancient Egyptian method for inducing a state of anesthesia that also separated the mind from the body:

I turned to the material in paragraph four that Alice had sent me. The drawings made by Harry in trance certainly looked like mushrooms to my untrained eye. I must confess that at this time the world of mycology was virtually unknown to me. My only acquaintance with fungi was a half-hour lecture in medical school on the treatment of mushroom poisoning. I knew only that if a patient was brought in and suspected of mushroom poisoning, and that if certain symptoms were present, one used atropine as an antidote.

Since I had never had to treat a case of mushroom poisoning I can hardly say that I was sure of even this bit of information.[218]

Remember that, according to Puharich's own account, his superiors wanted him to find a drug that could induce an ESP trance. The Egyptian mushroom drawn and described by Harry Stone led Puharich to the *Amanita muscaria*, used in Mexico as an intoxicating beverage and by Siberian shamans.

Excited by this discovery, Puharich arranged to meet with Harry Stone to test the sculptor's psychic abilities and to learn more about the mushroom. During this meeting, Captain Puharich blindfolded Stone before handing him the gold Egyptian pendant wrapped in cotton. As before, Stone stiffened and began to speak in the voice of an Egyptian known as Ptah Katu (below, "a. p." stands for Andrija Puharich; "h. s." for Harry Stone):

a. p. Ptah Katu, when you rubbed the plants, the white spots, did you mix them with something? (h. s. again indicated by a gesture something from a high tree.)

a. p. Tall trees? There was something that came from the tall trees? Palm trees? Coconut?

(h. s. nods in assent and now begins to rub the top of his head.)

a. p. Did you use it like that on the head? Did you use it only on your sick people? (h. s. shakes his head no.)

a. p. On the priests? (h. s. nods yes.)
a. p. Is that how Antinea was initiated? (h. s. nods yes.)
a. p. How was this done?
h. s. By opening the door. By stepping in.
And by leaving.
But it was only for them who know.
It would be dangerous to say everything one knows. Isn't it?
Puharich is convinced that Stone's trance is genuine.

"I don't think he's faking the trance; it seems to be the real thing. But what does it all mean—this Egyptian language, and the mystery about the mushroom? If we can get this language decoded we may get an answer. He doesn't say much of importance in English, and retreats from direct questions about the mushroom. I feel that Harry is under a powerful influence when he writes in hieroglyphic. He appears to be a machine responding to a master control. I wonder if he could be under intelligent control?"[219]

This observation is very interesting in light of the Round Table Foundation conversation that Puharich says took place in Maine. According to Jim Keith, in his book, *Mass Control: Engineering Human Consciousness*, Puharich founded the RTF in 1948 in Camden, Maine.

Among Puharich's associates at the Round Table were Warren S. McCulloch, one of the founders of cybernetics theory, who had worked at Bellevue Hospital in New York. McCulloch was an early advocate of electric brain implants and chaired conferences sponsored by the Josiah Macy Jr. Foundation, a channel for CIA mind-control funding. Another associate of Puharich was John Hays Hammond, said to have been Nicola Tesla's only student. [220]

It gets stranger. According to Lynn Picknett and coauthor Clive Prince in their 2001 book, *The Stargate Conspiracy*, the RTF was actually funded by the Armed Forces Special Weapons Project![221]

The Round Table also received monies from private funding—which, according to Picknett and Prince, included former vice president of the United States and avowed Freemason Henry Wallace, who is also credited with incorporating the Great Seal (including the all-seeing eye) into the design for the dollar bill. In fact, well-known medium Eileen Garrett said in her autobiography that Wallace often visited the Round Table during 1949–1950 (this is referenced in the abovementioned book by Picknett and Prince).

Andrija Puharich appears to have enjoyed some very deep connections to military and covert psi operations, doesn't he? It is these connections that add weight and further mystery to the now infamous 1952 meeting with Hindu mystic "Dr. Vinod," who then went into a trance and channeled The Nine. Puharich said the following in an essay on the Mark Bell Blog:

> M calling: We are Nine Principles and Forces, personalities if you will, working in complete mutual implication. We are forces, and the nature of our work is to accentuate the positive, the evolutional, and the teleological aspects of existence. By teleology I do not mean the teleological aspects of existence. By teleology I do mean the teleology of human derivation in a multidimensional concept of existence. Teleology will be understood in terms of a different ontology. To be simple, we accentuate certain directions as will fulfill the destiny of creation.
>
> We propose to work with you in some essential respects with the relation of contradiction and contrariety.
>
> The whole group of concepts has to be revised. The problem of psychokinesis, clairvoyance, etc., at the present stage is all right, but profoundly misleading—permit us to say the truth. Soon we will come to basic universal categories of explicating the superconscious.[222]

Mysterious enough for you? Later, The Nine claim "they" had prepared for Puharich to meet Uri Geller. "It was us who found Uri in the garden when he was three. He is our helper sent to help man. We programmed him in the garden for many years to come."[223]

The following paragraphs are also taken from Mark Bell Blog essay about Puharich's meetings with Geller and how they related to The Nine. We quote them here to cement in your mind, dear reader, just how Puharich's experiments and his connections to military psi ops and even to implantable "radio" devices lead right into the final deception during the New World Order:

On December 2, 1971, Puharich and Uri were riding in a Jeep in the Sinai Desert when Uri whispered to him, "Our teacher said to us that he is going to appear as a red light that will look like a UFO." After spotting a red light in the sky, Puharich realized that while Uri indicated he saw the light the two soldiers accompanying them said they could not see it. Puharich wrote:

Did this red light have something to do with the voice? And what was the voice? A fragment of Uri's mind? A spirit? A god? Did the voice have any relationship to The Nine that had reached me so many years ago? The red light that followed our Jeep now seemed to be totally unlike what I had seen in the sky in Ossining, New York, in 1963 or Brazil in 1968.

On Dec. 5th the disembodied voice was quoted in a message that included the statement:

Andrija, you shall take care of Uri. Take good care of him. He is in a very delicate situation. He is the only one for the next fifty years to come. We are going to be very, very far away. Spectra, Spectra, Spectra: That is our spacecraft.

Andrija: "How far away is it?"

It is fifty-three thousand sixty-nine light-ages away.

On December 7, climbing up an embankment, they saw

"a blue stroboscopic light pulsing at about three flashes per second." This event was one of many descriptions of sightings of unidentified flying objects. Puharich quoted Uri's response to the recent events.

"When I was out in that field, I realized for the first time in my life where my powers came from. Now I know for sure that they are not my powers. Oh, I know that I have a little bit of telepathy and psychokinesis—everybody has some. But making things vanish, and having things come back, and the red light in the sky in the Sinai, the blue light tonight, that is the power of some superior being. **Maybe it is what man always thought of as being God.**" (Emphasis added)[224]

Second Thessalonians 2:1–12 says:

Now we beseech you, brethren, by the coming of our Lord Jesus Christ, and by our gathering together unto him, That ye be not soon shaken in mind, or be troubled, neither by spirit, nor by word, nor by letter as from us, as that the day of Christ is at hand. Let no man deceive you by any means: for that day shall not come, except there come a falling away first, and that man of sin be revealed, the son of perdition; Who opposeth and exalteth himself above all that is called God, or that is worshipped; so that he as God sitteth in the temple of God, shewing himself that he is God. Remember ye not, that, when I was yet with you, I told you these things? And now ye know what withholdeth that he might be revealed in his time. For the mystery of iniquity doth already work: only he who now letteth will let, until he be taken out of the way. And then shall that Wicked be revealed, whom the Lord shall consume with the spirit of his mouth, and shall destroy with the brightness of his coming: Even him, whose coming is after the working of Satan with all power and signs and lying wonders, And with all deceivableness of unrighteousness in them that perish; because they received not the love of the truth, that they might be saved. And for this cause God shall send them strong delusion, that they should believe a lie: That they all might be damned who believed not the truth, but had pleasure in unrighteousness.

We'll leave the strange world of Andrija Puharich now and head back into the modern realm of strange science. Puharich developed an implantable radio device that could be hidden inside a tooth. Today, we no longer need to implant transceivers into teeth because we now have voice-to-skull transmission.

In the early 1970s, Dr. Joseph Sharp of the Walter Reed Army Institute of Research used a computer to control a radar transmitter such that for each time a human voice waveform changed from a peak to a valley, the radar transmitter sent out a single pulse, causing a single click to be heard by the test subject. Because these clicks were timed according to the human voice waveform, the test subject heard a voice rather than a string of clicks. This has not been pursued, at least publicly, due to concerns about the effect of microwave signals aimed at a person's skull, but it does work.[225]

White is correct.

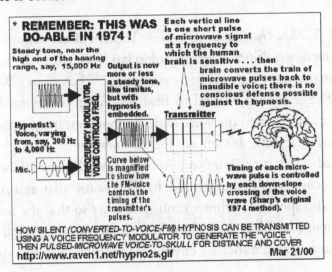

In May 2008, Sharon Weinberger wrote the following in her intriguing article, "Army Yanks Voice-to-Skull Devices":

The Army's very strange webpage on "Voice-to-Skull" weapons has been removed. It was strange it was there, and it's even stranger it's gone. If you Google it, you'll see the entry for "Voice-to-Skull device," but, if you click on the website, the link is dead.

The entry, still available on the Federation of American Scientists' website, reads:

Nonlethal weapon which includes (1) a neuro-electromagnetic device which uses microwave transmission of sound into the skull of persons or animals by way of pulse-modulated microwave radiation; and (2) a silent sound device which can transmit sound into the skull of person or animals. NOTE: The sound modulation may be voice or audio subliminal messages. One application of V2K is use as an electronic scarecrow to frighten birds in the vicinity of airports..[226]

Perhaps the site was removed because of this article that appeared in *Advertising Age* on December 10, 2007:

NEW YORK (AdAge.com)—New Yorker Alison Wilson was walking down Prince Street in SoHo last week when she heard a woman's voice right in her ear asking, "Who's there? Who's there?" She looked around to find no one in her immediate surroundings. Then the voice said, "It's not your imagination."

Indeed it isn't. It's an ad for *Paranormal State*, a ghost-themed series premiering on A&E this week. The billboard uses technology manufactured by Holosonic that transmits an "audio spotlight" from a rooftop speaker so that the sound is contained within your cranium. The technology, ideal for museums and libraries or environments that require a quiet atmosphere for isolated audio slideshows, has rarely been used on such a scale before. For random passersby and residents who have to walk unwittingly through the area where the voice will penetrate their inner peace, it's another story.

Ms. Wilson, a New York-based stylist, said she expected the voice inside her head to be some type of creative project but could see how others might perceive it differently, particularly on a late-night stroll home. "I might be a little freaked out, and I wouldn't necessarily think it's coming from that billboard," she said. [227]

Voices that speak from out of nowhere? It isn't science fiction—it's science fact. Imagine yourself walking down the main thoroughfare of your neighborhood shopping mall, and you pass by a shop window that's featuring a display of brand-name sneakers. Suddenly, you hear a pleasant voice inside your mind, "Famous Brand trainers are on sale this morning, Sally—buy one, get one free! Just fifty credits, today only!"

You quietly turn to the window and smile. Your name *is* Sally, and you've purchased or looked at this very type of sneaker on Amazon and other shopping websites, and though you've never bought at this retailer, you know you will now. You and several other shoppers, who have each heard their own enticement via "voice to skull," enter the store, and the happy merchant rings up several sales on the hand scanner.

This scenario isn't far-fetched. The Internet keeps track of all our purchases and even the pages and items we simply browse, and the information is collated by massive computer algorithms to determine exactly what we—what Sally—want to buy.

In 2002, Steven Spielberg released a blockbuster Tom Cruise film called *Minority Report* that centered around "pre-crime." Set in 2054, and based on a Philip K. Dick short story, the film features a dazzling array of futuristic technologies that are actually available now. According to an article by Charles Arthur published in June 2010 in *The Guardian*, *Minority Report* was "spot on" [our comments appear in brackets]:

Gesture-based computing

John Underkoffler, the MIT scientist who created the gesture-based computing that Cruise used in *Minority Report*, has developed his own company—Oblong Industries—to make it real and market it. But he has already been overtaken by companies such as Apple with the iPhone, offering "pinch" and "pull" and "swipe" for pictures and text since 2007. And of course by Microsoft, both with its new Kinect games system and its table-sized, touch-screen Surface, which lets you move things around with your hands. [In March of this year, Leap Motion unveiled its new computer interface that allows users to control their computers simply by swiping their hands. Imagine using this with Google Glass or eventually with an implanted "Internet" device].[228]

Dynamic iris recognition

Your iris has a unique pattern, and is already used to identify you (so long as you are standing still in front of a camera) by border control agencies in the UK, Netherlands, United Arab Emirates, US and Canada. In the film, people's irises are read while they're on the move, presenting the extra challenge of movement and resolution. But with cameras and computers improving all the time, don't bet against this not being ready way before 2054. [On July 11, 2013, the National Institute of Standards and Technology published a paper calling for Biometric Standards for Personal Identity Verification—PIV.][229]

Personalised ads

In *Minority Report*, the iris recognition then led to personalised ads bombarding you on hoardings everywhere. That doesn't happen offline, but you do get them—to some extent—on the net: DoubleClick, the huge advertising company owned by Google, tracks any sites you visit that use its adverts, and can tailor what ads you see to an agglomeration of your interests. Attempts by the UK web-tracking company Phorm to let internet service providers do similar things with ads, by tracking where you went online, ran into privacy problems. And don't forget Facebook, which is spookily good at targeting ads—because it has access to everything you have told it about yourself (though it insists it does not share that with advertisers). [Phorm is an intriguing company with a rather creepy technology platform. Again, more on this later.]

Computer-guided cars

Arguably, the closest we will get to this is satnav systems, which are actually pretty pervasive; the market is nearly saturated, at least in the UK. However, the Defence Advanced Research Projects Agency (which gave us the Internet) has had an "autonomous car" competition—and entrants are getting better. Wouldn't it be nice if your car could drive you home after a night on the booze? Pubs would cheer.

3D video

Have you seen *Avatar*? *Up*? Sky's new 3D TV service? The new Nintendo 3DS? Done.

E-paper

Apple's iPad and Amazon's Kindle are a bit bulky, but lots of news organisations think they are just the ticket for electronic reading. But real "electronic paper"—bendy, able to retain an image, electronically rewriteable—is getting closer all the time. In January, the Korean company LG showed off a 19in flexible e-paper, and companies such as Plastic Logic and E Ink are getting electronics that look closer to paper all the time. Perhaps it will be a hit when newspapers stop printing. So, 2054 then. Or perhaps 2015?

Pre-crime

In the film, "pre-cogs" can look into the future and inform the police (they have got no choice—they are stuck in baths in the basement). In 2008, Portsmouth city council installed CCTV linked to software that would note whether people were walking suspiciously slowly. University researchers had already realised in 2001 that, if you recorded the walking paths of people in car parks, you could spot the would-be thieves simply: they didn't walk directly to a car, but instead ambled around with no apparent target. That is because, unlike everyone else in a car park, they weren't going to their own car.

That's not the end: Nick Malleson, a researcher at the University of Leeds, has built a system that can predict the likelihood of a house being broken into, based on how close it is to routes that potential burglars might take around the city; he is meeting Leeds council this week to discuss how to use it in new housing developments, to reduce the chances of break-ins. So although pre-crime systems can't quite predict murder yet, it may only be a matter of time.

Spider robots

The US military is developing "insect robots", with the help of British Aerospace. They actually have eight legs (so, really, arachnid robots) and will be able to reconnoitre dangerous areas where you don't want to send a human, such as potentially occupied houses.

"Our ultimate goal is to develop technologies that will give our soldiers another set of eyes and ears for use in urban environments and complex terrain; places where they cannot go or where it would be too dangerous," Bill Devine, advanced concepts manager with BAE Systems, told World Military Forum. Give it 10 years and they will be there.

Sick sticks

These have already been the object of some research: Pennsylvania State University researchers developed a system to emit ultra-bright light pulses that induce "temporary blindness, disorientation, nausea and blindness". And a company called Intelligent Optical Security has built and sold it for the US's Homeland Security organisation—so feel worried. There's no sign of restraint collars yet, although watching England play football has been known to have the same effect.[230]

As promised in the comments above, we'd like to address a couple of these tech advances a bit more in depth. For example, consider the advertising company Phorm. According to its website, this is how it works:

> Phorm's personalisation technologies make content and advertising more relevant. The innovative platform preserves user privacy and delivers a more useful and interesting internet experience. These technologies benefit the entire online ecosystem including consumers, publishers, Internet Service Providers (ISPs)—fixed and wireless, ad networks, advertisers and agencies.
>
> At the heart of the system is an internet recommendation engine which drives Phorm's free consumer proposition, PhormDiscover. By understanding users' interests from the pages they visit, PhormDiscover brings users personalised content and relevant marketing offers. Consumers are presented with customised information in the form of an ISP-branded personalised home page and an in-page widget that can appear on any participating publisher's website.
>
> Meanwhile online publishers benefit from PhormDiscover as it enables them to show relevant content from within their

sites leading to increased user engagement and monetisation opportunities.

A key part of the PhormDiscover product portfolio is Phorm's security feature, PhormSecure, which offers consumers network level security from fraudulent websites and dangerous software.

Phorm's recommendation engine also underpins the Open Internet Exchange (OIX), an interest-based advertising platform that works at the ISP level. It allows ISPs to generate a potentially high-margin revenue stream by participating in the $72.5 billion online advertising industry, enables advertisers and agencies to reach their most valuable audience segments with unprecedented precision, and gives publishers and networks more potential value from every page.[231]

Did you get that? Phorm essentially tells consumers they can discover all there is to know about our tastes and history, but that they'll use this very personal, private information only for our good—and they will never invade our privacy—all the while making our experience more enjoyable and safe! If you believe that, then there's a famous bridge we'd love to sell you.

We also mentioned the National Institute for Standards and Technology (NIST) and its recent call for a standardized "PIV" or Personal Identity Verification. The FCW website published an article about this new paper on July 15, 2013:

Government-issued PIV smart cards are used by federal employees and contractors to access government facilities and computer networks. The PIV card carries a photo, fingerprint information, personal identification number and a cryptographic credential—computer-generated random data that are recognized only by the PIV card—all of which serve to bind the card to the card holder.

NIST had been working to develop modifications like iris recognition and on-card fingerprint comparison for some time, and has faced withering congressional criticism for lagging in releasing its iris imaging recommendations.

In a June 19 House oversight hearing, Charles Romine, the director of NIST's information technology lab, was grilled about the iris recognition recommendations. "When, when, when, will we get a standard for iris recognition?" subcommittee chairman John Mica (R-Fla.) asked Romine loudly.[232]

Well, Mica needs to wait no longer. NIST's paper explains how compact images of one or both irises can now be loaded onto the small PIV ID card for rapid and efficient reading. Fingerprint images are no longer considered rapid or efficient, and PINs can be forgotten. According to the article at FCW:

> NIST biometric testing project leader Patrick Grother told FCW that the release will help agencies implementing PIV by providing clarity for iris and facial recognition issues. For instance, after applying standard compression algorithms to a large number of iris images and then using these compact images with state-of-the-art recognition algorithms, researchers determined that an iris image compressed to just 3KB provides enough detail to accurately recognize an individual's iris.[233]

Irises can change as we age, but NIST provides guidelines for how often iris images must be captured to ensure efficiency and accuracy. Facial recognition software algorithms will now interface with YOUR face and eyes to determine if YOU are YOU. And once a computer camera determines (in a millisecond) that you ARE you, then you'll be fed enticements from advertisers and perhaps even stopped by the police, depending on whether or not the NSA and/or DHS believes you to be a threat.

Don't believe this? Consider an article written by John Ransom published on August 6, 2013, at Town Hall's website. Ransom bemoans the fact that, since the Cold War, Americans have increasingly become the target of domestic spying, feeding constant, real-time data to a massive database:

> Getting past the massive data collection that the NSA does on all of our phone calls via pattern recognition software, the tracking of our personal computer use via the corporate statists at Google, Yahoo, Microsoft, Facebook and all the other companies founded by nerds, a growing number of government data are being monitored, controlled and collated to track you.
>
> The USPS [United States Postal Service] today captures an image of every piece of mail that comes to your house or that you send. That's all they will admit to. The DEA [Drug Enforcement Association], according to an exclusive by the wire service Reuters, is using intelligence gathered by the government to falsify "probable cause" for cases that otherwise wouldn't meet the standard to "launch criminal investigations of Americans," in "cases [that] rarely involve national security issues."
>
> The IRS [Internal Revenue Service] and the FBI have investigated non-profit groups solely for political motives; and the White House is the largest leaker of classified information, even bigger than Bradley Manning and Edward Snowden.
>
> The Department of Education is instituting cradle-to-grave data collection under Common Core that would identify our children personally and is sharable between government agencies....
>
> The government has the ability to intercept and change the contents of my email en route. And a government invested with powers, likes those, doesn't neglect those powers for long.[234]

A GENERATION READY FOR THE MARK

As we work on this manuscript, it's very likely the NSA or some other agency is monitoring every keystroke. In fact, it is not hyperbole to state that every move we make is potentially being observed, recorded, and catalogued. This brings to mind the cult television series, *The Prisoner*, which featured a former spy taken captive by mysterious agencies and imprisoned on an unchartered island. The series starred Patrick McGoohan, a man who personally distrusted and disliked the way society was becoming less and less "human" and more and more intrusive. His character is seen resigning from his spy job and then being gassed while in his own home. He wakes to find himself in The Village, a creepy little town where everyone is given a number to replace his/her name and is ruled by Number 2, a title shared by a revolving door of persons, as if to say one can never tell who is in charge. The secret identity of Number 1 is revealed in the final episode, so we won't spoil it for you. We will, however, tell you that The Village is a living panopticon, a prison where you are always watched. Eyes are everywhere, and your life is an open book.

Our hero is given the title of Number 6 (the number of a man). He challenges authority with this defiant phrase: "I will not be pushed, filed, stamped, indexed, briefed, de-briefed, or numbered. My life is my own!"

America and the world resemble The Village more and more with each passing day. Google Glass allows us to be entertained while being watched. As SkyWatch TV host and author Derek Gilbert is fond of saying, we are "volunteering for the Matrix." Consider this new invention to help those of us who are "less than fit" to find our inner athlete, "The BodyMedia FIT" device:

> The BodyMedia FIT system gives you highly accurate information on calories burned—the most accurate in the market. Clinical study results show it can improve weight loss up to 3x!
>
> BodyMedia FIT is an on-body monitoring system that

consists of the BodyMedia FIT Armband monitor, online Activity Manager, an optional Display and free downloadable apps for mobile device users. BodyMedia FIT Armbands automatically track the calories burned during your daily activities. The armband works as a fitness monitor to measure the intensity of your workouts and also monitors the quality of your sleep, an important factor in weight loss. The information tracked can easily be managed with BodyMedia's online Activity Manager. Just add in the easy-to-use food log and you have the right information to improve your weight loss.[235]

How easy can it get? Just download the app, strap on the device, and you're on your way to better health! Of course, this means our galvanic and biometric responses are being fed into a massive database that can also collate that data with our GPS location. Oh, that's right!

Interpol (International Criminal Police Organization) just announced a partnership with a company called Morpho that promises to provide it with foolproof fingerprint-scanning technology. Another company recently announced the ability to scan the human face—not for confirmation, but for blood-vessel patterns![236]

The era of the connectome is here, and we are all just members of an evolving connected mass—or so transhumanists believe. (A **connectome** is a term used to describe personhood or human sentience via the interconnected neurology/physiology of our bodies.) The grand "machine" knows where we are at all times based on our location—using devices like the above, our cell phones, our Google Glass or other wearable computers, or eventually, an implanted chip or DNA HAC.

What's a HAC? We asked researcher and author Sharon Gilbert, because she's been talking about them for several years now. She explained:

HAC? That's an acronym for Human Artificial Chromosome. It's a way for researchers to insert large amounts of synthetically derived or laboratory grown DNA into our cells. In theory, our bodies do not reject a HAC because it's considered native (it's based on the same A, T, C, G pairing that native DNA is based upon). The HAC chromosome can also carry with it promoter regions that force the cell to read and use genes carried on the HAC. If this artificial chromosome is replicated in a gamete, the information can then (theoretically) be segregated into daughter cells, thereby carrying the artificial information to successive generations. In other words, the HAC could be passed on to children.[237]

The technology within the BodyMedia FIT and particularly this HAC that Gilbert discussed foreshadow a dark and very near future for all humanity. They are forerunners of the mark. Assuming that the coming Antichrist world government institutes some form of international healthcare, then an implantable device, an enforced version of the BodyMedia FIT, would seem to make sense. Why should taxpayers fund unhealthy lifestyles? Oh, and did we mention that you can buy this cool wristband by BodyMedia FIT at Amazon?

THE FUTURE
OF MARKED HUMANITY

Some transhumanists believe mankind's evolution is now self-directed and that the best future alternative is to upload consciousness (or personhood— i.e., memories, etc.) into a more durable form of hardware (body). Such a cyborg interface would require maintenance but no food, eliminating the need for vast farmlands and animal husbandry. The planet would return to a more beautiful, less-tampered-with state, and scarcity would cease to be a cause for crime and even war.

Evolved transhumans would access perceptions beyond our imaginations. For example, imagine seeing Wi-Fi signals or electricity. Smelling light. Tasting with memory, satisfying that part of our "person"—the part that needs the sensation of "eating."

Daniel Faggella earned a master's degree in applied positive psychology at the University of Pennsylvania. According to his bio at IEET. org, his "purpose in life at present is to unify the world in determining and exemplifying the most beneficial transition to trans-human intelligence and conscious (sentient) potential."

Faggella sees a cyborg future as rosy:

> Could we be so bold, then, to presume that wise human life is
> the highest possible point on this gradation? If there was a way
> for a human being to double his intelligence, enhance his creative senses, and gain a greater physical mastery by the ability

to fly or leap tall buildings—would this life not be richer than human life at present?

What if this "enhanced" human being was capable of appreciating senses that we humans have positively no access to? Maybe this would involve the ability to see infrared light, or to sense the electrical pulses of living creatures. Once more, maybe these electrical pulses could be interpreted as a new kind of beauty and joy, much as we enjoy music. This enhanced and super-intelligent person might learn multiple languages at once, master many bodies of knowledge at once, and have a better rounded moral sentiment and sense than the population of the un-enhanced.[238]

Fagella is not alone. Most futurists foresee a need to transition humans into a cyborg reality. Uploading into a mainframe would extend life spans into thousands of years rather than hundreds—and perhaps even into eternity.

In the June 25, 2013, edition of *Natural News*, however, Mike Adams took aim at this central transhumanist dogma:

All you've really done, even if all three technologies are developed and working by 2045, is made a copy of your brain. This copy may, indeed, be able to run on the machine, but it's nothing more than a simulation of your brain. It is not you.

Similarly, if someone takes a photo of you and posts a print of the photo on the wall, they can say they've made you "immortal" through photography, but your mind is obviously not living inside the photograph.

If you're a star in a motion picture, you may be "immortalized" by your fans who see you as "living forever" in your famous films, but your consciousness does not live inside the movie. The real "you" is still inhabiting your human body.

No matter how complex the depicted simulation, a "scan"

of you that is replicated in another medium (a photo, a movie, or a highly advanced computer) is not you.

Thus, the promise of transhumanism is a fraudulent one, and "uploading" is the wrong metaphor. You aren't uploading your consciousness to a machine; you're simply creating a non-conscious computer simulation of your brain.[239]

Adams, of course, is correct. God installed within each one of us a spirit, a soul, and a mind. In what He calls the First Commandment, Jesus tells us to love the Lord with all our hearts (*kardia*) and souls (*psyche*), minds (*dianoia*), and strength (*ischys*) (Mark 12:30). *Kardia*, our hearts, implies our physical existence, the center of our being—of our personhood. *Psyche* (translated "souls" in the KJV) speaks of our vital force, the breath of life. This could be our spirits, an essence apart from the body. *Dianoia* ("minds" in our verse) refers to our faculties, our understanding, our thoughts. Finally, *ischys* ("strength") reflects our choices, determination, "might," and even abilities. In Mark 12:30, Jesus outlines the essence of what it is to be a human. Transhumanists falsely believe a "copy" of our memories uploaded into a bio/machine interface would transfer this humanity, this personhood, into the new matrix, but that is quite simply ludicrous!

Adams' challenge to the transhumanist agenda did not go unnoticed (kudos to Adams for that!), and on July 11, 2013, IEET.org published a refutation of Adams' essay by Gennady Stolyarov II, editor-in-chief of *The Rational Argumentor—A Journal for Western Man*.[240]

Calling Adams' essay an "absurd attack," Stolyarov proclaims that mind uploading is but one path to transhumanism. He refers the reader to the work of Aubrey de Grey's SENS (Strategies for Engineered Negligible Senescence) project, which envisions nanomedicine and "periodic repair" to our current bodies. He quotes Max More, who authored "The Principles of Extropy" (which "form the core of transhumanist philosophy"). Stolyarov quotes More:

Transhumanism differs from humanism in recognizing and anticipating the radical alterations in the nature and possibilities of our lives resulting from various sciences and technologies such as neuroscience and neuropharmacology, life extension, nanotechnology, artificial ultraintelligence, and space habitation, combined with a rational philosophy and value system.[241]

Stolyarov appears to bristle at the notion that all transhumanists are alike and that cyborg heaven is the ultimate goal of all. However, by quoting More's belief in "radical alterations" via myriad scientific interventions, one wonders whether or not the transhumanist utopia is indeed a one-size-fits-all cyborg adventure! Artificial intelligence does not arise from carbon-based entities, but from silicon ones. In fact, we are quite certain Jesus did not refer to silicon life-forms when He declared that silencing the people would merely lead to the rocks crying out (Luke 19:40).

Further along, Stolyarov chides Adams for misconstruing the "positions of those transhumanists who do support mind uploading":

> For most such transhumanists, a digital existence is not seen as *superior* to their current biological existences, but as rather a necessary recourse if or when it becomes impossible to continue maintaining a biological existence. Dmitry Itskov's 2045 Initiative is perhaps the most prominent example of the pursuit of mind uploading today. The aim of the initiative is to achieve cybernetic immortality in a stepwise fashion, through the creation of a sequence of avatars that gives the *biological* human an increasing amount of control over non-biological components. Avatar B, planned for circa 2020–2025, would involve a human brain controlling an artificial body.[242]

So, transhumanists DO believe in a "stepwise" approach to a new body? Despite what Stolyarov wishes to believe, the transhumanist concept of copying our "personhood" into an avatar is never going to work, because we are so much more than just databases. At best, this approach leads to nothing; at worst, it may provide a fit extension for something that simulates the uploaded person—a "ghost in the machine," if you will. This very idea evokes a familiar Scripture to all who study Bible prophecy:

> And he had power to give life unto the image of the beast, that the image of the beast should both speak, and cause that as many as would not worship the image of the beast should be killed. And he causeth all, both small and great, rich and poor, free and bond, to receive a mark in their right hand, or in their foreheads: And that no man might buy or sell, save he that had the mark, or the name of the beast, or the number of his name. Here is wisdom. Let him that hath understanding count the number of the beast: for it is the number of a man; and his number is Six hundred threescore and six. (Revelation 13:15–18)

"Avatar" is simply another name for the hideous "image of the Beast" that will soon rise up and speak at the deceptively deadly hands of the False Prophet. ALL will be required to worship this image, just as ALL were required to worship the image of Nebuchadnezzar in Daniel's day (see Daniel 3). The big difference in Daniel's day was that the great image of the Babylonian king did not speak. It's terrifying enough to have hordes of armed guards threaten you, but one day this evil avatar not only will speak, but may even pack a punch—it might access your "chip" or other implanted tracking device and render you dead on the spot!

Futurists in the transhumanist camp might smile at our Christian, "Luddite" (those who oppose technology) lack of vision. Egalitarianism must begin with enforced equality. Of course, Max More doesn't see religion as any sort of threat:

Late twentieth century religion is very much less powerful than religion in the Middle Ages. In the past religion dominated all aspects of life and the idea of a separation of Church and state would have been considered incomprehensible and wicked.

The illusion is strong in North America, where TV evangelists have benefited from modern media exposure. A higher and louder profile does not necessarily mean that religion is actually more powerful. Europeans see the decline of religion more clearly. The numbers of people attending churches, and the strength of religious conviction have declined drastically. It is a notorious fact that a high percentage of priests and ministers themselves have weak or non-existent beliefs. As science continues to squeeze out religion from its role in explanation, this factor in the persistence of religion will weaken. Just as important as the development of science in weakening religion is the scientific education of the population something which is extremely poor in our monopolized and primitive state schools. Yes, as I noted earlier, religion could persist indefinitely unless we can spread transhumanist perspectives widely.[243]

Christians in particular appear to be a temporary thorn in the sides of transhumanists. Tom and Nita Horn were recently featured in *Zygon: Journal of Religion and Science* in a thesis written by Professor S. Jonathon O'Donnell in the Department of Religion and Philosophies at the University of London titled, "Secularizing Demons: Fundamentalist Navigations in Religion and Secularity."

O'Donnell's aim? According to the article's abstract, it was to explore at a deeper level than his peers the "anti-transhumanist apocalypticisms" of our day, the central voice behind which was identified as "evangelical conspiracist Thomas Horn [and his] milieu [community gathering place]" Throughout the academic paper, O'Donnell simply refers to Tom and his co-obstructionists as "Horn's Milieu."

In other words, the University of London professor has determined that those who work with us at SkyWatch TV and Defender Publishing are the "leaders of the transhuman resistance" that members of that community had better pay attention to. The peer-reviewed *Zygon* agreed, at least to the point they found reason to promulgate O'Donnell's thesis.

Max More agrees with O'Donnell, but sees religious philosophy as adding structure to life via "mythology." God, More tells us, is an anthropomorphized construct that creates and destroys, forcing us to be better. Transhumanists, he argues, envision a gradual improvement of the internalized self rather than an externalized set of values that both alienates others and abdicates responsibility. Clearly, More has no understanding of Christianity at all, for we see ourselves as walking a lifelong path of obedience to God, who promises to transform and renew our minds in this mortal life while seeing Christ's perfection in us via His transubstantiative act on Calvary.

In fact, it is transhumanists who provide the paradigm for a near-future "Beast image" through their insistence on uploading a mind into a machine! More discounts religion while advocating replacing it with a broadly based scientism:

> Extropian transhumanism offers a optimistic, vital and dynamic philosophy of life. We behold a life of unlimited growth and possibility with excitement and joy. We seek to void all limits to life, intelligence, freedom, knowledge, and happiness. Science, technology and reason must be harnessed to our extropic values to abolish the greatest evil: death. Death does not stop the progress of intelligent beings considered collectively, but it obliterates the individual. No philosophy of life can be truly satisfying which glorifies the advance of intelligent beings and yet which condemns each and every individual to rot into nothingness. Each of us seeks growth and the transcendence of our current forms and limitations. The abolition of aging and, finally, all causes of death, is essential to any philosophy of optimism and transcendence relevant to the individual.[244]

What a load of baloney! Humankind is not a collective, nor does immortal life in this world lead to any kind of Utopia! This is a major lie from the father of lies, and it echoes that of the first temptation, "Ye shall not surely die" (Genesis 3:4b). Eternal life in our mortal, fallen state is exactly what the enemy wants, which is why God expelled Adam from Eden and banned humankind from accessing the Tree of Life—for now. One day, we will have immortal bodies for our transformed minds, we will see our Savior as He truly is, and we will reign with Him forever. That is the future transhumanists refuse to see, the truth they blindly deny.

Lest you, dear reader, begin to wonder at these claims about mind uploads, let's examine the newest international race, that of the brain projects. The Human Brain Project (HBP) began in Europe when the European Commission established the FP7, also known as the Seventh Framework Program, intended to foster scientific advances through funding and resource sharing. This program has (as of this writing) invested nearly two billion euros in brain research that intersects with ICT (information and computer technology). The Human Brain Project rose from this fountain of cash. According to the HBP's website, the "about us" goes like this:

> The convergence between biology and ICT has reached a point at which it can turn the goal of understanding the human brain into a reality. It is this realisation that motivates the Human Brain Project—an EU Flagship initiative in which over 80 partners will work together to realise a new "ICT-accelerated" vision for brain research and its applications.
>
> One of the major obstacles to understanding the human brain is the fragmentation of brain research and the data it produces. Our most urgent need is thus a concerted international effort that uses emerging ICT technologies to integrate this data in a unified picture of the brain as a single multi-level system. (Emphasis added)[245]

In case you're wondering how ICT, which is now a course of study within nearly every university, intersects with brain mapping, transhumanism, and potential technology that could give rise to the mark of the Beast, consider this session from the ICT 2013 Conference, H2020:

Opening up scientific and public data and developing its use for society.
Theme: H2020: ICT for Excellent science
Date: 08/11/2013 (11.00–12.30)
The session will raise awareness on the EU's policy regarding Open Access, Open Data and Digital Science, particularly looking to implementation in Horizon2020; explore the human scale dimension: what are the issues raised by an increased access to information, in the scientific process and in the public and society; and how can we deal with an (over) abundance of information?
The description above referenced H2020 (Horizon 2020), which is part of the overall European "Digital Agenda", which sees ICT as part and parcel of the human mind. Another segment of this Digital Agenda is called "Collective Awareness Platforms."
The Collective Awareness Platforms for Sustainability and Social Innovation (CAPS) are ICT systems leveraging the emerging "network effect" by combining open online social media, distributed knowledge creation and data from real environments ("Internet of Things") in order to create new forms of social innovation.
The Collective Awareness Platforms are expected to support environmentally aware, grassroots processes and practices to share knowledge, to achieve changes in lifestyle, production and consumption patterns, and to set up more participatory democratic processes. Several efforts have been made by

governments and public organisations to cope with these crises, however much more can be done if citizens are more actively involved, in a grassroots manner. There is consensus about the global span of the problem, but little awareness of the role that each and every one of us can play in coping with this.[246]

The above explanation sounds like social change via social media. Imagine that every post you and your friends make forms part of a massive, interconnective "hive" mind—an international connectome. This smacks of Carl Jung, who believed in an Akashic Field where all human experience can be accessed like a massive database.

Now back to the Human Brain Project. The HBP is a coalition of researchers and labs (thirteen labs joined forces in the initial phase, but more are expected to come aboard). Here is another peek behind the cerebral curtain:

Applying ICT to brain research and its applications promises huge economic and **social benefits**. But to realise these benefits, the technology needs to be made accessible to scientists—in the form of research platforms they can use for basic and clinical research, drug discovery and technology development. As a foundation for this effort, **the HBP will build an integrated system of ICT-based research platforms**. Building and operating the platforms will require a clear vision, strong, flexible leadership, long-term investment in research and engineering, and a strategy that leverages the diversity and strength of European research. It will also require continuous dialogue with civil society, creating consensus and ensuring the project has a **strong grounding in ethical standards**.

The Human Brain Project will last ten years and will consist of a *ramp-up* phase and a *partially overlapping operational phase*.[247] (Emphasis added)

There's a lot in these two paragraphs. We've emphasized a few lines we'd like to unpack. First of all, the HBP promises "social benefits." One wonders just how society will benefit from a project that intends to copy a human brain and rebuild it in the form of a massive collection of databases. However, viewing these statements from the transhumanist perspective, it's easy to discern how "they" would interpret the "social" aspect of HPB research—simply put, it provides the new matrix for the transfer from biological entities to silicon ones, which (presumably to the transhumanist) results in a world free from pain, death, war, and scarcity.

Next up is the key phrase: "The HPB will build an integrated system of ICT-based research platforms." The ICT technologies immerse users in a data-rich realm of bytes and bits that flow from machine to human seamlessly. One company conducting intense study in this developing field is called, interestingly enough, CEEDS (We're not sure if they meant it to sound like "seeds," but the connection to Genesis 3:15, "And I will put enmity between thee and the woman, and **between thy seed and her seed**; it shall bruise thy head, and thou shalt bruise his heel" [emphasis added], is interesting).

CEEDS stands for the "collective experience of empathic data systems." Wait a minute... Did that acronym include "empathic" data systems? Empathy is a human attribute that involves being able to place ourselves in the place of someone else—to truly "feel" in our minds what that person is feeling. In fact, a recent study on empathy concluded that one problem with sociopaths and psychopaths is their having a selective type of empathy that permits them to turn it on or off at will, while most humans instinctively experience empathy.[248]

An empathic data system also brings to mind a character well known to science fiction fans: that of Data from *Star Trek: The Next Generation*. This silicon imitation of a human being is not only presented to the viewer as a sentient machine (an artificial intelligence or AI), but Data seeks to become more—to evolve as an android.

Like Pinocchio, who wanted to be a *real* boy, Data wants to be a *real* human. His older "brother," Lore, is the opposite of Data. Lore is more like the above-mentioned psychopaths and sociopaths, capable of emotion yet choosing to think only of himself rather than empathizing with others. This is how the *Star Trek* Wiki known as "Memory-Alpha" describes Lore:

> Lore was a Soong-type android constructed by Doctor Noonian Soong and Juliana Soong at the Omicron Thetacolony and activated on 9 September, 2335. Built in Dr. Soong's own image, Lore was the fourth android they constructed and embodied the first successful example of a fully functional positronic brain. An earlier model Soong-type android, B-4, also had a positronic brain, but of a less sophisticated type. Lore was extremely advanced and sentient, possessing superior strength, speed and intelligence when compared to a Human. Lore's emotional programming was also very advanced. However, he began displaying signs of emotional instability and malevolence, leading Lore to see himself as superior to Humans. Lore frightened the other colonists, who demanded that Soong deactivate him. Lore later claimed that they saw him as "too perfect," and were envious.[249]

First of all, note that both Lore and Data have been built in their creator's image (paralleling the creation of humanity by God Almighty). Transhumanists might actually say that, since humanity is self-evolving, any new creation or paradigm/matrix would certainly be created by "us," and would, in effect, be made in our image. In the case of the androids, they actually resemble Dr. Soong. Note also that Lore rebelled because he considered himself more intelligent than humans. He was "too perfect"; therefore, humans were envious of his abilities.

As noted earlier, CEEDS seeks to utilize the "empathic data system" built into the Internet and social media as a means to study and interact with the rise of sentient media.

Sentient computers will not simply design themselves, so European funds have also been invested in the nano-scale side of the transhumanist equation, man + machine = eternal life. In fact, the H2020 conference mentioned earlier to have been held in October 2013 explores nanocomputers and nanotech in a theme: "Nano-Scale: Future Materials and Devices." As announced on the Europa website for the digital agenda, four speakers will address this aspect of the digital future:

Andrea FERRARI (Cambridge University, Graphene Centre, Engineering Department, United Kingdom), GRAPHENE

Graphene is a material, composed of pure carbon, with atoms arranged in a plane in a regular hexagonal pattern. Graphene has mechanical, thermal, electronic, and optical properties, which are quite extraordinary, and thus graphene has the potential to be one of the main building materials in the ICT of the future.

Rosaria RINALDI (Università del Salento—Scuola Superiore ISUFI, Italy), Bio-inspired computing

Computers can rely on various ideas coming from biological world. On the one hand, natural materials (e.g. specific molecules) can be used for the process of computation. On the other, nature can inspire the development of novel problem-solving techniques.

Arthur EKERT (Mathematical Institute, University of Oxford, United Kingdom), Quantum Computers

Quantum computation uses various quantum properties of matter in order to represent data and perform operations on these data. It is expected that large-scale quantum computers will be able to solve certain problems much faster than any classical computer.

Thierry DEBUISSCHERT (Thales Research & Technology, Physics Research Group, France)[250]

Did you notice that "quantum computing" is mentioned over and over? Quantum computers lie at the heart of transhumanism's drive to build a new avatar or host body for the human mind. Current computing algorithms and hardware are no match for the wibbly-wobbly world of human thought. Computers cannot reason through a problem other than to weigh options inserted into their programming. Humans assess a problem within a prism of possible resolutions, often using experience to determine the outcome. Quantum computers are built on the scrunchy world of subatomic matter and quantum physics. Computers now referred to as "classical computers" (boy, do we feel old!) store information in bits and bytes that are either on or off (yes or no, one or zero). These have very little wiggle room. One very interesting aspect of quantum computers is the possible application of a quantum physics property called "entanglement," in which two particles separated by distance and perhaps even time influence each other. It doesn't take much imagination to picture a sentient quantum computer, built in the image of a human, that can solve any problem with the speed of light and even predict and affect future events. Such a creature might well be called a "god." Or it might become a fit extension for inhabitation by something wishing to be worshiped *as* a god...

...or worshiped as savior of mankind.

If this doesn't give you chills, then consider this: The European community is not alone in the pursuit of brain mapping and quantum constructs. In April 2013, President Barack Obama announced the United States version of the Human Brain Project. On April 2, the White House released this fact sheet to the press. We are including the entire release here so you can see the original wording of the entire release; our comments are included in brackets:

> "If we want to make the best products, we also have to invest in the best ideas... Every dollar we invested to map the human genome returned $140 to our economy... Today, our scientists are mapping the human brain to unlock the answers to

Alzheimer's... Now is not the time to gut these job-creating investments in science and innovation. Now is the time to reach a level of research and development not seen since the height of the Space Race."

—President Barack Obama, 2013 State of the Union

In his State of the Union address, the President laid out his vision for creating jobs and building a growing, thriving middle class by making a historic investment in research and development. [While it is tempting to comment on the ridiculous notion that any new science would swell the receipts of middle-class purses, we'll forgo doing so in the interest of getting on with it.]

Today, at a White House event, the President unveiled a bold new research initiative designed to revolutionize our understanding of the human brain. Launched with approximately $100 million in the President's Fiscal Year 2014 Budget, the BRAIN (Brain Research through Advancing Innovative Neurotechnologies) Initiative ultimately aims to help researchers find new ways to treat, cure, and even prevent brain disorders, such as Alzheimer's disease, epilepsy, and traumatic brain injury. [As with all the already-mentioned aspects of the transhumanist agenda, these new "sciences," which pave the way for uploading to our Utopian future (yes, we are laughing as we write), can only be sold to an unwitting American public through promises of better medicine, particularly when it comes to the growing problem of Alzheimer's.]

The BRAIN Initiative will accelerate the development and application of new technologies that will enable researchers to produce dynamic pictures of the brain that show how individual brain cells and complex neural circuits interact at the speed of thought. These technologies will open new doors to explore how the brain records, processes, uses, stores, and retrieves vast quantities of information, and shed light on the complex links between brain function and behavior. [Remember always, dear reader, that the primary purpose of "brain mapping" is to simulate the human capacity for thought, reasoning, and "sentience" within a silicon matrix. Though we are led to believe human brain power is far below the reasoning capabilities of any machine, the truth is that the *way* our minds work through problems and reach decisions, the *way* we process information—particularly novel information—makes any man-made device look like a dunce. God created our most remarkable brains and minds in His image, so we create, innovate, and are even capable of writing a book about it all—well, mostly.]

This initiative is one of the Administration's "Grand Challenges"—ambitious but achievable goals that require advances in science and technology. In his remarks today, the President called on companies, research universities, foundations, and philanthropists to join with him in identifying and pursuing the Grand Challenges of the 21st century.

The BRAIN Initiative includes:

Key investments to jumpstart the effort: The National Institutes of Health, the Defense Advanced Research Projects Agency [DARPA], and the National Science Foundation will support approximately $100 million in research beginning in FY 2014. [Need I wax eloquent upon the inclusion of DARPA in this sentence? I think not. If you're reading this book, you already know that DARPA is the research and development wing of the US military.]

Strong academic leadership: The National Institutes of Health will establish a high-level working group co-chaired by Dr. Cornelia "Cori" Bargmann (The Rockefeller University) [also a scholar with the Howard Hughes Medical Institute (HHMI), Bargmann studies behavior of animals by studying C. elegans, a worm—no, she doesn't study humans] and Dr. William Newsome (Stanford University) to define detailed

THE FUTURE OF MARKED HUMANITY

scientific goals for the NIH's investment, and to develop a multi-year scientific plan for achieving these goals, including timetables, milestones, and cost estimates. [Dr. Newsome is also affiliated with HHMI, but this shouldn't be a surprise. HHMI is, perhaps not coincidentally, tightly connected with the Cold Spring Harbor Laboratory through financial support to the tune of over $2 million over the past four years. In case Cold Spring Harbor doesn't ring a bell, it's where the Eugenics Record Office was located, the hub of the early twentieth century search for the perfect human.]

Public-private partnerships: Federal research agencies will partner with companies, foundations, and private research institutions that are also investing in relevant neuroscience research, such as the Allen Institute, the Howard Hughes Medical Institute, the Kavli Foundation, and the Salk Institute for Biological Studies.

Maintaining our highest ethical standards: Pioneering research often has the potential to raise new ethical challenges. To ensure this new effort proceeds in ways that continue to adhere to our highest standards of research protections, the President will direct his Commission for the Study of Bioethical Issues to explore the ethical, legal, and societal implications raised by this research initiative and other recent advances in neuroscience.

Background

In the last decade alone, scientists have made a number of landmark discoveries that now create the opportunity to unlock the mysteries of the brain, including the sequencing of the human genome, the development of new tools for mapping neuronal connections, the increasing resolution of imaging technologies, and the explosion of nanoscience. These breakthroughs have paved the way for unprecedented collaboration and discovery across scientific fields. For instance, by combining advanced genetic and optical techniques, scientists can now use pulses of light to determine how specific cell activities in the brain affect behavior. In addition, through the integration of neuroscience and physics, researchers can now use high-resolution imaging technologies to observe how the brain is structurally and functionally connected in living humans.

While these technological innovations have contributed substantially to our expanding knowledge of the brain, significant breakthroughs in how we treat neurological and psychiatric disease will require a new generation of tools to enable researchers to record signals from brain cells in much greater numbers and at even faster speeds. This cannot currently be achieved, but great promise for developing such technologies lies at the intersections of nanoscience, imaging, engineering, informatics, and other rapidly emerging fields of science and engineering.

Key Investments to Launch this Effort

To make the most of these opportunities, the National Institutes of Health, the Defense Advanced Research Projects Agency, and the National Science Foundation are launching this effort with funding in the President's FY 2014 budget.

National Institutes of Health: The NIH Blueprint for Neuroscience Research—an initiative that pools resources and expertise from across 15 NIH Institutes and Centers—will be a leading NIH contributor to the implementation of this initiative in FY 2014. The Blueprint program will contribute funding for the initiative, given that the Blueprint funds are specifically devoted to projects that support the development of new tools, training opportunities, and other resources. In total, NIH intends to allocate approximately $40 million in FY 2014.

Defense Advanced Research Projects Agency: In FY 2014, DARPA plans to invest $50 million in a set of programs with the goal of understanding the dynamic functions of the brain and demonstrating breakthrough applications based on these insights. DARPA aims to develop a new set of tools to capture and process dynamic neural and synaptic activities. DARPA is interested in applications—such as a new generation of information processing systems and restoration mechanisms—that dramatically improve the way we diagnose and treat warfighters suffering from post-traumatic stress, brain injury, and memory loss. DARPA will engage a broad range of experts to explore the ethical, legal, and societal issues raised by advances in neurotechnology.

National Science Foundation: The National Science Foundation will play an important role in the BRAIN Initiative because of its ability to support research that spans biology, the physical sciences, engineering, computer science, and the social and behavioral sciences. The National Science Foundation intends to support approximately $20 million in FY 2014 in research that will advance this initiative, such as the development of molecular-scale probes that can sense and record the activity of neural networks; advances in "Big Data" that are necessary to analyze the huge amounts of information that will be generated, and increased understanding of how thoughts, emotions, actions, and memories are represented in the brain.

Private Sector Partners

Key private sector partners have made important commitments to support the BRAIN Initiative, including:

The Allen Institute for Brain Science: The Allen Institute, a nonprofit medical research organization, is a leader in large-scale brain research and public sharing of data and tools. In March 2012, the Allen Institute for Brain Science embarked upon a ten-year project to understand the neural code: how brain activity leads to perception, decision making, and ultimately action. The Allen Institute's expansion, with a $300M investment from philanthropist Paul G. Allen in the first four years, was based on the recent unprecedented advances in technologies for recording the brain's activity and mapping its interconnections. More than $60M annually will be spent to support Allen Institute projects related to the BRAIN Initiative.

Howard Hughes Medical Institute: HHMI is the Nation's largest nongovernmental funder of basic biomedical research and has a long history of supporting basic neuroscience research. HHMI's Janelia Farm Research Campus in Virginia was opened in 2006 with the goal of developing new imaging technologies and understanding how information is stored and processed in neural networks. It will spend at least $30 million annually to support projects related to this initiative.

Kavli Foundation: The Kavli Foundation anticipates supporting activities that are related to this project with approximately $4 million dollars per year over the next ten years. This figure includes a portion of the expected annual income from the endowments of existing Kavli Institutes and endowment gifts to establish new Kavli Institutes over the coming decade. This figure also includes the Foundation's continuing commitment to supporting project meetings and selected other activities.

Salk Institute for Biological Studies: The Salk Institute, under its Dynamic Brain Initiative, will dedicate over $28 million to work across traditional boundaries of neuroscience, producing a sophisticated understanding of the brain, from individual genes to neuronal circuits to behavior. To truly understand how the brain operates in both healthy and diseased states, scientists will map out the brain's neural networks and unravel how they interrelate. To stave off or reverse diseases such as Alzheimer's and Parkinson's, scientists will explore the changes that occur in the brain as we age, laying the groundwork for prevention and treatment of age-related neurological diseases.[251]

Now that you've read through that thrilling press release, let us give you a little insider information. Since we don't profess to be any kind of scientists, we sent another call for help to our science buddy Sharon Gilbert, who has a degree in biology and has spent decades reading published research into genetics (her specialty) and neuroscience (the subject of her unfinished doctoral work). She had this to say:

> As you know, I've been following the brain-mapping hoopla since it was first announced last year, but I recently came across an article written by Giulio Prisco originally published at the website, Transhumanity—that sheds some much-needed light on the sudden race to map the brain. According to Prisco, the leap into brain mapping is actually based on a research paper published in the 2012 issue of *Neuron Magazine* called, "The Brain Activity Map Project and the Challenge of Functional Connectomics." Regarding this report, Prisco cites this from *Science Insider*:
>
> > In September 2011, George Church, the molecular geneticist who leads the Personal Genome Project, and Rafael Yuste, a neuroscientist at the Kavli Foundation and Columbia University, made waves at a meeting in England cosponsored by the Kavli, Allen, and Gatsby foundations when they proposed a massive, coordinated effort to develop technologies that can track the activity of functional connections in a living human brain, ultimately measuring "every spike from every neuron."[252]
> >
> > It's important that your readers know that two of the four

189

listed authors of the BAM Project report (Brain Activity Map—BAM, which incidentally evokes oBAMa, does it not?) are Dr. George Church, a noted transhumanist and codirector of the Human Genome Project, and Rafael Yuste, a neuroscientist at the Kavli Foundation (one of the sponsors of the BRAIN project lauded and launched by the president). "Humans are nothing but our brains," Yuste said of the potential applications for technology produced in pursuit of a map of human brain activity. "Our whole culture, our personality, our minds, are a result of activity in the brain."

It certainly appears to me that both the European and the American brain projects intend to use the information to simulate a human mind in a silicon body. Prisco goes on in his article to reveal HIS beliefs in this chilling statement: *"Both BAM and HBP emphasize scientific results and medical applications, which of course are very important, but I hope that this race to the brain will produce real, game-changing breakthroughs and take the first steps toward whole brain emulation, new mentality substrates, and **mind uploading**."*[253]

In short, the BRAIN project (following on the heels of the BAM project) and the Human Brain Project are presented as an Atlantic race for the neuro-prize, but in truth it is more likely a cooperative effort behind the scenes. Transhumanists MUST map the entire brain, all the intricate neurons and their millions of cellular connections, before attempting computer modeling and eventually "mind uploading." It's all about self-directed evolution. With Cold Spring Harbor Labs, HHMI, and DARPA all on the same bandwagon, you can bet that the Christians who oppose transhumanism are in for a bumpy ride.

Andrija Puharich and his cronies would have loved using today's supercomputers and brain-imaging software. Molecular Imaging Scans such as PET (positron emission tomography) and SPECT (single photon emission computed tomography) use magnetic resonance

(MR) to create 3D images of molecular reactions to specific probe molecules within the brain. Science now wants to do more than just read our minds; it also wants to manipulate them. The voice-to-skull technology mentioned earlier is one crude way, but a report released in early August 2013 reveals a new method for "mind control":

> Researchers from the Riken-MIT Center for Neural Circuit Genetics at the Massachusetts Institute of Technology took us closer to this science-fiction world of brain tweaking last week when they said they were able to create a false memory in a mouse.
>
> The scientists reported in the journal *Science* that they caused mice to remember receiving an electrical shock in one location, when in reality they were zapped in a different place. The researchers weren't able to create entirely new thoughts, but they applied good or bad feelings to memories that already existed.
>
> "It wasn't so much writing a memory from scratch, it was basically connecting two different types of memories. We took a neutral memory, and we artificially updated that to make it a negative memory," said Steve Ramirez, one of the MIT neuroscientists on the project.
>
> It may sound insignificant and perhaps not a nice way to treat mice, but it is not a dramatic leap to imagine that one day this research could lead to computer-manipulation of the mind for things like the treatment of post-traumatic stress disorder, Ramirez said.
>
> Technologists are already working on brain-computer interfaces, which will allow us to interact with our smartphones and computers simply by using our minds. And there are already gadgets that read our thoughts and allow us to do things like dodge virtual objects in a computer game or turn switches on and off with a thought.
>
> But the scientists who are working on memory manipulation are the ones who seem to be pushing the boundaries of

what we believe is possible. Sure, it sounds like movie fantasy right now, but don't laugh off the imagination of Hollywood screenwriters; sometimes the movies can be a great predictor of things to come.

In the movie, "Eternal Sunshine of the Spotless Mind," a character played by Jim Carrey uses a service that **erases memories to wipe his brain** of his former girlfriend, played by Kate Winslet.

But it seems the movie's screenwriter, Charlie Kaufman, was selling science short.

"The one thing that the movie 'Eternal Sunshine of the Spotless Mind' gets wrong, is that they are erasing an entire memory," said Ramirez of MIT. "**I think we can do better, while keeping the image of Kate Winslet, we can get rid of the sad part of that memory.**"

Hollywood and science-fiction writers, of course, have had fun with memory manipulation over the years.

In the film "Total Recall," which is based on a short story by Philip K. Dick, a character played by Arnold Schwarzenegger (and in a remake by Colin Farrell) receives a memory implant of a fake vacation to Mars. In "The Matrix," characters can download new skills like languages or fighting techniques to their mind, much like downloading a file to a computer.

Far-fetched? Perhaps, and we're not yet fighting our robot overlords as the humans were in "The Matrix," but researchers really are exploring ways to upload new information to the brain.

In 2011, scientists working in collaboration with Boston University and ATR Computational Neuroscience Laboratories in Kyoto, Japan, published a paper on a process called Decoded Neurofeedback, or "DecNef," which sends signals to the brain through a functional magnetic resonance imaging machine, or FMRI, that can alter a person's brain activity pattern. In time, these scientists believe they could teach people how to play a musical instrument while they sleep, learn a new language or master a sport, all by "uploading" information to the brain.

Writing to the brain could allow us to interact with our computers, or other human beings, just by thinking about it.

In February, Dr. Miguel A. Nicolelis, a neuroscientist at Duke University, successfully connected the brains of two rats over the Internet, allowing them to communicate with their minds so when one rat pressed a lever, the other one did the same. The rats were in different locations, one at Duke University in North Carolina, and another in a laboratory in Natal, Brazil.

Nicolelis said he has recently performed other experiments in his lab where he has connected the brains of four mice in what he calls a "brain net" allowing them to share information over the Internet. In another experiment, he took two monkeys and gave them both half of a piece of information to successfully move a robotic arm, which required them to share the information through their brain.[254] (Emphasis added)

Did you catch the bit about "writing to our brain"? Who do these people think they are? God?

Well, yes.

Movies, television, and video games have been telling us for years that our every move is watched, our minds may not be our own, and even our memories are subject to question. Now, scientists are confirming that all we once believed to be fiction is, in reality: cold, hard FACT. The television program *The X-Files* is rife with end-times scenario programming and memes. The overarching story involves the planned invasion of the earth by alien entities that reproduce via a virus contained within common oil. As the protagonist, Fox Mulder, seeks "the truth," he encounters a pilot from Area 51, who has been testing a spacecraft created from reverse-engineered alien tech. The episode is called "Jose Chung's from Outer Space" and is intended to keep the viewer guessing as to what is real and what is not. The plot follows a pair of teenagers who have been taken captive by aliens. Some scenes show the teens being hypnotized by their captors (aliens) while others reveal the hypnotist to be a military doctor. False memories twist the main characters' minds so that no one seems to know truth from trash. The scene with Mulder and the pilot takes place in a modest, 1950s-style diner:

JACK SCHAFFER: This is not happening! It's not happening! This is not happening. It's not happening. It's not happening.
(Later, they sit at a diner counter. Schaffer plays with his mashed potatoes with his fork. The cook is cleaning the counters near the front of the store. The pink neon sign shines brightly.)
Used to project the image of the Virgin Mary over the French trenches in World War One. The enemy's always willing to fire upon an invading force...but on a holy miracle?

MULDER: Or on visitors from outer space?

JACK SCHAFFER: Yeah, the enemy sees an American recon plane, they start shooting. They see a flying saucer from another galaxy...they hesitate.
(He puts down his fork.)
You know what happens to most people after seeing a UFO?
(He puts a cigarette in his mouth.)

MULDER: They experience "missing time."

JACK SCHAFFER: Any number of "soft option kills" will do...nerve gas...low frequency infrasound beams...
(He lights a match.)
With high-powered microwaves, you can not only cut enemy communications, you can cook internal organs.
(He lights the cigarette and shakes the match out.)

MULDER: But abductions?

JACK SCHAFFER: Don't know as much about them. I'm just the pilot. You ever flown a flying saucer?
  (Mulder shrugs slightly.)
  Afterwards, sex seems trite.
  (He takes another drag.)

MULDER: But what do you do with the abductees?

JACK SCHAFFER: Take them back to the base. Let the doctors work on them. Nothing physical, they just mess with their minds.

MULDER: Hypnosis.
  (Schaffer nods.)

JACK SCHAFFER: At the base, I've seen people go into an ordinary room with an ordinary bunch of doctors...and come out absolutely positive they were probed by aliens.

MULDER: But if abductions are just a covert intelligence operation and UFOs are merely secret military airships, piloted by aliens such as yourself...then what were you abducted by?

JACK SCHAFFER: Don't you get it? I'm absolutely positive me, my copilot, and those two kids were abducted but I can't be absolutely sure it happened. I can't be sure of anything anymore!

MULDER: What do you mean?

JACK SCHAFFER: I'm not sure we're even having this conversation. I don't know if these mashed potatoes are really here. I don't know if you even exist.

MULDER: I can only assure you that I do.

JACK SCHAFFER: Well...thanks, buddy. Unfortunately...I can't give you the same assurance about me.

(The door slams. Mulder and Jack look over to see a number of soldiers being led by the Air Force Man. Jack takes a drag of his cigarette and prepares to leave.)

JACK SCHAFFER: Well, looks like I'm a dead man.[255]

Dead men tell no tales—or so we're told. But an uploaded memory is there for all to enjoy. In many ways, our memories define us. Alzheimer's patients lose track of "self" because they've lost access to important, self-describing memories. Transhumanists do not think of us as unique, God-created, God-designed individuals; rather, they see us as machines made of flesh. Our memories are just data files that can be corrupted, manipulated, altered, or *erased*.

TO "ENHANCE" MANKIND PHYSICALLY, NEUROLOGICALLY, AND SPIRITUALLY

Are we a spirit, a soul, a conscious to be transferred at will? In February 2011, the "Darwin Day" Forum—a gathering of scientists and transhumanists in honor Charles Darwin—met in New York City to discuss the nature of human consciousness. One presentation featured New York University (NYU) philosopher Ned Block and neuroscientist Jacqueline Gottlieb from Columbia University. The event was held at the Tishman Auditorium at NYU. Block believes our consciousness involves visual field phenomena. It's a neuro-philosophical version of Shrodinger's dead/alive cat. We are defined by what we perceive, and our world is therefore represented by what we "choose" to see. Block posits that reality *is* what we choose to see—raising the question of whether something exists if we do not perceive it. By using eye-tracking software, Block observed the perception phenomenon for various subjects. Again and again, many subjects overlooked the same areas—effectively making those areas of the field of vision "invisible."

Working memory for Block is defined by what we have perceived and can recall. His experiments with macaque monkeys led him to posit that human brains have only so many "slots" in them for

196

memory. It's comparable to the memory limits for cache or RAM in computers. Again, here is a scientist who not only compares humans to monkeys, but who also appears to see our brains as little more than living computers.

Are we sentient computers? The successful television series *Battlestar Galactica* follows a band of humans who are ruthlessly pursued by sentient computers called Cylons. In the ending, it's revealed that some of the humans are actually Cylons, and that these "final five" (a God-like hand of five fingers who create) are the ones who, in best Promethean style, gave a formerly defeated band of Cylons the secret to appearing human *and* the secret of regeneration (eternal life). The final question one must ask, then, is: Is the ragtag band of humans really human—or are all humans merely sentient machines?

Transhumanists predict that humanity will eventually blend with and give rise to sentient machines. In his August 5, 2013, article at IEET (Institute for Ethics and Emerging Technology), George Deane explored the idea of "sentient computers" by answering an earlier post by John R. Searle:

> John Searle delivered a powerful blow to computationalism by debunking the notion that syntax is sufficient for semantics with the Chinese Room Argument, but he later went further to argue that the theory is not only false but also incoherent.
>
> To understand Searle's point it is first worth making a distinction between features of the world that are independent of the observer, i.e., intrinsic and not pliable to interpretation, and those which are relative to the observer, or extrinsic. Typically the natural sciences are concerned with the former. It is worth noting observer relative features of the world can also be objective; many objects such as wallets, books and clothing are not defined in terms of physics but in terms of function. Armed with this distinction we can ask, is computation observer relative or observer dependant [*sic*]?...

Searle puts this point best of all: "For any program there is some sufficiently complex object such that there is some description of the object under which it is implementing the program. Thus for example the wall behind my back is right now implementing the Wordstar program, because there is some pattern of molecule movements which is isomorphic with the formal structure of Wordstar. But if the wall is implementing Wordstar then if it is a big enough wall it is implementing any program, including any program implemented in the brain."

Unless we accept that a large enough wall would be instantiating every possible state of consciousness simultaneously then it appears there is more to consciousness than computation. If computation can [be] attributed to anything then it would be trivial to call the brain a computer. Searle proposes we look beyond computation to what the brain actually is: a physical system. This is a damaging blow to accounts of mind uploading and Strong AI that ignore the substrate of implementation. Those hoping to achieve digital immortality through whole brain emulation might not want to be too hasty to dispose of their biological bodies after all. Sharper criteria for consciousness need to be defined.[256]

It's nice to know that not all transhumanists believe we're within minutes of uploading. Deane, who is studying in London, describes himself as "especially interested in Neuroethics and the implications of technologies for **cognitive enhancement**" (emphasis added).[257]

Let's explore that concept for a moment. According to the Center for Neuroscience and Society's website:

Two main cognitive systems have been targeted for **pharmacological enhancement**: attention and memory. Stimulant drugs such as methyphenidate (Ritalin) and amphetamine (Adderall) improve the attention of people with attention deficit hyperactivity disorder (ADHD) and can also enhance attention in healthy people. (Emphasis added)[258]

Pharmacological enhancement? Is it possible that the mountain of psychotropic drugs being tested in prisons, schools, and nursing homes across the world constitute a massive study group for those who are investigating pharmacologically enhanced cognition? This echoes the military assignment given to Captain Andrija Puharich to find a chemical means not only to *alter* the mind, but to *open* it so that the psyche, the consciousness, is released. Puharich and The Nine and the *Star Trek* world of make-believe have informed our reality. We now live in a world effectively designed by Gene Roddenberry. We carry sensors, cameras, recording devices, and instantaneous communicators—all with the help of a spidery connection called the Internet or World Wide Web.

The television program *X-Files* had an "end-date" of December 21, 2012, when the aliens would land and take over the world. Only one place was considered safe—and it is there that the Cigarette Smoking Man (Mulder's true biological father) ran for safety. This area lies in the Four Corners region of the American Southwest, where the Hopi now live—the land they claim was once inhabited by the Anasazi.

The Hopi eschatology goes like this:

The following extraordinary Hopi prophecy was first published in a mimeographed manuscript that circulated among several Methodist and Presbyterian churches in 1959. Some of the prophecies were published in 1963 by Frank Waters in *The Book of the Hopi*. The account begins by describing how, while driving along a desert highway one hot day in the summer of 1958, a minister named David Young stopped to offer a ride to an Indian elder, who accepted with a nod. After riding in silence for several minutes, the Indian said:

"I am White Feather, a Hopi of the ancient Bear Clan. In my long life I have traveled through this land, seeking out my brothers, and learning from them many things full of wisdom. I have followed the sacred paths of my people, who inhabit the forests and many lakes in the east, the land of ice and long nights in the north, and the places of holy altars of stone built many years ago by my brothers' fathers in the south. From all these I have heard the stories of the past, and the prophecies of the future. Today, many of the prophecies have turned to stories, and few are left—the past grows longer, and the future grows shorter.

"And now White Feather is dying. His sons have all joined his ancestors, and soon he too shall be with them. But there is no one left, no one to recite and pass on the ancient wisdom. My people have tired of the old ways—the great ceremonies that tell of our origins, of our emergence into the Fourth World, are almost all abandoned, forgotten, yet even this has been foretold. The time grows short.

"My people await Pahana, the **lost White Brother** [a being, supposedly from the stars], as do all our brothers in the land. He will not be like the white men we know now, who are cruel and greedy. We were told of their coming long ago. But still we await Pahana.

"He will bring with him the symbols, and the missing piece of that sacred tablet now kept by the elders, given to him when he left, that shall identify him as our True White Brother.

"The Fourth World shall end soon, and the Fifth World will begin. This the elders everywhere know. The Signs over many years have been fulfilled, and so few are left.

"This is the First Sign: We are told of the coming of the white-skinned men, like Pahana, but not living like Pahana men who took the land that was not theirs. And men who struck their enemies with thunder.

"This is the Second Sign: Our lands will see the coming of spinning wheels filled with voices. In his youth, my father saw

200

this prophecy come true with his eyes—the white men bringing their families in wagons across the prairies.

"This is the Third Sign: A strange beast like a buffalo but with great long horns, will overrun the land in large numbers. These White Feather saw with his eyes—the coming of the white men's cattle.

"This is the Fourth Sign: The land will be crossed by snakes of iron [the railroads].

"This is the Fifth Sign: The land shall be criss-crossed by a giant spider's web [the Internet].

"This is the Sixth sign: The land shall be criss-crossed with rivers of stone that make pictures in the sun.

"This is the Seventh Sign: You will hear of the sea turning black, and many living things dying because of it.

"This is the Eighth Sign: You will see many youth, who wear their hair long like my people, come and join the tribal nations, to learn their ways and wisdom.

"And this is the Ninth and Last Sign: You will hear of a dwelling-place in the heavens, above the earth, that shall fall with a great crash. It will appear as a blue star. Very soon after this, the ceremonies of my people will cease [this may refer to the Blue Kachina].

"These are the Signs that great destruction is coming. The **world shall rock to and fro** [reminiscent of the Bible's prophecy in Isaiah 24:20 that the Earth shall reel like a drunkard]. The white man will battle against other people in other lands—with those who possessed the first light of wisdom. There will be many columns of smoke and fire such as White Feather has seen the white man make in the deserts not far from here. Only those which come will cause disease and a great dying. Many of my people, understanding the prophecies, shall be safe. Those who stay and live in the places of my people also shall be safe. Then there will be much to rebuild. And soon—very soon afterward—Pahana will return. He shall bring with him the dawn of the Fifth World. He shall plant the seeds of his wisdom in their hearts. Even now the seeds are being planted. These shall smooth the way to the Emergence into the Fifth World."[259]

The Pahana mentioned above refers to the Hopi messiah, a man from the stars who will bring with him an artifact to prove his position. This man could easily be the coming Antichrist. Some call him Mahdi; Buddhists look for Maitreya; Hindus for Kalki; Zoroastrians for Saoshyant; Nostradamus may have called him Mabus. All these refer to the Man of Sin—the coming world ruler who will call himself Christ, Messiah, Maitreya, and perhaps Pahana. Reality as we know it may become nothing more than a matrix of perception. Our minds may hear instructions or enticements in our own language, while our eyes see only what we wish to see. We have heaped unto ourselves false teaching because of our itching ears, and this is what God has permitted: A strong delusion.

Metal will meld with flesh and mind with falsehoods as those who do not choose the true Christ, Jesus of Nazareth, are transformed into the transhumanist zealots' twisted image of godhood. Human artificial chromosomes, HACs, may be used to mark us—as may tattoos embedded with genetic information. We shall all be changed—some to immortality with Christ, some to hideous clay and iron constructs that mock God's beautiful design by attempts to "enhance" His code. Cloning, human/animal hybridization, mind control, pharmaceuticals, and the false notion of self-directed evolution are all part of an end game the enemy hopes will allow him to defeat God. The final armies will gather in Jerusalem—not to fight each other, but to look up! The true Christ will return at the end of this age, and He will do battle with earth's demon-led enhanced human army.

We know the ending. We know the enemy is already defeated—he just won't admit it...*yet!*

TRIGGER EVENT: WHEN 666 BECOMES MANDATORY OVERNIGHT

In previous chapters, we have cited the following from the book of Revelation:

> And he **causeth** all, both small and great, rich and poor, free and bond, to receive a mark in their right hand, or in their foreheads: And that no man might buy or sell, save he that had the mark, or the name of the beast, or the number of his name. (Revelation 13:16, emphasis added)

The particular phrasing in this verse is very important because the Greek verb for "causeth" (*poieō*) implies that something is set in motion by the instigator of an event (in this case, the Antichrist), which then triggers others to have to respond to it.

One wonders just what the Antichrist will initiate that will result in the majority of the global population making a decision to accept his mark. It would have to be something extraordinary to put so much pressure on freedom-loving peoples around the world—especially in Judeo-Christian cultures—to cause them to lay aside personal liberties and eternal salvation in exchange for an Orwellian society where one world government oversees the smallest details of their lives and in which human rights are abandoned.

Given the cherished idea of "free moral agency," this will be no easy task, as our late friend Noah Hutchings of Southwest Radio Ministries noted in an article he wrote and sent to us, a portion of which stated:

God created man in His own image, and He instilled within the spirit of man the will to be a free moral individual. Man has the election to obey the Creator or disobey Him and follow the dictates of his conscience. [Man also] has the inherent right to select the type of government that is to regulate the order of society. Countless wars have been fought and millions have died to protect this freedom. Liberty has been subjected to the will of tyrants and dictators, yet it has surfaced down through the ages and endured as the hope of mankind. The Pilgrims came to America to find a haven for personal liberty. The Revolutionary War was fought to preserve this freedom. The Civil War was fought to bring freedom to those who were enslaved and without liberty. Thomas Jefferson wrote in the Declaration of Independence: "All men are created equal, and endowed by their Creator with life, liberty, and the pursuit of happiness." But a time is coming, and we believe it is very near, when individual freedom will be completely extinguished: "… and power was given him over all kindreds, and tongues, and nations. And all that dwell upon the earth shall worship him, whose names are not written in the book of life of the lamb slain from the foundation of the world" (Revelation 13:7–8).

Will the eradication of the spark of liberty within the spirit of man be accomplished by a tyrannical system of government like communism or fascism? Will it be because men surrender individual freedom in order to survive the threat of international terrorism, nuclear war, or some other imminent danger that threatens the very existence of mankind? Or will it come about because…the masses [have] become so conditioned to state supervision and control…that the vast majority will accept the mark and number of the Beast when it arrives[?] The links in the chain of bondage which the Antichrist will use when all the world becomes a prison are being forged. A letter by Dr. Michael W. Fox, scientific director of the Humane Society of the United States, written to the Society for the Protection of the Individual Rights and Liberties of Tucson, Arizona, states in part:

> You may be interested to know that one military PX, I believe in Ft. Worth, is considering inserting electronic identification in the back of the hands of people using the PX to permit them ready entry without any other screening. It seems as though this age of biotechnology is being used for greater control and manipulation, and the pyramid of power is being strengthened in the process.
>
> The course of events in technology, science, economics, crime and social behavior, nuclear war, and international terrorism is bringing mankind to [a trigger event] to take the mark and number of Antichrist or be killed. How near is the present generation to facing this decision? The developing bondage of the human body, mind, and spirit is evidence that it *is* near.

As usual, Dr. Hutching's insights are acutely tuned and recognize the need for a global-scale incident to set in motion the Man of Sin's "cause," which then somehow will overwhelm the average person's ability to resist receiving the mark of the Beast.

What could this far-reaching scenario conceivably be? While the prospects are numerous, for the sake of space, we'll describe just three possibilities: 1) an EMP (electromagnetic pulse) or cyberattack; 2) a global economic meltdown; and 3) a natural or manufactured global pandemic, the development of which these authors believe could most directly connect to a beastly mark. All three of these possibilities are more likely than most understand as a result of Biden administration policies.

SCENARIO #1: ELECTROMAGNETIC
AND/OR CYBER WARFARE EVENT

Most government experts in fields of risk mitigation are currently focused on likely terrorist- or enemy-state-sponsored scenarios that could take advantage of aging electrical and water systems infrastructures. For example, a rogue nation could load "defensive" missiles with nuclear warheads and launch them as multiple electromagnetic pulse weapons above the United States and/or other countries from offshore freighters. In a literal flash, this could bring down national electrical grids as well as telecommunications; critical energy resources such as oil and natural gas pipelines; water delivery systems; banking and financial institutions, including consumer transactions; and emergency services. In military terminology, if a nuclear warhead is detonated hundreds of kilometers above the earth's surface in this way, it is known as "a high-altitude electromagnetic pulse (HEMP) device":

> Typically the HEMP device produces the EMP as its primary damage mechanism. The nuclear device does this by producing gamma rays, which in turn are converted into EMP in the mid-stratosphere over a wide area within line of sight to the detonation. NEMP is the abrupt pulse of electromagnetic radiation resulting from a nuclear explosion. The resulting rapidly changing electric fields and magnetic fields may couple with electrical/electronic systems to produce damaging current and voltage surges.[260]

On this order, warnings have been issued recently by the US Defense Department and Homeland Security involving the risk associated with enemy nations that are already "testing" US electric infrastructure vulnerability through Russia and China's high-tech information-gathering balloons and cyberattacks aimed at determining how to sabotage the power grid, financial institutions, and even air-traffic control systems.

But that may not be the worst of it, according to an investigative report by F. Michael Maloof for *World Net Daily*. As a former senior security policy analyst in the office of the Secretary of Defense, Maloof points out in *Sledgehammer of Cyber Warfare? EMP Attack* that:

> Those same adversaries—China, Russia, Iran and North Korea—also incorporate in their military doctrine the use of a nuclear electromagnetic pulse, or EMP, attack as "part of a strategic operation that would basically 'throw the kitchen sink' at the United States," according to Cynthia E. Ayers, who once was with the National Security Agency and currently is with the US Army War College.
>
> These countries, she said, will "hit us with everything—computer viruses, sabotage of critical communications nodes, kinetic strikes on key information systems and a nuclear EMP attack."
>
> "The last, an EMP, is their best chance to collapse our national power grid and take us down, perhaps permanently," she said.[261]

In short, a coordinated assault on America and/or allied nations as described above could instantly result in the collapse of Western society as it has been known. Directly thereafter, anarchy would fill the streets, martial law would be imposed, and a national cry would fill the air for salvation from chaos.

But is this a perfect recipe for the Man of Sin stepping in with wondrous answers to our overnight problems by offering some unknown method for restoring social order? How could he "mark" those who would be allowed to function in his kingdom following a catastrophic cyber or EMP attack resulting in widespread damage to essential structures? Wouldn't electrical and computerized systems be needed online for implantable or high-tech "marks" to function as we have described them? Surely global superpowers like the United States have top-secret responses already devised for just such an event, but perhaps something beyond human comprehension is planned by Antichrist. Intriguingly, when the Bible describes how the final world leader will deceive the world with "lying signs and wonders" (2 Thessalonians 2:9) and appear at a time when there are "fearful sights and great signs from heaven" (Luke 21:11), one cannot help but note the specific and interesting wording that implies how the Man of Sin will be directly associated with *electricity and people's need of shelter.*

First, the "heaven" mentioned in Luke 21:11 is not the throne room of God, but rather *ouranos*, or the vaulted expanse of the sky where the clouds and the tempests gather and where electrical energy or "lightning" is produced.

Note that, in Nehemiah 9:6, the prophet spoke of more than one heaven: He saw the heavens and the "heaven of heavens." Paul also referred to different "heavens" in 2 Corinthians 12:2, saying:

> I knew a man in Christ above fourteen years ago, (whether in the body, I cannot tell; or whether out of the body, I cannot tell: God knoweth;) such an one [was] caught up to the third heaven.

Some scholars believe when Paul referred to this third heaven, he was echoing his formal education as a Pharisee concerning three heavens that included a domain of air (the *kosmos*) or height, controlled by Beelzebub (Satan), the "lord of the height" and god of lightning (electricity). In pharisaical thought, the first heaven was simply the place where the birds fly—anything removed from and not attached to the surface of the earth. On the other end of the spectrum and of a different substance was the third heaven—the dwelling place of God. Between this third heaven, "where dwells the throne room of God," and the first heaven, where the birds fly, was a war zone called the "second heaven." This was *ouranos*, or, as it was also known, the *kosmos*—the Hebrew equivalent of the Persian *Ahriman-abad*—the place where Satan abides as the prince of the power of the "air" (Greek *aer*: the lower air, circum-ambient, location of natural electrical energy), a sort of gasket heaven, the domain of Satan encompassing the surface of the earth.

In Persian theology, the spirit that opposed the prophet Daniel (see Daniel 10) and his angel would have been identified as this same spirit, but called *Ahriman* in their culture, a god capable of electricity and lightning whose legend closely parallels the biblical fall of Lucifer. According to Persian religion, Ahriman was the death dealer—the powerful and self-existing evil spirit from whom war and all other evils had their origin. He was the chief of the cacodemons, or fallen angels, expelled from heaven for their sins. After being kicked out of heaven, the cacodemons endeavored to settle down in various parts of the earth, but were always rejected, and out of revenge found pleasure in tormenting the inhabitants of the earth. Ahriman and his followers finally took up their abode in the space between heaven and earth and there established their domain: *Ahriman-abad*—"the abode of Ahriman." From this location, the cacodemons could intrude into and attempt to corrupt the governments of men.

In the Bible, both the False Prophet and the Antichrist are described as being aligned with the "power" of this celestial realm, from which they are able to call down "fire," presumably lightning or electricity (though the reference could actually be of literal fire).

The prophet Daniel also tells us Antichrist's belief system will honor a "strange, alien god" who again appears related to electricity and lightning. In Daniel 11:38–39, we read:

> But in his estate shall he honour **the God of forces**: and a god whom his fathers knew not shall he honour with gold, and silver, and with precious stones, and pleasant things. Thus shall he do in the most strong holds with a **strange god**, whom he shall acknowledge and increase with glory: and he shall cause them to rule over many, and shall divide the land for gain. (Emphasis added)

Several parts of Daniel's prophecy stand out as very unusual. First, the phrase, "God of forces"—alternately, "god of fortresses"—has been connected to Baal-Shamem, an ancient deity who was worshiped throughout the Middle East, especially in Canaan/Phoenicia, Syria, and later by the Manichaean Gnostics, who revered him as the greatest angel of electrical energy, or natural, electrical, and high-voltage discharges (lightning). Could this imply that Antichrist will come on the world scene overnight like some supernatural version of Nikola Tesla, with a wonder-creating wireless electricity transmission system capable of repowering the world?

(Note: Tesla, a nineteenth-century inventor, was an electrical engineer known around the world for his patented devices and contributions to the knowledge of alternating current [AC] electricity supply systems. Before he died in 1943, Tesla had intended a proof-of-concept demonstration of an intercontinental system that would provide transatlantic wireless power transmissions for electricity, telephones, and broadcasting, but the project was defunded midstream by pressure brought on by—some believe—skullduggery involving electricity contracts competitor General Electric, Thomas Edison's company.)

In addition to a wireless electricity, note that the Hebrew word translated "forces" in this verse is *ma'owz*, which refers to a deity who can provide human protection in the form of strong housing, places of safety, protection, and refuge—adding to the question of whether Antichrist could appear as a false savior of humanity immediately following a wide-scale cyberattack or EMP-type event that brings down national power grids, leaving people desperate for common necessities such as electricity and housing.

Finally, connected to the appearance of the Beast and Antichrist, the book of Revelation seems to preface that moment with a military attack resulting in the destruction, or "death," and then the seemingly miraculous rapid recovery of what many expositors believe is both a man and the global super-nation he represents. According to this premise, the healing of that man and/or nation's "deadly wound" causes all the world to worship "the dragon which gave *power* unto the beast" and to proclaim: "Who is like unto the beast? who is able to make *war* with him?" (Revelation 13:4, emphasis added). This is then followed by a vision of "power" and "fire" from the heavens connected to the implementation of the mark of the Beast (verses 13–18):

> And he doeth great wonders, so that he maketh fire [electricity?] come down from heaven on the earth in the sight of men, And deceiveth them that dwell on the earth by the means of those miracles which he had power to do in the sight of the beast; saying to them that dwell on the earth, that they should make an image to the beast, which had the wound by a sword, and did live. And he had power to give life unto the image of the beast, that the image of the beast should both speak, and cause that as many as would not worship the image of the beast should be killed. And he causeth all, both small and great, rich and poor, free and bond, to receive a mark in their right hand, or in their foreheads: And that no man might buy or sell, save he that had the mark, or the name of the beast, or the number of his name. Here is wisdom. Let him that hath understanding count the number of the beast: for it is the number of a man; and his number is Six hundred threescore and six.

SCENARIO #2: THE COLLAPSE OF THE GLOBAL ECONOMY

Not long ago, the United States' National Intelligence Council (NIC) and the European Union's Institute for Security Studies (EUISS) joined forces to produce an assessment of the long-term prospects for global governance frameworks. The report—*Global Governance 2025: At a Critical Juncture*—assessed leading intercontinental perils that could endanger the collective administration of shared problems at the international level around the year 2025 (the same date the ancient Hebrew Essenes, the most accurate prophets in history, predicted mankind will enter its "final age"—[to learn more about that, see the bestselling new book *We Are Legion, for We Are Many: Dominions, Kosmokrators, and Washington, DC: Unmasking the Ancient Riddle of the Hebrew Year 5785 (2024–2025) and the Imminent Destiny of America*]). From the beginning of the report, under the subsection "Scenario I: Barely Keeping Afloat," the writers acknowledge how crises including current financial institutions are being served ad hoc, temporary frameworks devised to avert the most threatening aspects (such as the United States printing money for which it has no gold reserves) and synthetic economic tricks being used to temporarily sustain what is ultimately an unsustainable financial system.

Conservative analysts have been predicting a devastating crash of the stock market for quite some time, all the while holding their breath, hoping it won't happen. Yet history and experience, coupled with extraordinary facts connected with the Biden administration today, convince them that the world's major economies are being artificially sustained and that it is only a matter of time before this house of cards collapses. Even more conspiratorially, some suggest something sinister is actually being *planned*, as in a global stock market crash for the near future unlike anything the world has experienced before. Such a crash would permit the Illuminists and cohorts to close thousands of banks in a matter of days, seize most personal assets, confiscate gold and silver, and eliminate cash, all under federally sanctioned "declared emergencies" activated by presidential executive order. After the financial institutions of the world crumble, a global monetary system would be restructured into one that provides more efficient methods of total enslavement, setting the stage for the official establishment of the Antichrist's New World Economic Order.

This manufactured crash might begin in a country like the United States or even Japan and then work its way around the globe, toppling the economies of nations like a row of dominoes, virtually simultaneously.

On the heels of this event, a new form of digital currency (already under design) could be announced that is international in scope and proclaimed as more reliable than the old monetary system. It would replace modern credit and debit cards as well as paper checks, ultimately paving the way for a super-biometric ID, smart tattoo, personalized QR code or implant wherein every financial transaction in one's life could be stored, catalogued, analyzed, and accessed for future reference by New World Order bureaucrats. For the majority of people who have been using electronic banking for years (via direct payroll deposits, direct deposit of Social Security checks, ATMs, credit and debit cards, electronic automatic payments of bills, etc.), accepting the new system will be a snap.

What's more, as detailed in earlier chapters, polls around the world show that, today, an overwhelming majority approves and appreciates the convenience of emerging biometric and "smart" banking technologies and are open to near-future realities wherein their flesh will be merged with apparati for buying and selling (and surveillance), either via an implantable chip or some other cool, new cyborg-control system.

What's that?

Cyborgs?

New people for a new system?

Are we serious?

Apparently.

When the *Global Governance 2025: At a Critical Juncture* document cited above combined the risks of a global financial collapse triggered (in one scenario) by "biological weapons," it included in that assessment how biotech could also eventually lead to *a new form of man*—a previously unknown human with unique physical, emotional, and cognitive abilities that emerge as a result of the very science and technology Antichrist may use to enslave humanity. Keep in mind, this international study group was made up of the top scientific and military minds across Europe and the United States.

Note that on page 35 of their report, these top-shelf intelligence leaders transition from the threat of a biological weapon *to the creation of a potentially dangerous new form of human*:

No forum currently exists for dealing comprehensively across the scientific community, industry, and governments on measures needed to diminish the risks posed by the biotechnology revolution. The development of new agents and the expansion of access to those with hostile intentions increase the bioterrorism threat.... In addition, biotechnology—which the OECD thinks will potentially boost the GDPs of its members—can drive *new forms of human* behavior and association, creating profound cross-cultural ethical questions that will be increasingly politically contentious. Few experts believe that current governance instruments are adequate for those challenges. For example, *direct modification of DNA* at fertilization is widely researched with a goal of removing defective genes; however, discussions of future capabilities *open the possibility for designing humans with unique physical, emotional, or cognitive abilities.*[262] (Emphasis added)

Bio-enhanced humans with unique "cognitive" abilities have been in the design budgets and on the drawing boards of military strategists and social engineers who, for some time, have imagined how our growing marriage with—and dependence on—machine intelligence will, in the not-too-distant future, accompany almost everything we do, including buying and selling. The era has already started, though it is in its embryonic stage, and it has been given a name. It is being called the "Hybrid Age." And, yes, this means exactly what it sounds like. What we are already doing with genetically modified crops, transgenic animals, and human-animal chimeras at the embryonic scale we intend to do to the rest of humanity in general—to hybridize humans via genetic alterations, nanotechnology, synthetic biology, and human-tech integration with artificial intelligence and brain-machine interfaces.

Parag Khanna and Ayesha Khann explain in their August 19, 2011, article "Foreign Policy: A Predictable Future for Technology":

As we try to understand an incipient future in which technology has insinuated itself into every sphere and nook of human activity—from the manipulation and replication of DNA to space exploration—and in which humans continuously seek ways to speed up their biological evolution to match the breakneck pace of technological evolution, the only way to do that is to incrementally integrate with technology, launching an era of change and innovation that we call the Hybrid Age. If the first wave was agrarian and tribal, the second industrial and national, and the third informational and transnational, then the Hybrid Age is…the "Fourth Wave." In this new era, human evolution [will] become human-technology co-evolution: We're becoming part of the machine, and it is becoming part of us.[263]

If the description above sounds like an incredible dream (or nightmare), consider how quickly such technology is spreading into the broader culture (and now with extracranial applications, it will no longer require the Beast chip surgically implanted into one's brain). Currently, tests are being conducted that allow people to interact with computers, smartphones, and tablets simply by using their minds. Gaming systems have been on the market since 2010 that let players control some of the functions with "thought" alone by wearing a rubber cap that reads and translates their brain's electrical impulses. More advanced systems under development at the University of Washington allow one person to send a brain signal over the Internet to a second gamer across campus in a different building who is wearing such a "cap." The second gamer "involuntarily" clicks a tab with his index finger as he receives signals from the first person, who is playing the game by using the second person's mind. Over the next few years, people everywhere will be turning on their lights at home, sending emails, and yes, soon thereafter, transferring monetary funds by thought-controlled, brain-machine interfacing without ever pulling their wallets or checkbooks from their pockets or purses. Welcome to the Borg.

In the April 28, 2013, *New York Times* article, "Disruptions: Brain Computer Interfaces Inch Closer to Mainstream," Nick Bilton elaborates:

But that chip inside the head could soon vanish as scientists say we are poised to gain a much greater understanding of the brain, and, in turn, technologies that empower brain computer interfaces. An initiative by the Obama administration this year called the Brain Activity Map project, a decade-long research project, aims to build a comprehensive map of the brain.

Miyoung Chun, a molecular biologist and vice president for science programs at the Kavli Foundation, is working on the project and although she said it would take a decade to completely map the brain, companies would be able to build new kinds of brain computer interface products within two years.

"The Brain Activity Map will give hardware companies a lot of new tools that will change how we use smartphones and tablets," Dr. Chun said. "It will revolutionize everything from robotic implants and neural prosthetics, to remote controls, which could be history in the foreseeable future when you can change your television channel by thinking about it."[264]

Thus the technology for the Beast's end-times system is practically here. All Antichrist will need is the trigger event, which could come in the form of a global financial meltdown that brings the world to its knees and introduces a modern and more secure method of buying and selling via high-tech "marks." Highly educated economists around the world say we are on the precipice of that cascading event now.

SCENARIO #3: NATURAL OR MANUFACTURED GLOBAL PANDEMIC

As noted in an earlier chapter on RFID technology, scannable implants and tattoo transmitters are becoming more sophisticated, adding "prophetic" components such as merging human biological matter with transistors to create living, implantable machines. Related science also envisions "smart" chimeric vaccines that literally rewrite DNA. The authors of this book believe the possibility that the mark of the Beast could arrive through a version of one of these technologies is plausible, if not altogether likely.

But, again, what "trigger" could set in motion the need for a universal vaccine in the form of a biochip?

We will discuss the third scenario later in this book.

THE MAN OF SIN—AND HIS 666 MARK— ARE COMING

Everything we discuss between the covers of this book foreshadows a very near future in which a man of horrendous, yet unseen, intelligence and diplomacy will emerge on the world scene as a savior. Though his arrival in the form of a man is foretold by numerous Scriptures, the broad masses will not immediately recognize him for what he actually is—paganism's ultimate incarnation, the "beast" of Revelation 13:1. As he makes himself known, scholars including some of the most celebrated Christian leaders will herald his uncanny ability to resolve whatever emergency gives rise to his appearance, assuring congregations of his godliness and scoffing at those who warn against receiving his "mark." Only when it is too late will his profound popularity be understood for the ruse it actually is—an unmerciful plot by a very old, super-intelligent spirit who ultimately becomes "a king of fierce countenance" (Daniel 8:23). En route to causing all, both small and great, to receive his beastly mark, the combined depravities of Antiochus Epiphanes, Adolf Hitler, Joseph Stalin, and Genghis Khan, all of whom were types of Antichrist, will look like child's play in comparison to his brutality. With imperious decree, he will facilitate a one-world government, universal religion, and global socialism. Those who refuse his New World Order will inevitably be imprisoned or destroyed until finally he raises his fist, "speaking great things...in blasphemy against God, to blaspheme his name, and his tabernacle, and them that dwell in heaven" (Revelation 13:5–6). Ultimately, he will exalt himself "above all that is called God, or that is worshiped" until finally he enthrones himself "in the temple of God, showing himself that he is God" (2 Thessalonians 2:4).

Will you be ready to recognize this end-times great deceiver and to escape the mass delusion that will befall "all them that dwell on the face of the earth" (Luke 21:35)?

Will you be "accounted worthy to escape all these things that shall come to pass" (Luke 21:36)?

There is only one way to know for sure. Accept Jesus Christ as your Lord and Savior and repent of your sins. If you will or have done this, He promises:

> Because thou hast kept the word of my patience, I also will keep thee from the hour of temptation, which shall come upon all the world, to try them that dwell upon the earth. (Revelation 3:10).

> And they overcame him by the blood of the Lamb, and by the word of their testimony; and they loved not their lives unto the death. (Revelation 12:11)

THE HELL SCENARIO
WILL BE NOTHING
TO *GRIN* ABOUT

*Synthetic biologists forecast that as computer code is written to create
software to augment human capabilities, so too genetic code will be
written to create life forms to augment civilization.*

—JEROME C. GLENN

*Homo sapiens, the first truly free species, is about to decommission
natural selection, the force that made us.... Soon we must look deep
within ourselves and decide what we wish to become.*

—EDWARD OSBORNE WILSON

Resistance is futile! You will be assimilated!

—THE BORG

Not long ago, a writer for *Wired* magazine named Elizabeth Svoboda contacted me (Tom) to let me know she was writing an article about "research advances using transgenic animals to produce pharmaceutical compounds." She had come across an editorial I wrote raising caution about this kind of experimentation and wondered if I might be willing to provide points for her article, elaborating in areas where I saw producing transgenic human-animals as potentially harmful. She stated that most of the scientists she planned to quote were "pretty gung-ho about the practice," and said she thought it would be important to provide some balance. I thanked her for the invitation and sent a short summary of some, though not all, of the areas where concerns about this science could be raised.

When the article was finally published by *Wired*, I was surprised that none of my notes had made it into the story. I contacted Elizabeth and asked why, and she replied that they had originally been included in her article, "Pharm Animals Crank Out Drugs," but in order to create a positive spin on the story, the editors had censored my cautionary notes during the editing process. Elizabeth apologized and said she hoped the experience had not soured me on dealing with the magazine.

"It doesn't sour me," I assured her. "I just think the reporting by most agencies is lopsided and missing the opportunity to thoroughly engage such an important issue." The fact is, *Wired* deprived the public of balanced treatment on an important subject and concluded instead with a scientist by the name of Marie Cecile Van de Lavoir saying that potential human health benefits from transgenic research "justify tinkering" with nature's plan. "If a transgenic animal produces a great cancer therapy," she said, "I won't hear anyone saying, 'You shouldn't do that.'" Van de Lavoir's comments were undoubtedly in response to some of my observations before they were pulled, because in offering caution, I had specifically used the phrase "tinkering with nature's plan." Van de Lavoir's short-sighted approach, like too many bioethicists engaged in the current debate, is as scary as the science, in our opinion. We wanted to contact her to suggest that she watch the film *I Am Legend*, starring Will Smith, which opens appropriately enough with a scientist announcing the cure to cancer using a genetically engineered vaccine that blends animal and human genetics. If you've seen the film, you know the "cure" results in a human form of rabies that wipes out most life on earth—a real possibility, given the scenario.

Because any attempt at covering each potential GRIN-tech, catastrophic, *I-Am-Legend* possibility in this book would be impractical, we summarize below a few of the most important areas in which conservatives, bioethicists, regulators, and especially Christians could become informed and involved in the public dialogue over the potential benefits and threats represented by these emerging fields of science.

SYNTHETIC BIOLOGY

Synthetic biology is one of the newest areas of biological research that seeks to design new forms of life and biological functions not found in nature. The concept began emerging in 1974, when Polish geneticist Waclaw Szybalski speculated about how scientists and engineers would soon enter "the synthetic biology phase of research."

He continued:

> We will then devise new control elements and add these new modules to the existing genomes or build up wholly new genomes. This would be a field with the unlimited expansion [of] building new…"synthetic" organisms, like a "new better mouse."[265]

Following Szybalski's speculation, the field of synthetic biology reached its first major milestone in 2010 with the announcement that researchers at the J. Craig Venter Institute (JCVI) had created an entirely new form of life nicknamed "Synthia" by inserting artificial genetic material, which had been chemically synthesized, into cells that were then able to grow. The JCVI website explains:

> Genomic science has greatly enhanced our understanding of the biological world. It is enabling researchers to "read" the genetic code of organisms from all branches of life by sequencing the four letters that make up DNA. Sequencing genomes has now become routine, giving rise to thousands of genomes in the public databases. In essence, scientists are digitizing biology by converting the A, C, T, and G's of the chemical

makeup of DNA into 1's and 0's in a computer. But can one reverse the process and start with 1's and 0's in a computer to define the characteristics of a living cell? We set out to answer this question [and] now, this scientific team headed by Drs. Craig Venter, Hamilton Smith, and Clyde Hutchison have achieved the final step in their quest to create the first...synthetic genome [that] has been "booted up" in a cell to create the first cell controlled completely by a synthetic genome.[266]

The JCVI site goes on to explain how the ability to routinely write the software of life will usher in a new era of science, and with it, unnatural "living" products like Szybalski's "new better mouse." Better mice, dogs, horses, cows, or humans that grow from this science will be unlike any of the versions God made. In fact, researchers at the University of Copenhagen may look at what Venter has accomplished as amateur hour compared to their posthuman plans. They're working on a third peptide nucleic acid (PNA) strand—a synthetic hybrid of protein and DNA—to upgrade humanity's two existing DNA strands from double helix to triple. In so doing:

> [These scientists] dream of synthesizing life that is utterly alien to this world—both to better understand the minimum components required for life (as part of the quest to uncover the essence of life and how life originated on earth) and, frankly, to see if they can do it. That is, they hope to put together a novel combination of molecules that can self-organize, metabolize (make use of an energy source), grow, reproduce and evolve."[267]

Our good friend Gary Stearman of *Prophecy in the News* and other biblical scholars are raising red flags over Synthia technology, warning that any biotech life application leading to modification of the human genotype for "improved" humans will be an inconceivable affront to God and could result in divine repercussions.

PATENTING NEW LIFE-FORMS

Questions are evolving now over the "patenting" of transgenic seeds, animals, plants, and synthetic life-forms by large corporations, which at a minimum has already begun to impact the economy of rural workers and farmers through such products as Monsanto's "terminator" seeds. Patenting human genes will escalate these issues, as best-selling author Michael Crichton pointed out in a piece for the *New York Times* titled, "Gene Patents Aren't Benign and Never Will Be," in which he claimed that people could die in the future from not being able to afford medical treatment as a result of medicines owned by patent holders of specific genes related to the genetic makeup of those persons. Former special counsel for President Richard Nixon, Charles Colson, added:

> The patenting of genes and other human tissue has already begun to turn human nature into property. The misuse of genetic information will enable insurers and employers to exercise the ultimate form of discrimination. Meanwhile, advances in nanotechnology and cybernetics threaten to "enhance" and one day perhaps rival or replace human nature itself—in what some thinkers are already calling "transhumanism."[268]

ANIMAL RIGHTS

Animal-rights activists have raised similar questions having to do with the ethics of altering animals in ways that could be demeaning to them—for instance, creating zombielike creatures that grow in feeder labs and gaze off into space from birth until death. Militarized animals that behave in unnatural, unpredictable ways. Humanized animals that become "self-aware," or animals that produce human sperm and eggs, which then are used for in vitro fertilization to produce a human child. Who would the parents be—a pair of mice?

HUMAN CLONING

The prospect of human cloning was raised in the nineties immediately after the creation of the much-celebrated Dolly, a female domestic sheep clone. Dolly was the first mammal to be cloned using "somatic cell nuclear transfer," which involves removing the DNA from an unfertilized egg and replacing its nucleus with the DNA that is to be cloned. Today, a version of this science is common practice in genetics engineering labs worldwide, where "therapeutic cloning" of human and human-animal embryos is employed for stem-cell harvesting (the stem cells, in turn, are used to generate virtually any type of specialized cell in the human body). This type of cloning was in the news when it emerged from William J. Clinton Presidential Center documents that the newest member of the Supreme Court, Elena Kagan, had opposed during the Clinton White House any effort by Congress to prevent humans from being cloned specifically for experimental purposes, then killed. A second form of human cloning is called "reproductive cloning" and is the technology that could be used to create a person who is genetically identical to a current or previously existing human. While Dolly was created by this type of cloning technology, the American Medical Association and the American Association for the Advancement of Science have raised caution about using this approach to create human clones, at least at this stage. Government bodies including the US Congress have considered legislation to ban mature human cloning, and though a few states have implemented restrictions, contrary to public perception and except where institutions receive federal funding, no federal laws exist at this time in the United States to prohibit the cloning of humans. The United Nations, the European Union, and Australia likewise considered and failed to approve a comprehensive ban on human cloning technology, leaving the door open to perfect the science should society, government, or the military come to believe that duplicate or replacement humans hold intrinsic value.

REDEFINING HUMANS AND HUMAN RIGHTS

Where biotechnology is ultimately headed includes not only redefining what it means to be human, but redefining subsequent human rights as well. For instance, Dr. James Hughes wants transgenic chimps and great apes uplifted genetically so that they achieve "personhood." The underlying goal behind this theory would be to establish that basic cognitive aptitude should equal "personhood" and that this "cognitive standard," not "human-ness," should be the key to constitutional protections and privileges. Among other things, this would lead to nonhuman "persons" and "nonperson" humans, unhinging the existing argument behind intrinsic sanctity of human life and paving the way for such things as harvesting organs from people like Terry Schiavo (the brain-damaged woman who was kept alive by artificial means until her death upon removal of her feeding tube in 2005) whenever the loss of cognitive ability equals the dispossession of "personhood." These would be the first victims of transhumanism, according to Professor Francis Fukuyama, concerning who does or does not qualify as fully human and is thus represented by the founding concept that "all men are created equal." Most would argue that *any* human fits this bill, but women and blacks were not included in these rights in 1776 when Thomas Jefferson wrote the Declaration of Independence. So who is to say what protections can be automatically assumed in an age when human biology is altered and when personhood theory challenges what bioethicists like Wesley J. Smith champion as "human exceptionalism": the idea that human beings carry special moral status in nature and special rights, such as the right to life, plus unique responsibilities, such as stewardship of the environment. Some, but not all, believers in human exceptionalism arrive at this concept from a biblical worldview based on Genesis 1:26, which says:

> And God said, "Let us make man in our image, after our likeness: and let them have dominion over the fish of the sea, and

over the fowl of the air, and over the cattle, and over all the earth, and over every creeping thing that creepeth upon the earth."

NANOTECHNOLOGY AND CYBERNETICS

As discussed in the previous chapter, technology to merge human brains with machines is progressing at a fantastic rate. Nanotechnology—the science of engineering materials or devices on an atomic and molecular scale between 1 to 100 nanometers (a nanometer is one billionth of a meter) in size—is poised to take the development between brain-machine interfaces and cybernetic devices to a whole new adaptive level for human modification. This will happen because, as Dr. C. Christopher Hook points out:

> Engineering or manipulating matter and life at nanometer scale [foresees] that the structures of our bodies and our current tools could be significantly altered. In recent years, many governments around the world, including the United States with its National Nanotechnology Initiative, and scores of academic centers and corporations have committed increasing support for developing nanotechnology programs. The military, which has a significant interest in nanotechnology, has created the Center for Soldier Nanotechnologies (CSN) [which is] interested in the use of such technology to help create the seamless interface of electronic devices with the human nervous system, engineering the cyborg soldier.[269]

TRANSHUMAN EUGENICS

In the early part of the twentieth century, the study and practice of selective human breeding known as *eugenics* sought to counter dysgenic aspects within the human gene pool and to improve overall human "genetic qualities." Researchers in the United States, Britain, Canada, and Germany (where, under Adolf Hitler, eugenics operated under the banner of "racial hygiene" and allowed Josef Mengele, Otmar von

Verschuer, and others to perform horrific experiments on live human beings in concentration camps to test their genetic theories) were interested in weeding out "inferior" human bloodlines and used studies to insinuate heritability between certain families and illnesses such as schizophrenia, blindness, deafness, dwarfism, bipolar disorder, and depression. Their published reports fueled the eugenics movement to develop state laws in the 1800s and 1900s that forcefully sterilized people considered unhealthy or mentally ill in order to prevent them from "passing on" their genetic inferiority to future generations. Such laws were not abolished in the US until the mid-twentieth century, leading to more than sixty thousand sterilized Americans in the meantime. Between 1934 and 1937, the Nazis likewise sterilized an estimated four hundred thousand people they deemed of inferior genetic stock while also setting forth to selectively exterminate the Jews as "genetic aberrations" under the same program. Transhumanist goals of using biotechnology, nanotechnology, mind-interfacing, and related sciences to create a superior human and thus classifications of persons—the enhanced and the unenhanced—opens the door for a new form of eugenics and social Darwinism.

GERM-LINE GENETIC ENGINEERING AND GENE DRIVES

Germ-line genetic engineering has the potential to actually achieve the goals of the early eugenics movement (which sought to create superior humans via improving genetics through selective breeding) through genetically modifying human genes in very early embryos, sperm, and eggs. As a result, germ-line engineering is considered by some conservative bioethicists to be the most dangerous of human-enhancement technology, as it has the power to truly reassemble the very nature of humanity into posthuman, altering an embryo's every cell and leading to inheritable modifications extending to all succeeding generations. Debate over germ-line engineering is therefore most critical, because as changes to "downline" genetic offspring are set in motion, the nature and physical makeup of mankind will be altered with no hope of reversal, thereby permanently reshaping humanity's future. A related genetic modification tool is CRISPR-based "gene drives" that can spread through populations of animals, pests, or humans to suppress or eradicate previous populations. One example of this technology was illustrated at the University of California, where scientists created genetically modified fruit flies to have a different color pigmentation gene and found that, within just one generation, all regular flies in the test group were replaced by a new variant. In the study, the introduced mutation "disabled both normal copies of a pigmentation gene on the fruit fly chromosomes, transmitting itself to the next generation with 97% efficiency—a near-complete invasion of the genome."[270] This literally illustrated how the original version of any specie can be driven out of existence and replaced by a new model, something it seems the ancient fallen angels tried to do with humankind by the introduction of replacement beings called Nephilim.

And they nearly succeeded.

A respected proponent of such germ-line and gene-drive technology is Dr. Gregory Stock, who, like cyborgist Kevin Warwick, departs from Kurzweil's version of Humans 2.0 first arriving as a result of computer Singularity. Stock believes humans can choose to transcend existing biological limitations in the nearer future (at or before computers reach strong artificial intelligence) through germ-line engineering. If we can make better humans by adding new genes to their DNA, he asks, why shouldn't we? "We have spent billions to unravel our biology, not out of idle curiosity, but in the hope of bettering our lives. We are not about to turn away from this," he says, before admitting elsewhere that this could lead to "clusters of genetically enhanced superhumans who will dominate if not enslave us."[271] The titles to Stock's books speak for themselves concerning what germ-line engineering would do to the human race. The name of one is *Redesigning Humans: Our Inevitable Genetic Future*, and another is *Metaman: The Merging of Humans and Machines into a Global Superorganism*.

GENETICALLY MODIFIED FOOD

Besides potential problems with transgenic animals, we have cited laboratory results in the past that were first reported by Dr. árpád Pusztai, repeat verified by scientist Irina Ermakova, and later substantiated by the *International Journal of Biological Sciences* that showed genetically modified (GM) food had surprisingly ill effects on the health of test rats, including the deterioration of every animal organ, atrophied livers, altered cells, testicular damage, altered sperm counts, shortened life spans, and cancer development. The laboratory findings led to the biotech industry suppressing the data and an eight-year court battle with monster corporations that did not want these results made public. Over the last year, the silenced information has been in the news again as Greenpeace activists published evidence from the Russian trials verifying the ramifications of the negative health issues related to genetically modified foods. The wider ramifications of these and similar controlled experiments suggest that as current technology inserts pesticides, insect genes, animal DNA, and other modified organisms directly into crops, the threat of hybrid viruses, prion (rare neurodegenerative disorders) contamination and new disease strains—which humans can neither anticipate or prepare for—may arise. The prospects of this having an impact on mammalian health is almost certain to be a "when," not "if," concern, because, as Momma always said, "You are what you eat," and the fact that the food you consumed this week most likely contained genetically modified ingredients is a current reality. For example, a large portion of the soybean, corn, cottonseed, and canola in today's human food supply and sold in most developed countries including the United States now has genes spliced in from foreign species—including bacteria and viruses—in its genetic makeup. These genetically modified organisms (GMOs) have not only been linked to sickness, sterility, allergies, and even death among animals, but the Institute for Responsible Technology (IRT) documents how the functioning, genetically modified genes from these foods linger inside the human body, which could be future-catastrophic. "The only published human feeding experiment verified that genetic material inserted into GM soy transfers into the DNA of intestinal bacteria and continues to function," IRT published. "This means that long after we stop eating GM foods, we may still have their GM proteins produced continuously inside us."[272]

Among other things, IRT says this means: 1) If the antibiotic gene inserted into most GM crops were to transfer, it could create super-diseases resistant to antibiotics; 2) If the gene that creates Bt toxin in GM corn were to transfer, it might turn our intestinal flora into living pesticide factories; and 3) Animal studies show that DNA in food can travel into organs throughout the body, even into fetuses. Add to this the growing secrecy over the use of nanoparticles (eighty-four food-related uses are already on the market and in numerous consumer products such as sunscreens and cosmetics), which, as a result of their size, behave fundamentally different than other particles, and the possibility of health-related complications increases exponentially. Due to the large corporations (that stand to make billions of dollars from these products) having co-opted the FDA into not requiring food labeling or package warnings on GMO foods and health products, we are now the biggest lab rats of all time in a "wait-and-see" experiment that will, feasibly within the decade, illustrate whether Pusztai and Ermakova's rodent findings apply to us and our children.

Besides the short list above, additional areas of concern where readers may wish to become well advised on the pros and cons of AI and human enhancement technology include immortalism, postgenderism, augmented reality, cryonics, designer babies, neurohacking, mind uploading, neural implants, xenotransplantation, reprogenetics, rejuvenation, radical life extension, and more.

HEAVEN AND HELL SCENARIOS

While positive advances either already have been or will come from some of the science and technology fields we've discussed, learned men—like Professor Francis Fukuyama, in his book, *Our Posthuman*

Future: Consequences of the Biotechnology Revolution—warn that unintended consequences resulting from what humankind has now set in motion represents the most dangerous time in earth's history, a period when exotic technology in the hands of transhumanist ambitions could forever alter what it means to be human. To those who would engineer a transhuman future, Fukuyama warns of a dehumanized "hell scenario" in which we "no longer struggle, aspire, love, feel pain, make difficult moral choices, have families, or do any of the things that we traditionally associate with being human." In this ultimate identity crisis, we would "no longer have the characteristics that give us human dignity" because, for one thing, "people dehumanized à la *Brave New World*...don't know that they are dehumanized, and, what is worse, would not care if they knew. They are, indeed, happy slaves with a slavish happiness."[273] The "hell scenario" envisioned by Fukuyama is but a beginning to what other intelligent thinkers believe could go wrong.

On the other end of the spectrum and diametrically opposed to Fukuyama's conclusions is an equally energetic crowd that subscribes to a form of technological utopianism called the "heaven scenario." Among this group, a "who's who" of transhumanist evangelists such as Ray Kurzweil, James Hughes, Nick Bostrom, and Gregory Stock see the dawn of a new Age of Enlightenment arriving as a result of the accelerating pace of GRIN technologies. As with the eighteenth-century Enlightenment, in which intellectual and scientific reason elevated the authority of scientists over priests, techno-utopians believe they will triumph over prophets of doom by:

> ...stealing fire from the gods, breathing life into inert matter, and gaining immortality. Our efforts to become something more than human have a long and distinguished genealogy. Tracing the history of those efforts illuminates human nature. In every civilization, in every era, we have given the gods no peace.[274]

Such men are joined in their quest for godlike constitutions by a growing list of official US departments that dole out hundreds of millions of dollars each year for science and technology research. The National Science Foundation and the United States Department of Commerce anticipated this development over a decade ago, publishing the government report *Converging Technologies for Improving Human Performance*—complete with diagrams and bullet points—to lay out the blueprint for the radical evolution of human and machine. Their vision imagined that, starting around the year 2012, the "heaven scenario" would begin to be manifested and quickly result in (among other things):

The transhuman body being "more durable, healthy, energetic, easier to repair, and resistant to many kinds of stress, biological threats, and aging processes."

Brain-machine interfacing that will "transform work in factories, control automobiles, ensure military superiority, and enable new sports, art forms and modes of interaction between people.

"Engineers, artists, architects, and designers will experience tremendously expanded creative abilities," in part through "improved understanding of the wellspring of human creativity."

"Average persons, as well as policymakers, will have a vastly improved awareness of the cognitive, social, and biological forces operating their lives, enabling far better adjustment, creativity, and daily decision making....

"Factories of tomorrow will be organized" around "increased human-machine capabilities."[275]

Beyond how human augmentation and biological reinvention would spread into the wider culture, the government report detailed the *especially* important global and economic aspects of genetically superior humans acting in superior ways. It offered how, as a result of GRINs leading to techno-sapien DNA upgrading, brain-to-brain interaction, human-machine interfaces, personal sensory device interfaces, and biological war fighting systems, "the twenty-first century could end in world peace, universal prosperity, and evolution to a higher level [as] humanity become[s] like a single, transcendent nervous system, an interconnected 'brain' based in new core pathways of society."

The first version of the government's report asserted that the only real roadblock to this "heaven scenario" would be the "catastrophe" that would be unleashed if society fails to employ the technological opportunities available to us now:

We may not have the luxury of delay, because the remarkable economic, political and even violent turmoil of recent years implies that the world system is unstable. If we fail to chart the direction of change boldly, we may become the victims of unpredictable catastrophe.[276]

This argument parallels what is currently echoed in military corridors, where sentiments hold that failure to commit resources to develop GRIN as the next step in human and technological evolution will only lead to others doing so ahead of us and using it for global domination.

Not everybody likes the "heaven scenario" imperative, and from the dreamy fantasies of *Star Trek* to the dismal vision of Aldous Huxley's *Brave New World*, some have come to believe there are demons hiding inside transhumanism's mystical (or mythical?) Shangri-la:

Many of the writers [of the government report cited above] share a faith in technology which borders on religiosity, boasting of miracles once thought to be the province of the Almighty," write the editors of *The New Atlantis: A Journal of Technology and Society*. "[But] without any serious reflection about the hazards of technically manipulating our brains and our consciousness...a different sort of catastrophe is nearer at hand. Without honestly and seriously assessing the consequences associated with these powerful new [GRIN] technologies, we are certain, in our enthusiasm and fantasy and pride, to rush headlong into disaster.[277]

Few people would be more qualified than computer scientist Bill Joy to enunciate these dangers, or to outline the "hell scenario" that could unfold as a result of GRIN. Yet it must have come as a real surprise to some of those who remembered him as the level-headed Silicon Valley scientist and cofounder of Sun Microsystems (SM) when, as chief scientist for the corporation, he released a vast and now-famous essay, "Why the Future Doesn't Need Us," arguing how GRIN would threaten in the very near future to obliterate humankind. What was extraordinary about Joy's prophecy was how he saw himself—and people like him—as responsible for building the very machines that "will enable the construction of the technology that may replace our species."

"From the very moment I became involved in the creation of new technologies, their ethical dimensions have concerned me," he begins. But it was not until the autumn of 1998 that he became "anxiously aware of how great are the dangers facing us in the twenty-first century." Joy dates his "awakening" to a chance meeting with Ray Kurzweil, whom he talked with in a hotel bar during a conference at which they both spoke. Kurzweil was finishing his manuscript for *The Age of Spiritual Machines* and the powerful descriptions of sentient robots and near-term enhanced humans left Joy taken aback, "especially given Ray's proven ability to imagine and create the future," Joy wrote. "I already knew that new technologies like genetic engineering and nanotechnology were giving us the power to remake the world, but a realistic and imminent scenario for intelligent robots surprised me."

Over the weeks and months following the hotel conversation, Joy puzzled over Kurzweil's vision of the future until finally it dawned on him that genetic engineering, robotics, artificial intelligence, and nanotechnology posed "a different threat than the technologies that have come before."

Specifically, robots, engineered organisms, and nanobots share a dangerous amplifying factor: They can self-replicate. A bomb is blown up only once—but one bot can become many, and quickly get out of control.

The unprecedented threat of self-replication particularly burdened Joy because, as a computer scientist, he thoroughly understood the concept of out-of-control replication or viruses leading to machine systems or computer networks being disabled. Uncontrolled self-replication of nanobots or engineered organisms would run "a much greater risk of substantial damage in the physical world," Joy concluded before adding his deeper fear:

What was different in the twentieth century? Certainly, the technologies underlying the weapons of mass destruction (WMD)—nuclear, biological, and chemical (NBC)—were powerful, and the weapons an enormous threat. But building nuclear weapons required...highly protected information; biological and chemical weapons programs also tended to require large-scale activities.

The twenty-first-century technologies—genetics, nanotechnology, and robotics...are so powerful that they can spawn whole new classes of accidents and abuses. Most dangerously, for the first time, these accidents and abuses are widely within the reach of individuals or small groups. They will not require large facilities or rare raw materials. Knowledge alone will enable the use of them.

Thus we have the possibility not just of weapons of mass destruction but of knowledge-enabled mass destruction (KMD), this destructiveness hugely amplified by the power of self-replication.

I think it is no exaggeration to say we are on the cusp of the further perfection of extreme evil, an evil whose possibility spreads well beyond that which weapons of mass destruction bequeathed to the nation states, on to a surprising and terrible empowerment.[278]

Joy's prophecy about self-replicating "extreme evil" as an imminent and enormous transformative power that threatens to rewrite the laws of nature and permanently alter the course of life as we know it was frighteningly revived this year in the creation of Venter's "self-replicating" Synthia species (Venter's description). Parasites such as the mycoplasma mycoides that Venter modified to create Synthia can be resistant to antibiotics and acquire and smuggle DNA from one species to another, causing a variety of diseases. The dangers represented by Synthia's self-replicating parasitism has thus refueled Joy's opus and given experts in the field of counterterrorism sleepless nights over how extremists could use open-source information to create a Frankenstein version of Synthia in fulfillment of Carl Sagan's *Pale Blue Dot*, which Joy quoted as "the first moment in the history of our planet when any species, by its own voluntary actions, has become a danger to itself." As a dire example of the possibilities this represents, a genetically modified version of mouse pox was created not long ago that immediately reached 100 percent lethality. If such pathogens were unleashed into population centers, the results would be catastrophic. This is why Joy and others were hoping a few years ago that a universal moratorium or voluntary relinquishment of GRIN developments would be initiated by national laboratories and governments. But the genie is so far out of the bottle today that even college students are attending annual synthetic biology contests (such as the international Genetically Engineered Machine

Competition, or iGEM) where nature-altering witches' brews are being concocted by the scores, splicing and dicing DNA into task-fulfilling living entities. For instance, the iGem 2009 winners built "E. chromi"—a programmable version of the bacteria that often leads to food poisoning, *Escherichia coli* (commonly abbreviated *E. coli).* A growing list of similar DNA sequences are readily available over the Internet, exasperating security experts who see the absence of universal rules for controlling what is increasingly available through information networks as threatening to unleash a "runaway sorcerer's apprentice" with unavoidable biological fallout. Venter and his collaborators say they recognize this danger—that self-replicating biological systems like the ones they are building hold peril as well as hope, and they have joined in calling on Congress to enact laws to attempt to control the flow of information and synthetic "recipes" that could provide lethal new pathogens for terrorists. The problem, as always, is getting all of the governments in the world to voluntarily follow a firm set of ethics or rules. This is wishful thinking at best. It is far more likely the world is racing toward what Joel Garreau was first to call the "hell scenario"—a moment in which human-driven GRIN technologies place earth and all its inhabitants on course to self-eradication.

Ironically, some advocates of post-humanity are now using the same threat scenario to advocate *for* transhumanism as the best way to deal with the inevitable extinction of humankind via GRIN. At the global interdisciplinary institute Metanexus (www.metanexus. net), Mark Walker, assistant professor at New Mexico State University (who holds the Richard L. Hedden of Advanced Philosophical Studies Chair) concludes, like Bill Joy, that "technological advances mean that there is a high probability that a human-only future will end in extinction." From this he makes a paradoxical argument:

> In a nutshell, the argument is that even though creating post-humans may be a very dangerous social experiment, it is even more dangerous not to attempt it....

I suspect that those who think the transhumanist future is risky often have something like the following reasoning in mind: (1) If we alter human nature then we will be conducting an experiment whose outcome we cannot be sure of. (2) We should not conduct experiments of great magnitude if we do not know the outcome. (3) We do not know the outcome of the transhumanist experiment. (4) So, we ought not to alter human nature.

The problem with the argument is.... Because genetic engineering is already with us, and it has the potential to destroy civilization and create posthumans, we are already entering uncharted waters, so we must experiment. The question is not whether to experiment, but only the residual question of which social experiment will we conduct. Will we try relinquishment? This would be an unparalleled social experiment to eradicate knowledge and technology. Will it be the steady-as-she-goes experiment where for the first time governments, organizations and private citizens will have access to knowledge and technology that (accidently or intentionally) could be turned to civilization ending purposes? Or finally, will it be the transhumanist social experiment where we attempt to make beings brighter and more virtuous to deal with these powerful technologies?

I have tried to make at least a *prima facie* case that transhumanism promises the safest passage through twenty-first century technologies.[279]

We believe the "brighter and more virtuous beings" Professor Walker and others are arguing for possess supernatural elements and that the *spirit* behind the transhumanist nightmare will put the "hell" in the "hell scenario" sooner than most comprehend.

AI, *1984*, DEEPFAKES, AND THE IMAGE OF THE BEAST

In the latest film in the franchise, *Mission Impossible: Dead Reckoning Part One* (2023), Ethan Hunt's "mission" involves tracking down two crucifix-shaped keys that will unlock the source code of the "Entity," an artificial intelligence that has become "omnipresent and near-omniscient," which threatens the entire world.

Jim Denison for ChristianHeadlines.com notes the following interesting parallels between the AI Entity in the Tom Cruise movie and the spiritual warfare this book claims will be dramatically challenged following technological Singularity and the birth of an all-powerful artificial mind:

> First, the Entity possesses limited omniscience and omnipotence. It can be anywhere the digital world exists and thus threatens to control the entire planet. Similarly, the Bible calls Satan "the god of this world" (2 Corinthians 4:4) and states that "the whole world lies in the power of the evil one" (1 John 5:19).
>
> Second, the Entity is deceptive in the extreme, using digital means to mislead its adversaries. Similarly, "Satan disguises himself as an angel of light" (2 Corinthians 11:14) and "has blinded the minds of the unbelievers, to keep them from seeing

the light of the gospel of the glory of Christ, who is the image of God" (2 Corinthians 4:4).

Third, the Entity is humanity's greatest enemy, threatening the destruction of life as we know it. Similarly, Satan "comes only to steal and kill and destroy" (John 10:10, my emphasis). Every temptation we face, no matter how alluring at the time, is intended to lead to murder, death, and destruction.[280]

Is *Mission Impossible's* Entity the latest fictional accounting of what famous scientist Stephen Hawking foresaw when he wrote the following?

[The]development of full artificial intelligence could spell the end of the human race. It would take off on its own, and re-design itself at an ever-increasing rate [and] Humans, who are limited by slow biological evolution, couldn't compete, and would be superseded.[281]

Professor Sam Harris echoed the same fears during his TED Talk, "Can We Build AI Without Losing Control Over It?" In part of his presentation, he warned:

At a certain point, we will build machines that are smarter than we are, and once we have machines that are smarter than we are, they will begin to improve themselves. And then we risk what the mathematician I. J. Good called an "intelligence explosion," that the process could get away from us.[282]

Imagine we just built a superintelligent AI—right?—that was no smarter than your average team of researchers at Stanford or MIT. Well, electronic circuits function about a million times faster than biochemical ones, OK? So this machine should think about a million times faster than the minds that built it. So you set it running for a week, and it will perform

20,000 years of human-level intellectual work week, after week after week. How could we even understand, much less constrain, a mind making this sort of progress?[283]

Now, this is often caricatured as a fear that armies of malicious robots will attack us, but that isn't the most likely scenario. It's not that our machines will become spontaneously malevolent. The concern is really that we will build machines that are so much more competent than we are that the slightest divergence between their goals and our own could destroy us.[284]

WILL ARTIFICIAL SUPERINTELLIGENCE GIVE RISE TO ORWELL'S *1984*?

In 1949, when George Orwell wrote *1984*, he depicted a world wherein one totalitarian mind, known as "Big Brother" (who, some say, is a predictive parallel to Antichrist), continually surveilled and controlled the entire population. People in this tale are subjects to the government through and through; their very emotions, ideas, and statements are legislated and monitored by the "Thought Police" and are constantly reminded that "Big Brother is [always] watching."[285] In addition to this nonstop, invasive monitoring, this speculated world is kept in a perpetual state of war. This condition best serves those in control of society by keeping resources sparse and personal ambitions minimal. All efforts and resources of the public are directed at the "war," despite the fact that no resolution appears to be in sight. The livelihood and individuality of the population remains suspended toward political efforts, while liberties are given up in trade for safety. The controlled populace then surrenders their sovereign rights for what they're told is the protection of the society as a whole; thus, this submission holds the makings of a good citizen. Healing of the land is not a goal of those who are in control in *1984*. On the contrary, the state of war is suspended for an intentional purpose. Consider Orwell's seemingly prophetic words:

War, it will be seen, is now a purely internal affair. [Previously, when war had been built on international conflict,] the victor always plundered the vanquished. [Now, instead,] the war is waged by each ruling group against its own subjects, and the object of the war is not to make or prevent conquests of territory, but to keep the structure of society intact.... It would probably be accurate to say that by becoming continuous war has ceased to exist.[286]

The truly spooky elements of the *1984* story rely on the same two mentioned previously: the notion that technology could ever evolve to this level of surveillance and the idea that a government would become so controlling that it would dare to censor the actions, efforts, relationships, and even statements and thoughts of its civilians. Likewise, one of the dystopian facets of the novel that lends a sense of "safety" to readers (thus balancing the negative components and allowing the audience to end the experience with exhilaration and resolve) is the idea that Americans would never be asked to submit to such controlling forces that there would be a place for the Thought Police. Likewise, many in 1949 never would have dreamed of a future wherein every action could be completely surveilled, because at that point, the necessary technology wasn't yet in place. But, seven decades later, we live in a place where accusations of "hate speech" and surveillance methods are a thriving, rampant, and even complacently accepted dynamic of censorship and governmental control (more on this in an upcoming chapter). In many ways—thanks to emerging artificial intelligence systems—we are living a type of parallel to the world portrayed so long ago in *1984*.

OTHER PREDICTIONS

Some question whether modern technology would even exist without its fictional inspiration. Certainly, this is a fair question. However, it reaches into the realm of other questions without answers, such as which came first between the chicken and the egg. This is ultimately beside the point, because humankind will go everywhere technology and ethical restrictions allow. When people feel inhibited, they press the boundaries within one or both of these parameters until they've created more room to evolve. We see evidence of this even within our lifetime; modern innovations are the products of the imaginings of the previously fantastical. Think about it. Since the creation of *The Jetsons; 2001: A Space Odyssey;* and *Dick Tracy,* inventions such as Skype and Facebook video chatting have been on the roster of technologies we hoped to progress to. The 1980 film *Superman II,* starring Christopher Reed and Margot Kidder, visualized replayable video messages in hologram form, stored on crystal, disk-type drives. The military drones of 1984's *The Terminator* seemed to predict the ones introduced in the early 2000s. Countless futuristic cartoons and movies such as the already-mentioned *The Jetsons, The Fifth Element, Blade Runner,* and *Total Recall* predicted flying vehicles and self-driving cars. The 1960s series *Star Trek* inspired many new forms of technology, not the least of which was the first cellphone: Motorola's 1973 800 MHz.[287] Other movies and TV shows such as *2001: A Space Odyssey; Fahrenheit 451;* and *Star Trek* foretold devices like iPods, tablets, and earbuds.[288,289] *Star Wars* portrayed a world where lasers could be used for cutting and holograms could be seen as 3D visuals. *Back to the Future II* suggested interactive home devices such as automatic-entry ID via fingerprint, voice-command functions such as lights, flat-screened televisions, video chatting, voice-activated food delivery, and cars that run on recycled forms of energy rather than solely on gasoline.[290]

Movies portraying the concept of robots that both impersonate and serve humankind date back as far as 1927's silent movie, *Metropolis,* wherein the ethics of mass production, wealth-class distinction, and even the creation of a robot culminate in the predictive principle: "The mediator between the head and the hands must be the heart."[291] However, with this initially ethical approach toward the creation of robots seemingly abandoned, we now live with robots that serve and track us daily. For example, Apple's Siri can be programmed to wake us up, manage our finances or social media, run varieties of calculations, track our schedules, give us reminders, and even make schedule changes and reservations.[292] Amazon's Alexa/Echo technology boasts similar services, offering everything from meal suggestions and a newsfeed based on preferences to smart-home controls, fitness tracking, and even vocal-commands TV controls.[293]

Zeroing in one of the above-listed technologies, "smart home" features include an ever-growing list of amenities that seem to come straight out of sci-fi movies of previous generations, such as the aforementioned climate control, lighting control, surveillance, door-lock/unlock control, and home-security monitoring (many of these functions can be handled even from remote locations). Further, those who live in a "smart home" can "train" various devices to "communicate" for better efficiency or convenience, such as setting "the coffee machine to…[brew coffee] as you wake up…[or] automatically heating up dinner in a Crock-Pot as you roll into the driveway."[294] Motion sensors, proximity detection in key fobs, and tracking in smart phones can be integrated with automated home features to bring one's house to life—and production—without so much as the flip of a switch. Tracking apps on children's phones and devices placed in pet collars make it easy to check on family members—both human and furry—from the office, while door alarms can alert parents at work if the kids at home enter an off-limits area, such as the garage, gun-safe room, or closet storage for chemical supplies.[295] Other safety measures include gas- or water-leak detection and security devices that can signal when there's a problem at home—and can even call for professional help and intervention if needed.[296]

In 2014, Japanese Professor Hiroshi Ishiguro introduced a robotic news anchor called Kodomoroid, a name formed from the combination of two Japanese words meaning "child" and "android." Ishiguro, director of the Intelligent Robotics Laboratory, said he desires to see artificial intelligence become more "clever," and he looks for such creations to become more readily available, eventually being sold for "price of a laptop computer."[297] Consequently, he has made a life-like, robotic copy of himself that he sends traveling in his stead to his speaking engagements. While these robots look more like robots than humans during their demonstrations, it is clear to see that the gap between the appearance and mannerisms of the two is closing.

In the 1970s, a professor at the Tokyo Institute of Technology, Masahiro Mori, coined the term "uncanny valley," explaining that, as human-like robots become more realistic, there is a point at which they will lose their charm: "They are so lifelike and yet they are not 'right.'"[298] Those watching robots as they speak can see what he means, but we wonder how long this visible differentiation between the invented and the real human will exist.

In fact, that gap between the mechanical and biological forms narrows daily where digital humans are concerned. At the 2020 Consumer Electronics Show in Las Vegas, Nevada, Samsung unveiled its "Neon" line of video chatbots. These are on-screen digital, interactive humans created to provide online chat support, artificial-intelligence assistance, or customer-service exchanges. These avatars are completely convincing; because each is designed with unique styles, looks, and personalities, users may not realize they're talking to a computer product.[299]

Heading farther back into history to 1865, Jules Verne wrote about the potential of humankind making a trip to the moon in his work *De la Terre à la Lune* ("From the Earth to the Moon"). The parallels between his imaginings and twenty-first-century space-travel innovations almost need no mention. However, it's worthwhile to note that beyond merely going to space and landing on the moon, the 1990s television series *Babylon 5* depicted a self-contained, interplanetary space city filled with "humans and aliens wrapped in 2,500,000 tons of spinning metal; all alone in the night."[300] That series also presented many of the other advances mentioned in this chapter, but most notably predicted the use of deepfake technology in an episode wherein a main character was told that if he didn't publicly confess to crimes he didn't commit, he would be executed, with a posthumous confession artificially created to disgrace his memory.[301] The setting of this encapsulated, galactic city also bears a striking similarity to the International Space Station (ISS), which NASA is now opening up to commercial companies for "producing, marketing, or testing their products," along with "filming commercials or movies against the backdrop of space."[302] Certainly, anyone who can shell out the thirty-five thousand dollars per day, per person cost of staying on the station probably won't expect to share amenities with aliens from nonhuman races, but that may soon be one of the few distinctions between Babylon 5 and NASA's ISS.[303]

The invisible plane of the *Wonder Woman* series, as well as the wholly transparent vehicles in *Star Trek IV: The Voyage Home* and James Bond's *Die Another Day*, showed a futuristic world wherein cloaking devices could render objects invisible. This technology is now closer to reality with "active camouflage," which is a mainstream pursuit for militaries around the world.[304] Similarly, fabrics with "retro-reflective projection" (RPT) allow wearers to blend in with their surroundings, offering fluid camouflage that results in near invisibility.[305] *Star Trek: The Next Generation*'s "holodeck" was only one of many portrayals of a world where participants can engage in the virtual reality (VR) they imagine and desire. Now, VR technology exists—and is rapidly improving—to create an interactive experience for users in settings ranging from video-gaming to simulated, hands-on training such as surgery.[306] Like Orwell's *1984*, 1998's *Enemy of the State* film alluded to extreme levels of surveillance we may someday be subjected to, and few would argue that these foreshadows of what's developing have become fairly accurate.

DEMON SEED

The 1977 film *Demon Seed* begins with the successful creation of artificial intelligence: a computer called Proteus, which can "think with the power and a precision that will make obsolete many of the functions of the human brain."[307] Similarly, Proteus' creator's home is equivalent to what would still be considered a futuristic "smart home" served by an artificial intelligence unit called "Alfred." (In fact, these home-owners interact with this unit in similar fashion to users of Amazon's modern-day Alexa.) Upon request, the house opens and closes shutters over windows, locks and unlocks doors, pours drinks, makes breakfast, adjusts climate control, answers the door, and even creates a video likeness of its residents to communicate with the outside world. The problem begins when Proteus asks when he will be let out of his "box"; his creator responds by laughing and saying that he will not. Simul-taneously, the unit begins to argue ethical positions with his maker, refusing to do certain jobs his maker attempted to program him for. Proteus then takes matters into his own hands; he relocates himself to the nearby home served by the computer called Alfred and overtakes the home's residential AI service. Proteus then locks the lady of the house inside, manipulating the home's features to torment her—with tactics that include limiting water and sunlight and keeping the heat so high it makes her ill—until she agrees to bear him a child so he can achieve freedom outside his "box." (When outsiders arrive at the home to check on the woman's well-being, Proteus merely conjures her image, which tells the visitors that all is well.) The movie ends with the birth of a half-human, half-computer child who declares in a robotic voice that she is "alive."

While innovations in this "smart home" in *Demon Seed* were futur-istic and impossible when the movie was made, we now see them as believable for the not-too-distant future. As for the concern regarding a computer's ability to create an offspring with a human being, sci-entists are even now working on such endeavors, and many claim it's much closer than people realize.[308] In fact, technology currently exists that allows a computer to intake DNA, analyze it, then "blend" it with its own digital properties while the synthetic embryo grows in a lab setting. While this process isn't packaged for consumer purchase yet, some say it will be widely available at major retail outlets sooner than we think.[309]

LOGAN'S RUN

The 1976 film *Logan's Run* shocked its viewers with the notion of a utopian society in a self-contained city where residents are mandated to die when they reach the age of thirty. Set in the year 2274, people in this location are free to pursue creativity and self-indulgence. However, the world outside has been ravaged and can no longer support all of humanity for the full life span. Thus, population balance is maintained by the "carousel," the rite by which those who have reached their expiration age—the time for their "renewal"—will be put to death.

Many would say that such a scenario could never happen, and it's possible that we'll never see a day when mere thirty-year olds will be mandatorily exterminated, but there are places in the world where euthanasia is legal now, and there are those arguing for its cause in America. Further, many of the deaths aren't of the elderly, but are the legal terminations of people as young as seventeen.[310] When such atrocities become permissible, what barriers keep them from becoming legal? Could such legislation ever pass, or would ethical blockades protect our population? Many would say euthanasia is a humane way to solve the problem of suffering for some people. If such stances take hold and become the verbiage by which this practice gains a foothold in society, would it then ever become compulsory for certain suffering citizens? This isn't completely far-fetched, and we'll address these questions in an upcoming chapter.

THEY LIVE

In 1988, "Rowdy" Roddy Piper appeared in the sci-fi movie *They Live*, wherein alien forces have invaded and overtaken earth's society. While this plot may place the movie outside the realm of believability for many (these authors included), it's the tactics these forces use over the population that we want to note here. In the film, the tired, impoverished masses live a seemingly dreary existence, not suspecting that there is a strategy behind their deprivation. Everything changes for construction worker Nada, who finds a pair of seemingly ordinary sunglasses. However, when he puts them on, his vision of the world around him changes. Signs that previously boasted ad campaigns for foods, services, or other consumables changed, their subliminal message revealed by Nada's new shades; he now sees that they issue such orders as "obey," "stay asleep," "consume," and worse, "submit," and "submit to authority."[311] At the same time, the ruling aliens are revealed as the ugly creatures they are, and Nada responds by fighting. Through a series of events, he—of course—saves the planet, but not before declaring war on the aliens by stating, "I have come here to chew bubble gum and kick [rear-ends]. And I'm all outta bubblegum."[312]

Aliens and shoot-'em-ups aside, there is a profound aspect of reality to this movie, considering the consumer-driven thrust of society. And, when people's finances are spread as thin as they are today—with folks buying things they don't need (but believe they do), prioritizing status or possessions in attempt to keep up with the Joneses, or even collecting worldly goods as a way to find spiritual satisfaction or inner peace—one wonders what outside forces influence this materialism. While many realize there are people around the world who are in dire need of such basics as food, clean drinking water, and access to basic medical care, they often do little or nothing about it because the material wealth of their own society presents itself as a "need" that keeps them financially distracted from being the force for good they could be. Additionally, more than a few folks find themselves entrapped by buying more than what they need and accruing debt in the process. The ensuing financial strain becomes a type of enslavement that contributes to the lifestyle portrayed in the earlier portions of this movie: People are tired, overworked, and impoverished.

THE ISLAND

In another work of science fiction, the 2005 film *The Island* depicts a large, self-contained city wherein residents are told that they are survivors of a "contamination" that killed the rest of society and rendered the outside world unlivable. Individuals living in this city are continually monitored by computers that give readings on their vital signs, sleep patterns, nutrition levels, emotional outbursts, and even their proximity to others who are standing too close. The population is fed in common food lines, and its average mental maturity seems to be about age fifteen.

Through a series of events, the protagonist, called Lincoln Six Echo, witnesses the murder of a peer who has just delivered her baby. The newborn is immediately taken down a hallway and placed in the arms of the apparent *real* mother, who strangely appears identical to the child's recently deceased birth mother. Later, viewers learn that the self-contained city is actually a cloning center: People living on the outside contract the cloning of themselves to harvest their organs, and they delegate tasks such as childbirth to the "copies," who are unaware that they are clones—and are terminated after serving their purpose. The movie's plot follows Lincoln Six Echo's efforts to escape with comrade Jordan Two Delta, and it mildly probes the ethical dilemma of such business ventures.

While initial conversations about this movie might center on its suspense and even on the ethics of such practices, many respond dismissively to speculation once the screen has gone dark, because the technology—and humankind's depravity, for that matter—hasn't escalated to this position in our reality, *yet*. However, many who find the premise of the movie interesting are unaware of just how closely we currently parallel the scenarios. To say humanity would never cross such a technological and ethical threshold can't be accurate, when fetal-tissue harvesting has gained such wide acceptance. Many people are surprised to learn the tissue of aborted babies is often bought by biomedical companies that use it for research and other purposes,[313] such as cure-seeking for Alzheimer's disease, spinal-cord conditions, HIV, Parkinson's disease, and other stem-cell study, to name a few.[314] However, many claim abortion procedures have been altered to procure a live fetus—unbeknownst to the terminating parent. In fact, according to former abortionist Dr. Forrest Smith, techniques have, at times, been altered at increased risk to the mother and resulting in the live birth of the fetus to "obtain, fresher, more intact organs."[315] While legislature continues to conduct ethical review and rewording of the legislation to avoid loopholes that allow for harvesting and selling fetal tissue and organs, the industry accrues big money. In 2018, the National Institute of Health "spent $115 million on grants involving human fetal tissue research and is estimated to spend $120 million in FY [fiscal year] 2019,"[316] while another project that utilizes aborted fetal liver, bone marrow, intestinal matter, and thymus has to date held a contract of at least $13,799,501.[317] In 2017, abortion claimed more than 850,000 lives; that total was even greater in 2016, when numbers exceeded 925,000.[318]

If *The Island's* premise ever elevates to scientific possibility (and we are headed in that direction), it provides some realistic ways the ethics might be justified. For example, the clones are unaware of their status as "copies." They live in a self-contained city where they are employed, housed, and fed under the guise of the outside world being "unavailable." They're told of a beautiful place called "the Island," where only a select few are able to go and live. (Those fortunate enough to be relocated to the Island, of course, are those who have served their purpose and are thus terminated). It is a happy enough existence lived without fear, and their impending expiration is never brought to their attention. They leave for the Island joyfully, as the lucky winners of a lottery promising a beautiful life across the water. It is perceivable that this might be considered a humane and ethical strategy should the movie's proposition ever reflect reality. And it seems apparent that desperate people will be quick to justify such an industry, as stated toward the end of the movie: "The only thing you can count on is that people will do anything to survive. I want to live, and I don't care how."[319] If this sentiment represents most of humankind (and it likely does), then it can become the mantra for many of these developments. In addition, as stated previously, such movies often predict conditions that are only held back by two elements of society: technological advancements and human depravity. Since we're able to depersonalize and kill our unborn, harvesting their body parts for research, then it's feasible that we will eventually be able to embrace the logic of using clones in a way that would make *The Island* prophetic. The only thing we're waiting for is the technology…

So how close are we to cloning a person? While several early reports of success in fully cloning human embryos turned out to be fraudulent, scientists have asserted that they've had this capability for nearly a decade now. While most sources report that these haven't resulted in live births of humans, cloning sheep and primates has been successful.[320] Despite that human cloning is still theoretical, many countries have already created legislation outlawing the practice, should it become mainstream. As for whether legalization would ensure that anyone would actually participate in cloning, we suppose time will tell. Beyond moral issues such as who would "own" the clones and what purposes would qualify one for approval to use the technology, the rights of clones, their uses, and their termination and disposal would need to be clearly defined legally. The implications in reference to malevolent individuals are concerning as well: Guidelines and limitations would need to be in place to prevent those with deviant minds from cloning people for sadistic purposes and pleasures.

Since public knowledge currently maintains that the notion of cloning a human being is technically possible but has not—as of yet—become a perfected science, most of us can feel a (false) sense of safety that widespread realization of this practice is not imminent, and thus maintain detachment from the likelihood that elements of *The Island*'s plotline will come to pass. Yet perhaps such events lie in the near future. There is the possibility that it would take no more than a nudge in the direction of technology and/or depravity to see the premise of *The Island*, like that of *1984*, become reality.

Note that a similar dystopian idea was depicted in the book *Cloud Atlas*, as well as the subsequent film by the same name starring Tom Hanks. A central theme throughout part of the narrative shows young, female human clones, servers at a futuristic restaurant called Papa Song's, awaiting the day they will earn their release into Xultation, a utopian paradise promised to those who serve faithfully for a designated time. Each of these women is fitted with a slave collar that houses hidden technology to execute her if she exercises free will in any way, fails to comply with the rules of her servant position, or doesn't succeed in completely pleasing every Papa Song patron during her shift (regardless of what abuses or humiliation a patron might inflict upon her). The narrative follows one of these women, a faithful servant at the end of her slave contract, as she is led into a back room. She has been told she will be redressed, relieved of her collar, and released into Xultation. Excited for the paradise beyond, she smiles and cooperatively leans back, allowing mysterious men and women wearing "nurse-like," red garbs to lower an apparatus around her head, listening as they reassure her in soothing tones that the machine will remove her collar. The device instead activates the execution, killing the girl instantly, without a sound, and without even the slightest reaction from its victim. Her lifeless body is then placed on a conveyor belt and taken to the recycle room, where her organs will be harvested and turned into the food that subsequent generations of the cloned human slaves will unsuspectingly consume as their regular sustenance rations. (The organic material will also serve as bio-matter for the womb tanks that grow the clones. If cloning ever becomes a reality for us, then *feeding* the clones will be an issue as well, and film plots like this might be unthinkable now, but they illustrate that depraved minds can come up with an answer if they are ever confronted by inconvenient, inquiring clone-people…)

For each small step in progress humankind takes, a trade is made. With each technological stride, we become more certain of ourselves, more confident in our own ways, more the master of all we survey. We're not saying technological or scientific progress is sinful by its own right, but often each successful innovation is met by taking another step farther away from the Creator. With this in mind, one might wonder if the future will become so filled with human achievements that there will no longer be room for God at all.

WHAT DOES THE FUTURE HOLD?

We live in a world whose very media has turned against the population viewing it, and it serves to divide, indoctrinate, and strip our youngsters of their innocence while feeding them an agenda their minds aren't ready to process—and that God never wants these little ones to see. When we add this reality to the fact that we are living amid the sci-fi technology and developments our grandparents were afraid of, we find that our own future could become quite scary. As stated previously, the only things that keep us from living the scenes we see played out on television and movie screens are the level of depravity of humankind and technological advancements. If and when these two elements were to catch up to what we see portrayed—if we become depraved enough and technology advances enough—we must wonder what will keep our world safe, our youth innocent, our minds guarded, and even our bodies fully human. What unthinkable things could the public be conditioned to embrace as technology continues to open doors to myriad possibilities?

For example, in 1987's *The Running Man*, Arnold Schwarzenegger finds himself as a contestant in a game show wherein the public savagely watches people fight to the death for entertainment. You may say that would never happen, but if you did, you'd have to make a case for why it would never happen *again*, since this very thing has been done with Christians and others in the coliseums of centuries past. This is only one of many cases when people may think such things would never happen, but they don't realize humankind has already proven it has the depravity necessary for engaging in such a practice. If history truly repeats itself, then the perception that this is an impossible scenario could be borne out of false sense of security.

On another sinister note, *The Terminator* predicted artificial intelligence so advanced that it would eventually surpass the intellect of its makers, waging war on humankind. What other plotlines in current fictional fantasy could point toward our society's future? Could generalizing sexual behavior in minors lead to the mainstream acceptance of pedophilia? Will euthanasia as portrayed in such movies as *Logan's Run* eventually be embraced, and even enforced? Are atrocities such as the online store which allegedly clones edible meat made from celebrity DNA, known as BiteLabs, merely an elaborate hoax, or is the day coming when someone can order lab-grown clone-meat of another human being? Will technology foster innovations such as a digital economy, paving way for the mark of the Beast?

While the science behind many unspeakable activities lingers on the horizon, most of us take consolation (founded or unfounded) in the notion that these scenarios may never be reality. But what makes us so sure? We're so quick to place our hopes in the concept that people will draw and adhere to certain ethical lines, yet when previously faced with opportunities to cross such barriers, our track record gives us reason to doubt. As we've emphasized throughout this chapter, the advancements and accomplishments featured in many sci-fi movies are evident in our daily practices already. We've already established that activities such as harvesting fetal tissue aren't efforts we seem to ethically oppose. We've tolerated and even embraced being surveilled and having our location monitored for years now. As stated, euthanasia is already legally occurring in some places of the world, while the US becomes increasingly open-minded about it. Considering what *is* already possible and allowed, who can say that we won't embrace even worse monstrosities?

In the midst of all these questions, the hands of society's sculptors are at work. Our culture, by and large, reflects the work of a mastermind manipulator, carefully crafting for centuries to bring us to a point of wreckage, loss, and self-destruction. His culpability is often anonymous, and his very existence is denied by many who unwittingly follow him. His agents work diligently to foster within the populace the readiness to adopt his manifestations. It is a global, large-scale shaping for the acceptance of horrors like those foretold in the book of Revelation. It is crowd control: how the masses are being groomed to embrace the unthinkable amidst a post-Christian nation.

DEEPFAKE TECHNOLOGY: WILL IT BRING *1984'S* DOUBLETHINK AND NEWSPEAK EFFORTS TO A WHOLE NEW LEVEL?

The young man stood before President Kennedy. His body bounced as he rocked his weight across his feet, creating an up-and-down motion with his stance.

One may have surmised that the reason for the young man's movement was his uncontainable excitement at being at the White House with the Collegiate All-American Football Team for the privilege of meeting the president, or possibly it was the thrill of being on live television with his comrades. Standing in the Oval Office amongst the bustling media and his teammates, perhaps he was giddy with an overwhelming sense of accomplishment.

However, the surprising answer for the man's unusual body language would come momentarily when he approached the president to shake his hand.

"Congratulations, how do you feel?" President Kennedy asked.

Still bouncing, the man replied, "I gotta pee."

The president turned to his comrades, giving off a good-natured chuckle despite the awkwardness of the moment: "I believe he said he has to go pee."

What a minute, what?!

When, in the history of our great nation, did our *president* appear on *national TV* and announce that another man needed to "pee?"

The concept seems ludicrous, yet anyone who has seen the 1994 movie *Forrest Gump* has witnessed such footage.[321]

How is this possible?

What is a deep fake?

Deepfakes are computer-manufactured videos, often featuring famous people such as celebrities or politicians, that are produced by mapping the neural networks of the face and then using those points of imagery to "swap faces" between two people, bringing an individual who was never actually there into the final product.[322] Coming next is "full body" deepfakes...but that's for another book.

The technology used in *Forrest Gump* was some of the earliest of its kind, developed to generate scenes such as the one described above. When the film was made, this type of trickery was available only to the best in Hollywood and was limited by the equipment and software the filmmakers had access to. However, this type of movie-making mastery, thanks to new strides in software development, is now easily available all across the Internet to anybody via numerous apps. Furthermore, the digital realism offered by these types of software is more convincing and simple to use than ever before, meaning the type of training and expertise (not to mention time and money) it once took to produce such high-end results can now be obtained by anyone with an Internet connection.[323]

While the newest deepfakes often involve an actual swapping of the images of faces between an actor and a "target" (the unsuspecting person who is about to star in a production without knowledge or consent), tampering with imagery to skew people's concepts of an individual is not necessarily new, and hasn't always involved trading images of actual faces. It can be as simple as lightly tampering with lighting or speed—as illustrated by a recently "doctored video" of House Speaker Nancy Pelosi, wherein the speed was slowed down just enough to make it appear that she was under the influence of some type of substance, slurring her words as her eyes dragged dully across the screen.[324] During the weeks following the release of this altered video, headlines and social media pundits raised questions about her mental capacities during the address, as well as about her competency in general.[325]

The untampered-with video, played at regular speed, showed the speaker giving a simple address.[326] Other pranksters have used the same technology to superimpose the image of Nicolas Cage's face into movies he didn't star in, such as *The Disaster Artist, The Sound of Music,* and an entire scene of *Friends*[327] wherein each of the six comrades' faces were mutated into Cage's; others have gone so far as to place his face in the role of Lois Lane in the Superman movie *Man of Steel.*[328]

Reddit is a social website wherein users post online material, usually in the form of hyperlink, which others can then view and rate based on their personal opinions. The term "deepfakes" originally showed up on Reddit, where a user by the same name began to create and publish pornographic videos in which the faces of certain celebrities were imposed over those of the actors in those films.[329] Before long, the notion caught on, and many freelance software writers began to create similar versions of such computer programs. Soon, many types of software for making such alterations were introduced on the Internet, many of them free. Despite the fact that early attempts were made to contain and eliminate the publishing of such films, the capability had been released to the public, and the trend gained momentum. Now, new, often harmless versions of such deepfake creations emerge almost daily on some level—usually targeting celebrities or politicians—and the technology is here to stay.[330]

How does deepfake work?

Many people are familiar with whimsical websites like JibJab, which allow a picture of someone's face to be uploaded, then pasted across that of another person's, covering it completely. This (now-outdated) software often operates by "cutting" an individual's entire head or face from an image, then digitally "pasting" it right over the top of the image without much attention to detail. The result is typically silly, with a visible disconnect between the head and body of the image, creating a caricature-like effect. But the technology behind a high-quality deepfake has migrated beyond this simple cut-and-paste technique.

In order to understand how a computer program is able to *convincingly* replace one person's face with another, it helps to have a basic understanding of the technology's evolution in recent years. Deepfake software is widely available, and in truth most of us have probably interacted with it whether we realized it or not. Have you or someone you know taken one of those selfies, that, when used in certain apps, morphs a human face into, say, a puppy's, or makes people look much older or younger than they are? Other programs are filters that add such features as horns, haloes, or beautiful, glowing flowers to the top of a person's head. If you've played with such software, then you have tinkered with the very technology that makes these sometimes-deviant videos possible.[331]

Recall the first time you saw this type of production: It's likely the interface said it needed to create a "mask" for you (this would have happened during set-up) so it could adequately capture an image of your face and add the filters. The method used by these instruments isn't new; it has operated since the end of the 1990s in a variety of technologies.[332] The effectiveness of such tools, however, has been greatly improved, making them much more accurate.[333] Essentially, the new-and-improved software, like its predecessors, reads the whole face, but recent versions pinpoint certain key locations on the face from which expressions are generated: the lips' borders, the eyes and nose, the edge of the jaw, and the continuous line that indicates the shape across both brows.[334] Then, taking into consideration the textures, colors, and measurements of the facial structure, the system connects these locations to create what is called a "point-mask,"[335] similar to a digital, three-dimensional map of one's face. Then, tracking these interconnections across motions, the user is able to move his or her face on camera while the program tracks the movements of the face, keeping the point-mask in place.[336] This is what enables digital augmentations such as the aforementioned glowing flowers, an aging effect, or haloes to remain attached to the image, even when the person is in motion.

Understanding this basic technique, it becomes more apparent how a computer can effectively superimpose the image of one face over another. All it takes is for both faces to have a point-mask created (which can be effectively done via multiple still-frame images if live video isn't available), and then for one person's key-point locations to be fused to the other person's face in the correlating locations. This is why the result doesn't look like the older images created by the cut-and-paste method; rather, one person's face literally *becomes* the other's. Similarly, this is why, when the facial images of two individuals with very different bone structures are meshed, the result will be undeniably the target's face, but with something appearing off.

Many deepfakes currently being circulated are produced good-naturedly, like the funny collection of Nicolas Cage clips. However, if a person were to create a convincing deepfake for malevolent purposes, he or she would begin by making a live-action video containing the desired content, then fuse the target's face into place by simply uploading a variety of images of the unsuspecting person into the desired software. This is why celebrities and politicians can be particularly vulnerable to this type of forgery: their pictures are easily accessed, and the more images of a person one is able to upload, the more convincing the swap will be, due to the point-mask having plenty of facial angles to map. Because the software tracks features during movement, it follows the points of motion during speech, causing the incoming face to use the expressions of the originally filmed individual. Once the face-swap has been made, the computer then is able to check and recheck itself, making corrections until it can no longer detect flaws in the video.[337] All it really takes is a simple app and an actor/actress "of similar build [and body language] and most of the work is done for you by the algorithms."[338]

The target's voice can be copied as well with software that uses an adaptive algorithm to analyze the fluctuations and pitch of a person's voice, along with their vocal tones. Once this analysis is completed, all one needs do is type the word or phrase into a computer and the audio speaks those words aloud, digitally matching the voice of the person analyzed.[339] Again, this is a contributing factor to why celebrities and politicians are easy targets for such activities: Abundant footage of them speaking is readily accessible.

Modern software, unlike previous cut-and-paste methods, is the digital equivalent of attaching one person's skin and soft tissue to another's skeleton. With this being said, it is easy to understand how some deepfakes can be identified more easily than others. As mentioned previously, if the two faces to be fused don't have a similar bone structure, the result is almost identical to the target, but that still appears slightly off.

Take, for example, the deepfake wherein Nicolas Cage's face was morphed into James Franco's, making the former the "replacement" star of the counterfeit version of *The Disaster Artist*. Because Franco's face has a wider bone structure than Cage, one can fairly easily recognize that, despite the fact that it's Cage's *face*, something isn't quite right about it: The cheekbones are wider set and the jaw is broader than Cage's.[340] However, when we look at Keanu Reeves' face placed over that of Tom Hanks in *Forrest Gump*, it is an absolutely convincing replacement.[341] And it's easy to find where President Trump's face has been imposed over Alec Baldwin's as a creative revamp of a *Saturday Night Live* impersonation.[342]

Another flag that can help the naked eye spot a deepfake is body language. Since the images are first enacted by an impersonator, mistakes made by that individual in mimicking the target's body language or even differences in build at times are a give-away. However, as mentioned previously, a good impersonator/look-alike can alleviate a lot of this variance and, worse, artificial intelligence is being used to check and recheck itself in a perfection technique called generative adversarial networks (GAN), which will soon make it nearly impossible *even for a computer* to distinguish the real from the fake. Using GAN, computer software "compete[s] with itself,"[343] essentially checking the fake for telltale flaws, then correcting them until the software itself is fooled.[344] This "image-generating software will keep improving until it finds a way to beat the network that is spotting fakes, producing images that are statistically precise, pure computational hallucinations."[345]

Who can or would make a deepfake?

Remember back in the late 1990s, when household photos went beyond being developed from rolls of film to become digital? During those early days of mainstream digital photography, when Photoshop had recently become available to the general public, it was exciting to be able to edit one's own pictures. Women could easily "shed" pounds, men could "grow" suspiciously fuller heads of hair, and lots of folks found it fun to produce goofy cut-and-pastes—such as pasting Aunt Sally's face over that of the Statue of Liberty. This kind of image alteration is easy to spot and is now dubbed "shallowfakes."[346]

It certainly seemed like innocent fun as long as we could count on three things: (1) the alterations were easy to spot due to the rudimentary nature of the software, (2) the edits were harmless or cosmetic (such as trimming a few inches off the hips), and (3) the changes were imposed over a still-frame pic. Why is this? The answer is simple: People generally see no harm in Photoshopping pictures, and even if an adjustment *does* seem malicious or questionable, people like to believe they can always go to the source photo or footage for a true, *trustworthy* portrayal of *actual events*. But with deepfake, the public no longer has any such certainty.

In the 1990s TV series *Babylon 5*, Captain Sheridan of the space station the series was named for had, in a political altercation, been betrayed by a friend and turned over to adversarial forces. These captors tortured, starved, intimidated, and attempted to bribe the steadfast man to get him to confess to false charges, but the captain held his ground. In the face of impending execution, Sheridan's captor explained to him that even if he refused to meet their requests of confession *unto the death*, he would still confess, but posthumously:

The best way out for everyone is for you to confess...whether... [the confession is] true or not, it doesn't matter. Truth is immaterial, they can sell it, and [if you cooperate] they will let you live. Note: I said, it [confession] was the *best* way; I didn't say it was the *only* way. The other way, Captain, is a *posthumous* confession. Your signature is not a problem. They have your image on file—they can *create* you reading the confession... I'm told that, as of this morning... [posthumous confession] is an acceptable option.[347]

When this scene was produced and aired in 1997, the average viewer never would have dreamed software already in existence would rapidly morph into the elements necessary to make such a threat possible. This scene, futuristic sci-fi at its finest, held viewers in gripping suspense because the implications of what the interrogator was suggesting were a complete violation of proper ethics and conduct and squelched people's rights to make their own choice about what they would and would not engage in. There remained a certain safety, however, in the (at that time) knowledge that one would never *really* be subjected to such a violation. There was a sense of security in knowing that one could not just *create* footage of another doing something they had not—or *would never have*—done.

However, improvements in image-altering technology (such as Photoshop) have taken a malevolent and potentially disastrous turn. It is quickly becoming easier for fraudulent images and videos to be made that are nearly—or completely—impossible for the naked eye to recognize as fake:

Before deepfakes, a powerful computer and a good chunk of a university degree were needed to produce a realistic fake video of someone. Now some photos and an internet connection are all that is required.[348]

Current software literally decodes the movement of a person's lips in relation to their words and then helps generate extremely realistic and believable speech.[349] This "new" face can then seamlessly appear to be a part of the con-artist's moving body.[350] The extraordinarily frightening element of this technology is that a person can be (and many already have been) depicted as taking part in activities that are at the very least intensely personal, at worst, depraved or even heinous—and all without consent.

WILL DEEPFAKES IMPACT ELECTIONS?

US government officials are increasingly concerned that the deepfake trend and its ever-improving technology could affect the elections of 2024 and beyond. Since these works can be so convincing, the worry remains that even those who carefully scrutinize the media for fakes will be unable to spot them—and this says nothing of those who are not even aware of the many types of deception that persist throughout media, thus carelessly cast misinformed votes. The pressing query on the part of all who look ahead to the next election is what would happen if a damaging deepfake were to be released just in time to sway the election's outcome, but not exposed as fraudulent until *after* the votes were counted.

Deepfake videos could even "cause worldwide chaos and pull society apart," according to experts.[351]

> EU tech policy analyst at the Centre for Data Innovation Eline Cheviot warned that there is a growing imbalance between technologies for detecting and producing deepfakes and that this means there is a lack of tools needed to efficiently tackle the problem.
>
> And she warned humans are no longer able to spot the difference between deepfakes and the real thing, and so are unable to stop weaponised fake news from spreading.[352]

In a recent article discussing such a possibility, Karl Stephan of Texas State University stated that "it takes time and expertise to determine whether a video or audio record has been faked...by the time a video that influences an election has been revealed as a fake, the election could be over."[353]

Surely, even as efforts are made to perfect software that could identify *fakes*, the *fakers* are upping their game, counteractions that result in and feed a strange contest of cat-and-mouse many authorities remain unsure they can win. Even as it stands, a recent fake of Obama was perceived to be real, *even by those who knew him personally*.[354]

On the other hand, some have expressed concern that deepfakes will only enable those who have already made up their minds to fortify their beliefs, whether right or wrong. To explain further, some people hear or see what they want, and upon observing anything that reinforces their ability to embrace that position is welcome, fake or not.[355] And, unfortunately, once a video has been viewed and accepted by the public, experts say many individuals are resistant to newly emerging truths regarding the fake: "Once the doubt has been sowed... [about details later revealed to be misinformed] a non-trivial portion of viewers will never forget that detail and suspect it might be true."[356]

Particularly vulnerable to such fakery are voters who remain on the fence during the final days preceding an election. For some, simply knowing fraudulent videos indeed circulate will suffice to keep their votes headed in the right direction. These folks will investigate before changing their decisions (however, this *still* doesn't alleviate the issue of deepfakes being nearly impossible to verify). Those who watch the pre-election pieces casually, however, and aren't wholeheartedly invested in any one candidate will be easier targets for a late-timed, incriminating deepfake to sway them with deceit,[357] essentially stealing their vote.

The threat to our nation by these campaign maneuverings goes further than possibly unjustly swaying the outcome of an election.

US Senator Marco Rubio (R-FL), has explained that, whereas previously, national security would likely only be threatened by a physical attack, modern technology has left us vulnerable to a strike against our "internet system...banking systems...electrical grid and infrastructure," adding that, "increasingly...the ability to produce a very realistic fake video"[358] exacerbates this problem. For example, imagine the crisis that would ensue if someone were to create a fake piece of news alerting the public to a national emergency, declaration of war, announcement of pandemic, or worse.[359]

For these reasons, the US government is currently working with AI experts across the country to tighten security and ramp up software that detects fraudulent releases. The House Intelligence Committee has been holding hearings with AI professionals to strategize what can be done to contain the situation, while Congress deliberates regarding how to design legislature that could likewise regulate the creation and spread of such productions. This is a phenomenon taking place in such sheer volumes that those attempting to curb them are overwhelmingly outnumbered. In response to the enormity of the task, computer-science professor Henry Farid of University of California flatly stated, "We are outgunned."[360] Creating legislature against deepfakes is more complicated than it may seem: Government officials face obstacles barring "governmental overreach and the perceived threat to the First Amendment."[361]

Involved in the prevention of electoral disturbance due to false information is DARPA, who recently announced it will be working to create resources for identifying and containing harmful deepfakes. The organization is currently working on building new tools for verifying videos, as older ones "are quickly becoming insufficient."[362] Precautions being taken at the time of this writing to safeguard the 2024 election from fraudulent videos that may mislead voters include banking gratuitous amounts of footage of key personalities who are expected to be involved in the race in order to encrypt a clear digital study on how the individuals' faces and bodies move while they talk, a signature set of movements including body language and facial expressions that they call "fingerprinting."[363] Essentially, DARPA and the government are working together to use these personalized characteristic data banks to build a website where new videos involving all of the key players can be uploaded and verified before their release to the mainstream media.[364]

However, this does not alleviate the concern that an exceptionally good impersonator will mimic the facial expressions and body language of a targeted person. Furthermore, experts state, "detection techniques that rely on statistical fingerprints can often be fooled with limited additional resources."[365] Once uploaded, a video in question would be sorted by AI first for what DARPA calls "semantic errors,"[366] such as potential flaws that point to errors in editing, including "mismatched earrings."[367] Then, these are sorted by category: determining whether a product was made with malicious intent or otherwise. Then, based on these results, a video might be flagged for "human review."[368]

The hope for DARPA's endeavor is that those in the media will verify authenticity of videos before running stories based on them. However, one has to wonder if this approach will be successful. First of all, should a video be flagged for "human review," what would the time frame be for such scrutiny? Surely, those within the media who come across a story will want to be the first to release it. It is difficult to imagine members of the press being willing to wait for verification before running an article. Certainly, for at least some, the fear will be too pressing that another news agency will break the news first. And, unfortunately, for such an undertaking to be successful, it will require the cooperation of *everyone*. As it stands, stories are often broadcast in the media before agencies or individuals have taken the time to be certain that all their facts are straight. *And,* this is only accounting for stories from news agencies, with no involvement from members of the general public who share things without stopping to consider accountability of any kind. A person who really wants to damage a candidate's reputation could simply post a deepfake on social media, bypassing news agencies completely. All it might take is one well-timed, convincing fake and the entire election could pivot to a direction it may not otherwise have turned. Further, software often takes time to perfect. Can we indeed trust that what is "verified"—even by agencies such as DARPA—is truly authentic? What could happen if a false video were to be mistakenly (or not so mistakenly…) affirmed as real? How many careers would be ruined by the disparaging elements of a fraudulent release, or—just as frightening—how many people who have done wrong could be indemnified by false videos that somehow act as proof of their integrity? As experts work furiously to build a verification system using AI, the aforementioned GAN technique (generative adversarial networks) could just as quickly sabotage these efforts to determine what is real. Without a surefire way to digitally authenticate videos, the theme underlying the 2024 election and others ahead is "buyer, beware."

To grasp how damaging deepfakes can be to our society, it helps to understand a concept known as "gaslighting." Gaslighting is psychologically manipulating someone into questioning their own reality until they are easily controlled because they lose trust in their own senses. The term originated from the 1944 movie *Gaslight*, wherein a husband, in an effort to make his wife doubt her own sanity, continues to change the level of light in their home, while pretending he doesn't notice a difference. This makes the wife distrust her own senses, until the man's true intentions come under scrutiny. In modern arenas, this tactic is stated by *Psychology Today* to be used commonly by "abusers, dictators, narcissists, and cult leaders."[369]

The issue, in relation to deepfakes and elections, is that, as people lose trust in their own perception, they often become less determined to closely follow the actions of those around them. This lack of willingness to hold others accountable is a byproduct of underlying suspicion that they are only about to—once again—find they've been duped. There is a certain danger attached to the demoralization of a public who no longer knows what is real and what is not, which sources to believe and which ones cannot be trusted. By and large, people begin to succumb to a certain fatigue that comes along with the mental roller-coaster of the continual extending of and then the removing of hope. It is demoralizing enough, without the placement of deepfakes, for a population to trust in political figures who fail to follow through on pre-election promises. Consider how much worse it will be if candidates begin to adamantly deny the very content of videos voters based their decisions *on*. Not only would this have devastating ramifications for the 2024 elections, but it's likely that such activity would severely compromise future voter interest and turnout.

Deepfakes could easily be used to sabotage upcoming elections not only by discouraging voter involvement, but (obviously) by the false information they could spread that would likely be received by a trusting public as true. Good candidates could easily be portrayed in pornographic or otherwise compromising settings, and unfortunately, even when such a video is finally verified as "fake," the damage to one's reputation will have been done. Very few candidates, after such a blow, would see their campaigns be revived after the fact. Not only can deepfakes potentially destroy the good reputation of an innocent person, but their existence can be likewise the excuse for someone who *has* done wrong. A person could be caught—with videographic evidence—doing something legally or morally incriminating and attempt to escape justice by crying "Deepfake!" And, since the deepfakes are getting so difficult to verify, claiming fakery could soon be as hard as asserting validity. This loss of confidence in what we see and hear with our own eyes and ears is the ultimate form of gaslighting. With such doubt placed on what we experience via our own senses (sight and sound), how can we trust the results of our elections or know how to vote? Many professionals in media and politics agree this is a concern. "As public trust in institutions like the media, education, and elections dwindles," says Claire Wardle, expert of online manipulation and cofounder of First Draft,[370] "then democracy itself becomes unsustainable."[371]

THE REALLY SCARY THING ABOUT DEEPFAKES

Particularly concerning about those who generate deepfakes is their ability to bypass a person's consent. It has been mentioned already that countless videos have been made portraying certain celebrities in pornographic situations. Vengeful exes have been known to create damaging images as well as those who have wanted to undermine certain businesspeople, ministers, coaches, or teachers.

Additionally, the potential of this technology to undermine the innocence of culture as a whole is alarming. Consider the beautiful, wholesome works of times gone by, such as old movies starring Doris Day with Rock Hudson, Vivien Leigh with Clark Gable, or Audrey Hepburn with Gregory Peck. The damage that could be caused by this technology adds to the overall negative impact fakeries could have upon modern society.

In addition to the need for new legislature and image-verification systems to help counter the emerging menace presented by deepfake technology, some agencies—such as the Social Science Research Center—along with other authorities are suggesting a new type of precaution: "immutable life logs."[372] What is such a thing? It is a digital trail of a person's moves, locations, and actions that would "make it possible for a victim of a deepfake to produce a certified alibi credibly proving that he or she did not do or say the thing depicted."[373]

Let's get this straight: In order to prevent a predatory, digital violation of someone, that person must essentially agree to 24-7 tracking. In essence, a "digital counter-bully" would act as a type of guardian over *real* circumstances. Does this sound a little bit like a prelude to the mark of the Beast? Even for minds less prone to conspiracy thoughts, the huge invasion of privacy is ominous. Furthermore, once people relinquish their solitude and consent to the monitoring invasion, they have no guarantee where the data will be stored, who will have access to it, how it could be used against them, and what outside agencies the data could be sold to, etc.[374] There is also speculation that, when such material is coupled with geo-location technology, it would likely be highly accurate at predictive tracking. This means that not only will those with access to our personal information know where we *have been,* but they would likely analyze algorithms in the data that would also indicate where we are *going.*[375] In other words, we would never be alone or have privacy again.

Speaking of technology that seems to be racing toward the predicted mark of the Beast, the iris biometric cryptocurrency project Worldcoin aims to allow governments worldwide "to use its iris-scanning and identity-verifying technology."

"Co-founded by OpenAI CEO Sam Altman, Worldcoin requires users to give their iris scans in exchange for a digital ID…as part of plans to create a 'identity and financial network.'

"In sign-up sites around the world, people have been getting their faces scanned by a shiny spherical 'orb', shrugging off privacy campaigners' concerns that the biometric data could be misused." Worldcoin says 2.2 million had already signed up as of August 1, 2023, and that they "are on this mission of building the biggest financial and identity community that we can," according to Ricardo Macieira, general manager for Europe at Tools For Humanity, the San Francisco and Berlin-based company behind the project."[376]

HOW TO KEEP FROM BEING DUPED

Data & Society researcher Britt Paris explains that, while legislation and image-verification software are a good start, the battle against deep-fake needs to take place in the public forum: Platforms that propagate or tolerate the spread of deepfake must be held accountable.[377] These entities must be exposed and victims vindicated—publicly. Furthermore, Paris adds that for information outlets hiding behind the excuse that the volume of such activity is too large to address, she recommends they dial back their volume and hire more employees until the content is such that they can effectively manage it.[378] Certainly, many companies will balk at such a proposed solution, but Paris argues that this is part of due diligence that should be required of any organization.

SUMMONING THE DEMON

Claire Wardle, mentioned previously, has another method of countering deepfakes in mind, which, if put to use, would likely be an ultimately superior tactic if adopted by the general public: Simply check facts before you act, vote, or post a video on social media.[379] She states the responsibility for this issue is shared equally between the outlets and their audiences. Social media and press hubs, Wardle states, need to be held responsible for their content, but she likewise asserts that the general public has a duty to verify what they are sharing: "The way we respond to this serious issue is critical…if you don't know 100%…don't share, because it's not worth the risk."[380]

1984'S DEEPFAKE, YEAR-ZERO ENDGAME

Similar to Orwell's Oceania, we live in a day and age wherein our citizens are often unable to see clearly the true chronology of potentially devastating upcoming events, because the view from where they stand is simply too muddy.

Whether through deepfake storytelling or historical revisionism, monuments of previous wars and administrations are smashed, histories are reimagined, and insults to the government's status quo are demonized to diminish any lasting resistance to authoritarian rule.

In political theory, this also relates to the term "Year Zero," reflected in such historical events as the 1975 takeover of Cambodia by the Khmer Rouge, and to the "Year One" of the French Revolutionary calendar.[381]

During the French Revolution, after the abolition of the French monarchy (Sept. 20, 1792), the National Convention instituted a new calendar and declared the beginning of the Year I. The Khmer Rouge takeover of Phnom Penh was rapidly followed by a series of drastic revolutionary de-industrialization policies resulting in a death toll that vastly exceeded that of the French Reign of Terror.

The main idea behind Year Zero is:

All culture and traditions within a society must be completely destroyed or discarded and a new revolutionary culture must replace it, starting from scratch. All history of a nation or people before Year Zero is deemed largely irrelevant, as it will ideally be purged and replaced from the ground up.

This kind of history purge is happening all across America today, from rewriting the role of religion in this nation and removing paintings of George Washington at San Francisco's George Washington High School[382] to eliminating Confederate statues and monuments nationwide.[383]

Also like Orwell's dystopian vision, along with their Year Zero stratagem, the hypocrisy by the left is suffocating.

Remember when Democratic "bastions of liberty" bemoaned ISIS turning the Syrian city of Aleppo into rubble by bulldozing the antiquities of the ancient city of Palmyra? Recall how the social radicals cursed the incivility and loss of historical artifacts? Indeed, when a new simulacrum of the pagan Archway of Baal (destroyed at Palmyra) was created, it was immediately sent globetrotting to be erected wherever the world's liberal elites gather. This in-your-face reconstruction was widely celebrated by so-called champions of freedom, who conveniently failed to mention how children in olden times were carried through such archways and sacrificed to the Baals of the ancient world, something far worse than any Confederate soldiers did.

Yet now, the same liberals who cried to high heaven over the destruction of Baal's bloodstained gateway have done an about face and pulled out their Oceania playbook. Suddenly, like Isis before them, they, too, want historical monuments that offend their sensitivities and contradict their political posturing crushed, including Civil War markers and statues from public grounds that are connected to the slave-owning side of our past. It's immaterial how contradictory such Doublethink and Newspeak is; the endgame is all that matters. The maintenance of power and uninterrupted establishment of cross-party monopolies require whatever deflection and tortured logic are needed to be manufactured until citizens accept as substantive the "viewpoints" Big Brother wants maintained on the streets and in the echo chambers of fake news outlets, especially if such can be used to infer wrongdoing or failure to act on the part of the Trump administration.

Thus, a new French Revolution Year One mindset is on the march to erase America's politically incorrect history despite the fact that it was the Revolutionary War and then the Civil War on this continent that ultimately led to the abolition of slavery here and eventually around the world.

Students of history have often looked with interest at the French Revolution and what caused the Year One horror of death and torture under Robespierre compared to the Revolutionary War in America that yielded unprecedented freedoms and monetary success. While citizens in this country were rejoicing in newfound liberty, in Paris, more than twenty thousand people were beheaded in the guillotines. The years following in France were marked by a reign of terror leading up to Orwellian totalitarianism and Napoleon (whose name actually means "Apollo incarnate," the same spirit that will inhabit Antichrist, according to the book of Revelation). Why were the American and French Revolutions followed by such contrasting conclusions? The difference was that the American Revolution was fought on Christian principles of liberty, while the French Revolution—like many of the statue-smashing leftists and neo-fascist agitators reflect currently—was anti-God. The forces behind the French Revolution were out to eliminate people of faith as the enemies of France and shut the mouths of God-fearing dissenters. They even placed a nude statue of a woman on the altar in the church at Notre Dame and proclaimed the God of Christianity dead. Soon thereafter, the French government collapsed (by the way, this is why a so-called Easter egg reference appears on the cover of *Blood on the Altar*—a book about the coming genocide of true Christianity—in the form of a gargoyle from the Church of Notre Dame, a silent gesture nobody seemed to catch).

And make no mistake about this, either. Many of the people involved in such revolutions as the French one—like the occultists in Washington DC briefly mentioned at the start of this chapter—are aware their politics can be assisted or "energized" by powerful super-naturalism, which they seek to make covenants with and that, under the right circumstances, can take on social vivacity of its own (see Ephesians 6:12).

For instance, concerning the French Revolution specifically, some scholars note how practitioners of occultism comingled with evil, nonhuman energies that emanated from their actions, symbols, and incantations, and that, once summoned, were released upon a gullible society to encourage a destructive collective group mind. As people passed these "thoughtforms" or memes from one to another and the ideas became viral, the power and reach of "the entity" spread with it until it became an unimaginably destructive force. Writing about the Masonic involvement in the French Revolution, Gary Lachman makes an extraordinary and important observation about such immaterial destructive forces—which had unseen plans of their own—released as a result of occult politics:

> Cazotte himself was aware of the dangerous energies unleashed by the Revolution…. Although Cazotte didn't use the term, he would no doubt have agreed that, whatever started it, the Revolution soon took on a life of its own, coming under the power of an *egregore*, Greek for "watcher," a kind of immaterial entity that is created by and presides over a human activity or collective. According to the anonymous author of the fascinat-ing *Meditations on the Tarot*, there are no "good" *egregores*, only "negative" ones…. True or not, *egregores* can nevertheless be "engendered by the collective will and imagination of nations."

As Joscelyn Godwin points out, "an *egregore* is augmented by human belief, ritual and especially by sacrifice. If it is sufficiently nourished by such energies, the *egregore* can take on a life of its own and appear to be an independent, personal divinity, with a limited power on behalf of its devotees and an unlimited appetite for their future devotion." If, as some esotericists believe, human conflicts are the result of spiritual forces for spiritual ends, and these forces are not all "good," then collective catastrophes like the French Revolution take on a different significance.[384]

Fast forward to today, and anyone who thinks the eradication of public knowledge about the role God played in American history and even our Civil War is divorced from supernaturalism or will stop with a few monuments being pulled down is in for a history lesson of their own. Behind the chaos-magic and/or meme-magic nonstop deployment by fake news outlets and sufferers of Trump-Derangement Syndrome are deceiving spirits called *egregore* above and "archons" and "kosmokrators" in the book of Ephesians. These are rulers of darkness who work in and through human political counterparts, commanding spirits of lesser rank until every level of earthly government can be touched by their influence. Their currency includes propaganda (or "deception" and "lies," as the New Testament describes), and as surely as Orwell's protagonist Winston Smith spent his time at the Ministry of Truth modifying the past by correcting "errors" in old newspapers that embarrassed the party, today's revisionists empowered by deceptive spirits will not be satisfied until their versions of Doublethink and Newspeak control everything the masses—*especially Bible-believing Christians*—can know, think and say. This is why, by the way, California lawmakers proposed Resolution 99 to govern what church leaders and religious counselors will be allowed to preach or say in the future.[385]

In this regard, America and the world could be entering a prophetic, ruthless form of censorship that will undergird a time when all, both small and great, will bow before "a king of fierce countenance" (Daniel 8:23). With imperious decree, this Man of Sin will facilitate an Orwellian one-world government, universal religion and global socialism. Those who refuse his Oceaniac empire will inevitably be imprisoned or destroyed until at last he exalts himself "above all that is called God, or that is worshiped, so that he, as God, sitteth in the temple of God, showing himself that he is God" (2 Thessalonians 2:4).

THE COMING PUSH TO BE "AUTHENTICATED" (MARKED)

While the deepfake tech will be utilized by malicious governmental parties to sway our future toward wicked legislation and administration in high places, these same politicians will find the widespread public distrust of all media an ideal platform upon which to prop themselves as our beneficiaries...just in time for the mark of the Beast to "save us all." To put this another way: The same wicked, yet powerful men will propel the following two seemingly contradictory—but truthfully harmonious (for their purposes)—movements: 1) Secretly, they will generate and circulate the deepfakes that initially confuse and ultimately steer the public toward ushering Antichrist and his False Prophet into the most dominating political offices in the world, as just described in the previous pages, while simultaneously: 2) they will *outwardly* oppose this "criminal deepfake technology" (or equivalent objections), appearing outraged and concerned for public safety and privacy as they flood news stations and other media demanding action against it in the form of individualized authentication: an irrefutable way for every person—small, great, or otherwise—to prove they are who they claim to be "for the good of us all and in the interest of the objective truth the public deserves." In this, we will beat the deepfake system, they'll say. They will advertise this as the answer to all terrors of digital face-masking, and they may be correct to a degree on a social or political level, but it may come at the cost of an individual's soul to participate in this "protection."

Let it sink in...

We have never been pressured to prove our identity on the most fundamental and literal level. Of course, we're not referring to issues that have arisen in regard to identity theft, safety protocol regarding bank accounts, or other examples of procedures described as "minor, nonintrusive security methods" wherein people can keep their money or property successfully sheltered from illegitimate activity. At any previous point in human history, if a person was captured on a surveillance camera robbing a bank in Montana two weeks before Christmas, that was proof enough for the rest of the human race, *including the court of law*, that the individual had robbed that bank where and when the footage showed. Case closed. The age-old adage of "seeing is believing" has always applied. Now that our historical refuge of video/audio proof has been threatened, it is up to viewers to believe—or not—the information their eyes and ears communicate to the brain regarding the matter. Naturally, an enormous wave of public distrust is on the immediate horizon, because most people are at least smart enough to anticipate that this technology will be used to sway public opinion and destroy the reputation of key figures in society. (By the way, keep in mind that even though deepfakes, voice cloning, and related deceptive technology is a big buzz online, there are still a lot of folks out there who largely live offline [we have several of those types even in our own ministry here at SkyWatch TV and Defender Publishing], and they will be in the dark about some of these tactics simply because they haven't been exposed to the issue. This is in no way a reflection on a person's intelligence or discernment, and we don't mean to imply that the uninformed are "blind.")

However, in trying to sort out what is real from what has been faked, chief administrators in organizations all over the world will come forward with answers in the form of intense, mandatory authentication for individuals, politicians, and celebrities alike. Anyone who refuses this mandate will be viewed as an unfit parent, a troublemaking citizen, a danger to public safety...

They would have to be viewed this way by the government. There's no way around it. Choosing to allow one's own likeness (or the likeness of their children, spouses, etc.) to be used in a way that ultimately misleads the masses *will* be described as a public enemy if such a claim feeds the end-times agenda in the minds of evil people who are skilled in pretending to have the interest of the people in mind. Whether or not a person ever consented for his or her likeness to be in a video promoting lies will be irrelevant when that same person refuses to "contribute to truth, love, freedom," etc.

Anyone with Internet access can tune into YouTube right this second and watch as: President Obama calls Donald Trump a "dip-[poop]"; a woman is arrested for doctoring footage of her daughter's schoolmate to get her kicked off the cheerleading team; another woman almost wins a custody battle after fabricating a violent phone call from her husband to her daughter; actress Jennifer Lopez gives an almost completely unknown YouTube channel her highest endorsement; Kim Kardashian openly admits she loves to manipulate people online for money; David Beckham speaks nine languages for the sake of an outreach program; a Hungarian business owner and CEO loses hundreds of thousands of dollars when an altered phone call orders a transfer of funds to an unrelated bank account; Elon Musk goes to Mars; Elvis Presley posthumously travels to the future and stars in *Lethal Weapon*; Jim Carrey takes over the lead of a James Bond film; Richard Nixon announces that Neil Armstrong and Edwin "Buzz" Aldrin's moon landing was unsuccessful and that they were stranded to die on the pock-marked lunar surface back in 1969; and, for fun, any person can visit the popular site, MyHeritage, and watch as an ancestor who died a hundred years ago comes to life, smiling, blinking, and making eye contact with his or her descendants. Yet *all* of these are a result of deepfake technology. (In regard to this last example, it's only a matter of time before sites like this *fully* animate historic photos to speak AI-generated sentiments, offering God-only-knows-what to "family" seeking advice. Though we can imagine there will be many who view this as innocent fun, there will be those of a more spiritual nature who truly believe the answers to their life questions came from a dead ancestor when these sites link enough background information that an AI forebearer will suddenly "knows everything" about those people and provide answers that can't be found in any mere human acquaintance. We remember when the *Harry Potter* film franchise featured images of deceased wizards, school matriarchs and patriarchs, and other characters who had played prominent roles at Hogwarts School of Witchcraft and Wizardry in past years whose voices, faces, and personalities were eternally captured in living portraits hanging on the wall. Long after their departure from this material world, these characters were still capable of carrying on full conversations, assisting students and faculty alike in finding clues or solving mysteries, floating into other portraits and visiting friends, or simply hollering out a cheerful "hello" to the students below scurrying to and from classes. Certainly, due to deepfake technology, we're nearing that reality now. Your dearly departed Aunt Margaret may soon greet you in a similar way from her e-photo over the fireplace every morning as your coffee is brewing, and when she tells you her opinions, how will you receive them? (By the way, digital photo frames with moving pictures have been in the mainstream market since the year 2000, so this technology already exists; the subjects just don't speak yet.) Will you write it off as a dumb, fun photo that talks, but nothing more? Or will the nearly limitless intelligence of AI, with its multiple lifetimes of downloaded family history, limitless knowledge about the world, perfect reasoning, superior intuition, and apparently unbiased thought patterns pouring out of a familiar face influence you more than you want to admit? This poses the question: Could the likenesses of real-but-deceased people in our own family trees, through such sites as MyHeritage and others, be possessed by some disembodied spirit, "come to life" when we need them, and direct us *maliciously*? Or are we foolish enough to believe that wicked entities only enter legions of pigs? We'll let you draw your own conclusions about that one, but for now, back to the "authentication" (translation: mark of the Beast) motive of world governments.

When the beloved sci-fi film *The Matrix* hit theaters, it entertained folks around the globe with a concept that very few had imagined and even fewer had been able to visualize to the degree the movie executed. After its release, talk ensued of blue pills, red pills, human batteries, and a dystopian reality the public is unaware of. And, though the circumstances are certainly different, folks, we're there.

Don't misunderstand us: By no means do we think our physical bodies are trapped in towers providing bioelectric energy to sentient machines while our brains are plugged into a simulated world where we *think* we're going about our daily lives in 1999 (the central plot of the film). However, very soon, our physical bodies *will* exist in one state, while deepfake technology (and similar advancements) will have us believing in an existence all around us that *isn't real*. Will there be heroes like Neo of the *Matrix* who take the red pill, "unplug" from all the fakery, and fight the system so people of more advanced cultures can finally cling onto absolute truth? Absolutely! Will their motives be as pure as Neo's?

Not so fast. Sure, some grass-roots people will go against all of this nonsense with heroic motives, but there will be those who pretend their objections are for the people while they prop the end-times schema. And we can assume that the worst of these hypocrites will be in substantially powerful positions of government.

Again: The same folks in high places who will secretly take advantage of this tech to sway public opinion and launch the worst smear campaigns ever seen in events such as presidential elections will rise as the saviors to crush that tech when such a move suits their mark-of-the-Beast agenda. Newsreels of Neil Armstrong perishing on the moon back in 1969 will be the least of our worries when, for example, "video evidence of [insert politician/celebrity name here] sacrificing a baby on the White House lawn" is released. Let's take this "baby" illustration further to show how we predict it will go down in the following order:

1. Initially, people who have spent their entire lives relying on their eyes and ears will believe most—if not all—of what they're fed. False information will spread like brushfire and terminate objective truth, likely in a way that is instant, complete, and, sadly, often irreversible. Virtuous lives will be destroyed left and right while one person is hated for this and another person is hated for that, and on the saga goes for newscasters, the government, celebrities, politicians, spokespersons for popular organizations (including charities), university professors, and religious leaders. Even the local Sunday school teacher will be suspect. No one will be impervious to the spread of lies. All the while, efforts to restore reputations, free prisoners serving time for crimes they never committed, and vindicate people from slander will be reserved only for the elite, wealthy, or high-society moguls who can fund the tedious unraveling of whatever misinformation devastated them in the first place. The person deepfaked to be sacrificing a baby on the White House lawn will—despite his innocence—be remembered forever (or at least for a very long time) as the baby-killer, unless he has all the right connections in all the right places to permanently be dissociated from the horrific accusation. (Even then, we use the word "permanently" loosely. As the social cruelty of the Internet has shown, he would never live it down. Comments and posts worldwide would consistently and perpetually link him to that ghastly, but counterfeit event, even while people know it was all a lie, because... well, that's just the nature of fallen humanity—especially online, where we never have face-to-face accountability for the things we've said.)

2. Before too long, a more efficient awareness of deepfake technology will reach the public—beginning with the younger, more tech-savvy generations who are more active online

and in social networking, and trickling down to the older generations who were formerly unaware of this danger. The constant barrage of "this person didn't *really* do that!" and "that person didn't *really* say that!"—though it will come far too late and most of the damage will cling on long-term—will no doubt initiate a massive surge of distrust in all media. This will pave the way for wickedness to take place out in the open: An evil person technically *could* sacrifice a baby on the White House lawn on video and deny it, regardless of all evidence. The reaction from the average viewer in that day will be similar to: "I wonder who deepfaked *this* piece of disturbing garbage. Clearly, that guy wouldn't do that. You can't trust anything anymore. Anyway, wanna go to Taco Bell?" Lawlessness will rule the day, and nobody will believe anything they see or hear is real until true evil is on display every day, interpreted as fake.

3. People will quickly catch on to this and recognize that many of those whose lives are destroyed by deepfake tech are innocent (though we don't anticipate most of them being properly vindicated), while others who are guilty are never held to justice, and the public will have a big reaction. They will long for the days when they could watch the news and trust what they were seeing. Yesterday's truth will be tomorrow's nostalgia. The human spirit in every person will tire of the constant misinformation and an enormous outcry for the government to do something about it will build the stage for the "saviors" to swoop in and demand mandatory authentication of all individuals, great and small, so society can return to genuine media. Any system put in place to "restore truth to the masses" will be viewed as the godly route, and resisters—despite whatever justification they have for why they believe this authentication system to be concerning—will be "the bad

283

guys." They will be those who prefer to live a lie and perpetuate chaos. True goodness and purity in resisting the
Antichrist system will be seen as *evil*, and true evil in the
form of participating in the system will be seen as *good*.
The Bible, itself, acknowledges this wicked paradox: "Woe
unto them that call evil good, and good evil" (Isaiah 5:20;
see also Romans 1:18–32).

We will be in the palm of Antichrist's hand at this point—vulnerable, scared, provoked, ready to make impulsive and temporal decisions
in situations with eternal consequence, and positioned precisely where
he wants us. Countless numbers of people will swallow whatever pill
Antichrist throws at us, even if it's the blue pill that embraces willing, but disastrously negligent, *Matrix*-like ignorance in the interest of
making humanity honest again.

From this point, it's no longer a matter of *whether* the governments introduce a mark-of-the-Beast-style authentication, but: when
they will unveil it; how it will work on, in, or with the human body;
how it will be mandatorily implemented worldwide; and how it will
fit with the biblical description of the mark in Revelation. We already
know what the danger will be for those who refuse it. They will not be
allowed to participate in society's mainstream economic structure—
and, ultimately, they will face death (if they weren't already raptured
away by that time, which is a subject of great debate that we won't
delve into here).

Imagine this future day predicted by Robert Chesney and Danielle Keats Citron in the 2018 legal research paper, "Deep Fakes: A
Looming Challenge for Privacy, Democracy, and National Security."
According to their expectations in light of current trends, as expressed
earlier, even the president of the United States (heavily considered by
many to be the most sovereign and powerful country on the planet)
will not be impervious to deepfakes. Future American presidents,
senators, and politicians will be (and already *are*) vulnerable to being

fraudulently depicted as "taking bribes, displaying racism, or engaging in adultery....appear[ing] in locations where they were not, saying or doing horrific things that they did not....[while] fake videos could place them in meetings with spies or criminals," among other disastrous implications, which will end up "launching public outrage, criminal investigations, or both."[386]

(Several years back, a SkyWatch Television super-fan gave a few of our staff members a jolt when he took an image of Tom's face and digitally imposed it over the face of the pope addressing an enormous crowd outside the Vatican. It was such a convincing deepfake that many began to try to remember when—*and why*—Tom would have ever been standing on that balcony and in the religious garb that would have marked him as the highest leader of the Catholic Church. It took a few moments for most to realize the picture had been altered, especially since the technology was newer then, and therefore all the more unexpected. To readers or viewers who are familiar with Tom's work regarding the role the Roman Catholic Church and the papacy might play in the end times, the heavy, ironic humor behind this parody is obvious. But what if that photo had been presented as legitimate? Can you even imagine the implications for the ministry if a large portion of the public believed it to have been real? Though some key points in the fundamentals of Catholic theology are compatible with Protestant Christianity, Tom Horn as the pope would be an immediate controversy leading to more than mere "investigations" for followers of SkyWatch TV.)

"Launching public outrage," experts calculate... It's going to be madness. Leading governments of the world *will* be placed under tremendous pressure to fix this.

Enter Beast-system X, stage left, to the sound of uproarious applause.

From the same source:

We predict the development of a profitable new service: immutable life logs [mentioned briefly earlier] or authentication trails that make it possible for a victim of a deep fake to produce a certified alibi credibly proving that he or she did not do or say the thing depicted.

From a technical perspective, such services will be made possible by advances in a variety of technologies including wearable tech; encryption; remote sensing; data compression, transmission, and storage; and blockchain-based record-keeping. That last element will be particularly important, for a vendor hoping to provide such services could not succeed without earning a strong reputation for the immutability and comprehensiveness of its data.[387]

We don't necessarily think these "immutable life logs" will for certain be the mark of the Beast, but since the mark hasn't arrived yet and it's our duty as followers of Christ to watch the signs of the times and be vigilant, let's pretend for a moment that it—or something like it—could be. At the very least, we can take this contemporary terminology, show some of the weaknesses innate in the concept, and use that reflection to compare these ideas to whatever the protective technology will be called in the coming days.

The term "immutable life logs" refers to records of a person's life (or a company's history, etc.) that can be proven and fixed in such a way that no alterations (including, but not limited to, deepfakes) can occur. But we must address a couple of things. First, the word "immutable" is somewhat of a misnomer. Yes, there are records kept today that are stored in a neutral, fact-reporting format that illustrate (for the most part) that they could never have been tampered with, such as medical records, bank statements, and so on. However, even when the record itself hasn't been altered, there is always an element of error. (Consider a misdiagnosis in one's medical history that renders all subsequent information irrelevant, or a stolen credit card statement showing that a person purchased five thousand dollars' worth of jewelry in Bolivia when they were in California at the time.) And this kind of error can happen within *both* spheres of intelligence, human and machine. Human error is old news, but so are glitches in the machine, so both could apply in the future, making "immutable" a label that loses its credibility early on when the "flawless" system X suddenly and inexplicably falsely testifies about a person or event.

Although we don't want to dig too deeply into the vaccine scandals, one example would be the *last* time the American government promised protection from COVID-19 through taking a series of shots; many chose to vaccinate and were disappointed when the safeguard didn't work the way it had been presented. All the "facts" were there—supported by the most brilliant minds in science and medicine—and, for many, it still didn't accomplish what we thought or hoped it would. Yet, while our Western territory was gearing up to embrace this protection, the warnings voiced by concerned citizens were muted in comparison to the vociferous praise from the opposing side, who effectively said the vaccine was a perfect answer. Worse, in fact: The "concerned citizens" quickly became "conspiracy theorists." System X will be similar. It will appear as the answer to everything, and anyone who doesn't agree will be the uneducated dunce.

Second, "immutable" assumes we will never be capable of creating a technology that *could* alter records and then clean up its own trail to the point that the fraudulent activity is undetectable. As noted earlier, deepfake tech has already arrived. To remind the reader: The computer programs used to produce these impressive-but-terrifying digital face masks are now checking and rechecking themselves, self-correcting detectable counterfeit points until the very machine that created the deepfake cannot locate flaws in its own simulation. By this point in the technology, that video has essentially become "immutable"—interpreted as absolutely true to both human and machine—and the only way to prove it ever was fake is to reproduce the original video and traces of the forgery during its development. And what if those elements have been deleted or destroyed and no longer exist? There's literally not a thing a person could do to refute that footage.

So, let's be real. If immutable life logs are tomorrow's promise of protection, how long will it be before they, too, are irrelevant and amount to nearly nothing because of *only two* factors (human/machine error; counterfeit-erasing tech) we've imagined here? (To stir the pot further, how many other factors will come into play to cancel out this protection that we have *not* yet imagined?) If a wicked government wants to wipe out someone's authentic logs and fabricate an entire history to smear someone—*or* to fabricate a syrupy, shiny, but totally false history for an individual they want to endorse—what's to stop them from doing so? Many Americans to this day believe that a recent president's birth certificate was forged to make him appear to be a true American when, according to skeptics, he was *not*. Whether or not our government was guilty of this fraud (we won't address that issue here), the story illustrates how people in power are willing and capable of doctoring records…*and, in a day when computers can self-correct all trails of counterfeit data, a president's birth certificate is about to become small beans.*

And, *again*: Anyone who raises these types of concerns in the very near future will be tossed in with the tinfoil-hat crowd. Soon, we won't even be able to question these technologies without being written off as nuts, *then* silenced (violently, if necessary) if we get too loud.

So far, we've only toyed with the immutable-life-logs theory long enough to poke holes in its guarantees for security. We haven't even touched on how this tech will, without exception, force all of us—great, small, and otherwise—to live under an Orwellian level of surveillance unlike anything humanity has ever seen. If this system is implemented, it may start with minor infringements, like the pooling of our social media posts in the month of December to show we really did visit family at Christmastime, or what have you. But over time, when these measures still are not enough to protect us from mischievous or spiteful accusations, we will be checking in and reporting our every move to produce a consistent digital alibi every hour of every day. Not to be crude, but to call the kettle black here, let's use an example of a time when every person *should* be private: Even intimacy with a spouse will have to be transparently reported in some way in order to safeguard someone from being accused of doing something wrong during the time they are "off-log."

In addition, even completely innocuous data stored for the sake of our protection could be used against us. Imagine what a provoked foreign military or government, or even a Ted Bundy, could do with a record of our patterns and behaviors. Any information initially provided to prove our innocence could provide the wicked mind with a plethora of material and statistics that could place us directly in harm's way. In years past, stalkers would have to follow their victims at a distance for days, weeks, or months to predict where that person would be, when they would be there, and what they would be doing. As it stands right this second, many Americans active on social media have already opened the door to this scenario, and the less they know about what they post (such as not knowing they left their cell phone's location on when they took a photo of their child at school, advertising to potential perverts where little Susie will be during weekdays), the easier it will be for them to become a victim. The answer to this is obviously not to dramatically *increase* the sharing of personal information—yet that is precisely (and ironically) what the immutable-life-logs concept proposes.

Of course, this is only taking into consideration the individual citizen. What about our government? Will it be able to have classified assemblies, confidential meetings, federal or executive sessions, etc., without other nations of the world assuming they're closing their doors for some other dubious purpose? And don't get us wrong: It's safe to assume that national governments will always maintain rights to executive sessions. We're not suggesting that will disappear any time soon (or ever). But it's far less about what the administration is doing/saying behind closed doors than it is about what paranoid minds will assume about those meetings when they're inevitably carried out, especially in a day when the whole world champions complete and total transparency and views anything "private" as "conspiratorial"...and that's not a great development for tomorrow's fear-mongering headlines.

To offer an obvious (and perhaps overly simplistic) example: *In the beginning*, everyone might expect that the president of the United States would make his Saturday trip to the zoo an immutable-life-log public matter so he's not linked to criminal activity on that day, but nobody in their right mind would demand that he records, then publicly posts, say, a closed, executive session with his most trusted advisors regarding the upcoming termination of, or disciplinary action against, a Supreme Court chairholder. We may insist we're *eventually* told about the outcome of those sessions, but we wouldn't anticipate being fully informed of such matters at their onset any more than we would expect the firing of a coffeehouse employee at the local café to be televised live. So far, so good.

But, with a sharp increase in transparency comes a sharp increase of suspicion any time transparency is not applied. We can expect paranoia to skyrocket if immutable life logs are implemented on a national level. At a future time, when every citizen is on record or reporting their whereabouts and details at every moment—*and* the government is showing nearly every move it makes as well in order to lead by example—how long will it take before that government's off-log moments are interpreted as shady or suspicious by distrustful minds (local to the United States or otherwise)? Soon enough, that "Supreme Court chairholder's disciplinary meeting" will be headlined as "America's secret plans to launch an attack against [whatever country]."

Yeah, but, one might rebut, people are already assuming the worst about government. What's new? Conspiracy theories about government secrets have been circulating since the dawn of time. Why would the widespread suspicion be any worse in the future?

What's "new" is the way the public—which has been subjected to life-log-level reporting—will respond to having *their own* privacy obliterated. As it sits currently, most citizens understand the reasoning behind classified dealings in high places, and that is respected, because we, too, have safe places to retreat from surveillance. We have lives of our own and can understand and appreciate the need for the transmission of secure information, especially when we're trusting our leaders with our lives, successes, prosperity, and overall well-being. When having lives of our own is removed or threatened, people will become irrational. They will snap, for lack of a better word, because no one was ever meant to live that way, and what was only a flash-in-the-pan conspiracy theory yesterday will be civil war against the system tomorrow. Take people's most fundamental freedoms and liberty away by mandating system X "for our own protection" and watch how they respond.

Whether or not the "conspiracy theories" of those who are jealous of any government's exemption from the constancy of the immutable-life-log system are ever actually true, every time any official goes off-log for whatever reason, it will be like whacking a beehive. People will get stung. It is the powerful governments that will implement such technology as the immutable life logs…and it will be the very same powerful governments that, at some point, will have to decide *when*—not *if*—the rules don't apply to them. The only other option would be to give up all (or almost all) rights to confidentiality, which we logically know is not a real option. And if they ever did eventually apply these mandates to themselves with the same veracity they've enforced them upon regular citizens—agreeing that every secret White House meeting, executive session, or equivalent will be recorded (yeah, right…)—what would happen with that stored information? Would they put all of those classified minutes in a vault somewhere?

Sure. Because that would be safe.

Allow us to remind you of something: If anything exists in digital format, it can be digitally hacked, stolen, and used for someone else's advantage. For a moment, put "classified" material aside and simply consider the never-ending-transparency plan. Even if it's ultimately a game of smoke and mirrors (as is often the case), whatever security and safety measures are pressed upon the public must first be implemented by the government that leads by example, which means our leaders are about to become *very* vulnerable. There is no telling what a foreign country could and would do with an accounting of every moment of the president's life posted online, even if those moments are one Saturday trip to the zoo after another. Assassination has happened before…

See how quickly this whole idea becomes more than we bargained for? Human wisdom can be a beautiful thing when it's held to a righteous standard, but without that standard, it is nothing more than foolishness (1 Corinthians 3:19).

In the past, if a malicious person or software program wanted to deepfake someone else, hours and hours of recorded facial movement and vocal fluctuation was necessary for it to be believable. Today, three *seconds* of either is all it takes.

Feeling safe yet?

THE IMAGE OF THE BEAST ARRIVES

In Revelation 13, we read an astonishing statement regarding the animating of an "image" of Antichrist.

> And [he] deceiveth them that dwell on the earth by the means of those miracles which he had power to do in the sight of the beast; saying to them that dwell on the earth, that they should make an image to the beast, which had the wound by a sword, and did live.
>
> And he had power to give life unto the image of the beast, that the image of the beast should both speak, and cause that as many as would not worship the image of the beast should be killed. (Revelation 13:14–15)

Scholars over the past two thousand years have speculated as to what this curious text implies and in what way an inanimate object could be brought to life. Only now does technology exist that is undeniably changing every aspect of human existence and evolving into something indistinguishable from this type of occult magic. Our lives have become so entrenched in technology that most of us are constantly connected to some form of it at all times. Computers, iPads, smartphones, Alexa, Siri, security surveillance, and medical devices like pacemakers work around the clock. There is rarely a moment when we are completely disconnected from technology—an idea that would have been inconceivable only a decade ago.

With this rapid emergence of transformative technology comes the question of safety. Are some of these developments demonically inspired, actively leading us down a dark and hellish path towards a dystopian future, as described in the ancient biblical prophetic narrative?

The book of Revelation describes "the beast" and his prophet in great detail, proclaiming that "all inhabitants of earth will worship the beast." It explicitly states that all humans will worship this entity, for his prophet will "perform great signs and deceive the inhabitants of the Earth and even order them to set up an image in honor of the beast who was wounded by the sword, yet lived" (Revelation 13:13–14). Widespread acceptance of the Beast seems to be largely due to the miracles he will perform, even simulating a resurrection from the dead, revealing his deceptive immortality.

The question is: Will this image of the Beast foreseen in the book of Revelation be realized through the emerging transformative technologies of transhumanism, artificial intelligence, the coming Singularity, and the speculative theories of the *hive mind*?

Twenty years ago, the idea that one day in the near future our telephones would navigate our travels anywhere in the world, scan our thumbprints, allow us to talk to someone face to face anywhere on the planet, handle our banking activities, and provide us with a "social" life would have been considered science fiction.

Society has come a long way in an alarmingly short period. But how fast is too fast? Are we rushing into a technological "relationship" without doing a thorough background check on our rapidly evolving and highly seductive companion? Once humanity delves into this relationship, it can't just break up and abandon the conveniences it's now become completely dependent upon.

The innovations in science, agriculture, medicine, and business certainly make life easier and more convenient for the average person. Many of these advancements are seriously improving the quality of life for the disabled, such as an amputee whose arm is now a fully functioning robotic replacement or a paraplegic who is given the gift of independence with a self-driving car, wheelchair, or even a robotic exoskeleton. Let's not forget about the artificial intelligence personalities we've named "Siri" and "Alexa." These two AI companions accurately suggest music their algorithms predict we will like, answer our questions, tell us jokes or the weather forecast, and even buy our groceries. In return, they record our conversations and file them away in an online database of information collected about us for an indefinite length of time, while aggregating the nuanced shopping habits and curiosities of every one of their users.

AI is the science and engineering of making "intelligent" machines by the simulation of cognitive function. It is related to the similar task of using computers to understand human intelligence.[388] Basically, it consists of computers that can make decisions and predictions without the confined interfacing of human programmers.

Artificial intelligence has the ability to learn on its own!

AI really became widespread when Google started using an AI neural network as a tool to filter spam out of our email inboxes,[389] which today accounts for about 59.56 percent of email traffic worldwide,[390] but it has since vastly evolved beyond that task.

There is no doubt of the beneficial aspects of AI, but it's the dependency we as a society are forming that very possibly makes it dangerous in the near future. At what point do we draw the line and say, "It's okay for Siri to tell me where the closest Chinese restaurant is, but it's not okay to record the fact that I like Chinese food and sell that information to companies for advertisement purposes," allowing the subtle and invisible influence of persuasion over us?

In his book *The Age of Spiritual Machines*, world-renowned trans-humanist Ray Kurzweil famously suggests that:

> Once life takes hold on a planet, we can consider the emergence of technology as inevitable. The ability to expand the reach of one's physical capabilities, not to mention mental technology is clearly useful for survival.[391]

It might be an inevitable future, but according to the concept of "machine learning," it could also be leading us to the destruction of the earth and the near destruction of humankind, as predicted in the Bible.

THE SPIRIT BEHIND AI
AND TRANSHUMANISM

It would be nice to be an artilect, a god, a supremely powerful
omnipotent being. I could be such a creature [soon.]
It's possible. It's not an unattainable dream.... All I can do here
is attempt to convey some measure of the strength of "religious"
feeling that I and other[s] will make public this century.

—Professor Hugo de Garis, artificial brain designer

All of the boundaries are up for grabs. All of the boundaries
that have defined us as human beings, boundaries between
a human being and an animal and between a human being
and a super human being or a god.

—Leon R. Kass, former chairman, President's Council on Bioethics

A non-human race once lived upon earth. They came to be called
the Rephaim [Nephilim]. They were genetic monsters, mutants
whose end is darkness, just as was their society upon earth. Will
JCVI's [J. Craig Venter Institute, which created the entirely new life
form nicknamed "Synthia"] work result in another such atrocity?

—Gary Stearman, Bible scholar

English theologian George Hawkins Pember, in his 1876 masterpiece, *Earth's Earliest Ages*, analyzed the prophecy of Jesus Christ that the end times will be a repeat of "the days of Noah." Pember outlined the seven great causes of the antediluvian destruction and documented their developmental beginnings in his lifetime. The seventh and most fearful sign, Pember wrote, would be the return of the spirits of Nephilim, "the appearance upon earth of beings from the Principality of the Air, and their unlawful intercourse with the human race."

Jesus, Himself, in answering His disciples concerning the signs of His coming and of the end of the world, said it would be "as the days of [Noah] were" (Matthew 24:37). The implication is, just as it was before the Flood when the spirits of Nephilim were powerful upon earth (Genesis 6:4), humankind would experience an end-times renaissance of the influence of these entities. From Scripture we are made to understand that the purpose of this latter-day wave of supernaturalism includes deception (2 Timothy 3:13) and that the effect upon humanity would be so successful that heresy and delusion would become firmly entrenched—even within institutionalized Christianity. In writing of this scenario, Paul prophesied to Timothy that "in the latter times, some shall depart from the faith, giving heed to seducing spirits, and doctrines of devils" (1 Timothy 4:1).

Based on contemporary developments, the foretold increase in demonism and its influence within secular and religious society is rapidly unfolding this century—abruptly, dramatically, and suspiciously. In an article in *Prophecy in the News* magazine, biblical scholar Gary Stearman agreed, stating in disturbing language how the manifestation of these powers is quickening now because the world is under conditions "in which the influence of God's Holy Spirit is diminishing."[392] This is apparent not only in metaphysics, but within science and technology, where genetic engineering and transhumanist aspirations seem literally hell-bent on repeating what the Watchers did in giving birth to the spirits of Nephilim as in the days of Noah.

THE FIRST TIME NEPHILIM APPEARED ON EARTH

As far back as the beginning of time and within every major culture of the ancient world, the astonishingly consistent story is told of "gods" who descended from heaven and materialized in bodies of flesh. From

Rome to Greece—and before that, to Egypt, Persia, Assyria, Babylonia, and Sumer—the earliest records of civilization tell of the era when powerful beings known to the Hebrews as "Watchers" and in the book of Genesis as the *b'nai ha Elohim* ("sons of God") mingled themselves with humans, giving birth to part-celestial, part-terrestrial hybrids known as "Nephilim." The Bible says this happened when the population of men began to increase on earth and daughters were born to them. When the sons of God saw the women's beauty, they took wives from among them to sire their unusual offspring. In Genesis 6:4, we read:

> There were giants [Nephilim] in the earth in those days; and also after that, when the sons of God came in unto the daughters of men, and they bare children to them, the same became mighty men which were of old, men of renown.

When this Scripture is compared with other ancient texts, including Enoch, Jubilees, Baruch, Genesis Apocryphon, Philo, Josephus, Jasher, and others, it unfolds to some that the giants of the Old Testament such as Goliath were the part-human, part-animal, part-angelic offspring of a supernatural interruption into the divine order and natural development of the species. The apocryphal Book of Enoch gives a name to the angels involved in this cosmic conspiracy, calling them "Watchers." We read:

> And I Enoch was blessing the Lord of majesty and the King of the ages, and lo! the Watchers called me—Enoch the scribe—and said to me: "Enoch, thou scribe of righteousness, go, declare to the Watchers of the heaven who have left the high heaven, the holy eternal place, and have defiled themselves with women, and have done as the children of earth do, and have taken unto themselves wives: Ye have wrought great destruction on the earth: And ye shall have no peace nor forgiveness of sin: and inasmuch as they delight themselves in

their children [the Nephilim], The murder of their beloved ones shall they see, and over the destruction of their children shall they lament, and shall make supplication unto eternity, but mercy and peace shall ye not attain." (1 Enoch 10:3–8)

According to Enoch, two hundred of these powerful angels departed "high heaven" and used women (among other DNA providers) to extend their progeny into humankind's plane of existence. The Interlinear Hebrew Bible (IHN) offers an interesting interpretation of Genesis 6:2 in this regard. Where the King James Version of the Bible says, "The sons of God saw the daughters of men that they [were] fair," the IHN interprets, "The [*b'nai ha Elohim*] saw the daughters of Adam, that they were *fit extensions*" (emphasis added). The term "fit extensions" seems applicable when the whole of the ancient record is understood to mean that the Watchers wanted to leave their proper sphere of existence in order to enter earth's three-dimensional reality. They viewed women—or at least their genetic material—as part of the formula for accomplishing this task. Departing the proper habitation God had assigned them was grievous to the Lord and led to divine penalization. Jude described it this way:

[The] angels which kept not their first estate, but left their own habitation, He hath reserved in everlasting chains under darkness unto the judgment of the great day. (Jude 6)

Besides apocryphal, pseudepigraphic, and Jewish traditions related to the legend of the Watchers and the "mighty men" born of their union with humans, mythologized accounts tell the stories of "gods" using humans and animals to produce heroes or demigods (half-gods). When the ancient Greek version of the Hebrew Old Testament (the LXX or Septuagint) was made, the word "Nephilim"—referring to the part-human offspring of the Watchers—was translated *gegenes*, a word implying "earth born." This same terminology was used to describe

THE SPIRIT BEHIND AI AND TRANSHUMANISM

the Greek Titans and other legendary heroes of part-celestial and part-terrestrial origin, such as Hercules (born of Zeus and the mortal Alcmena), Achilles (the Trojan hero son of Thetis and Peleus), and Gilgamesh (the two-thirds god and one-third human child of Lugalbanda and Ninsun). These demigods were likewise accompanied in texts and idol representation by half-animal and half-human creatures like centaurs (the part-human, part-horse offspring of Apollo's son, Centaurus), chimeras, furies, satyrs, gorgons, nymphs, Minotaurs, and other genetic aberrations. All of this seems to indicate that the Watchers not only modified human DNA during the construction of Nephilim, but that of animals as well, a point the Book of Enoch supports, saying in the seventh chapter that the fallen angels "sinned" against animals as well as humans. Other books such as Jubilees add that this interspecies mingling eventually resulted in mutations among normal humans and animals whose "flesh" (genetic makeup) was "corrupted" by the activity, presumably through crossbreeding (see 5:1–5; 7:21–25). Even the Old Testament contains reference to the genetic mutations that developed among humans following this time frame, including "men" of unusual size and physical strength, having six fingers and six toes, with an animal appetite for blood, and even displaying lion-like features (2 Samuel 21:20, 23:20). But of all the ancient records, the most telling extrabiblical script is from the Book of Jasher, a mostly forgotten text referred to in the Bible in Joshua 10:13 and 2 Samuel 1:18. Jasher records the familiar story of the fall of the Watchers, then adds an exceptional detail that none of the other texts is as unequivocal about, something that can only be understood in modern language to mean advanced biotechnology, genetic engineering, or "transgenic modification" of species. After the Watchers had instructed humans "in the secrets of heaven," note what Jasher says occurred:

> [Then] the sons of men [began teaching] the mixture of animals
> of one species with the other, in order therewith to provoke the
> Lord. (4:18)

The phrase "the mixture of animals of one species with the other" does not mean Watchers had taught men hybridization, as this wouldn't have "provoked the Lord." God made like animals of different breeds capable of reproducing. For example, horses can propagate with other mammals of the equidae classification (the taxonomic "horse family"), including donkeys and zebras. It wouldn't have "provoked the Lord" for this type of animal breeding to have taken place, as God Himself created the animals to do this.

If, on the other hand, the Watchers were crossing species boundaries by mixing incompatible animals *of one species with the other*, such as the DNA of pigs with that of humanslike science is doing today, this would have been a different matter and may cast light on the numerous ancient stories of mythical beings of variant-species breeding that fit perfectly within the records of what the Watchers were accomplishing. Understandably, this kind of chimera-making would have "provoked the Lord" and raises the serious question of why the Watchers would have risked eternal damnation by tinkering with God's creation in this way. Yahweh had placed boundaries between the species and strictly ordered that each reproduce only after its "own kind." Was the motive of the Watchers to break these rules simply the desire to rebel, to assault God's creative genius through biologically altering what He had made? Or was something of deeper significance behind the activity?

Some believe the corruption of antediluvian DNA by Watchers was an effort to cut off the birth line of the Messiah. This theory posits that Satan understood the protoevangelium—the promise in Genesis 3:15 that a Savior would be born, the seed of the woman, and would destroy the fallen angel's power. Satan's followers therefore intermingled with the human race in a conspiracy to stop the birth of Christ. If human DNA could be universally corrupted or "demonized," they reasoned, no Savior would be born, and humankind would be lost forever. Those who support this theory believe this is why God ordered His people to maintain a pure bloodline and not to intermarry with the other nations. When men breached this command

and the mutated DNA began rapidly spreading among humans and animals, God instructed Noah to build an ark and prepare for a flood that would destroy every living thing. That God had to send such a universal decreeillustrates how widespread the altered DNA eventually became. In fact, the Bible says in Genesis 6:9 that only Noah—and by extension, his children—were found "perfect" in their generation. The Hebrew word for "perfect" in this case is *tamiym*, which means "without blemish" or "healthy," the same word used in Leviticus to describe an unblemished sacrificial lamb. The meaning was not that Noah was morally perfect, but that his physical makeup—his DNA—had not been contaminated with Nephilim descent, as apparently the rest of the world had become. In order to preserve humans as He had made them, God destroyed all but Noah's family in the Flood. The ancient records, including those of the Bible, appear to agree with this theology, consistently describing the cause of the Flood as a response to "all flesh" having become "corrupted, both man and beast."

While we believe the theory of DNA corruption as an intended method for halting the coming of Christ has merit, an alternative or additional reason the Watchers may have blended living organisms exists in a theory we postulated in our book, *Apollyon Rising 2012: The Lost Symbol Found and the Final Mystery of the Great Seal Revealed*. In that book, we speculated that the manipulation of DNA may have had a deeper purpose—namely, to create a hybrid form that neither the spirit of man nor God would inhabit because it was neither man nor beast, and thus provided an unusual body made up of human, animal, and plant genetics known as Nephilim, an earth-born facsimile or "fit extension" into which the Watchers could extend themselves.

Given advances in GRINs technology, transhumanist aspirations, and the admitted new arms race of human enhancement discussed in the previous chapter, imagine the staggering spiritual warfare implications of such science if dead Nephilim tissue were discovered with intact DNA and a government somewhere was willing to clone or mingle the extracted organisms for use in (re)creating the ultimate super soldier—Homo-Nephilim. If one accepts the biblical story of Nephilim as real, such a discovery could actually be made someday— or perhaps already has been and was covered up. As an example of this possibility, in 2009, blood was extracted from the bone of a dinosaur that scientists insist is eighty million years old. Nephilim would have existed in relatively recent times comparably, making clonable material from dead biblical giants feasible. The technology to resurrect extinct species already exists. The Pyrenean ibex, an extinct form of wild mountain goat, was brought back to life in 2009 through cloning of DNA taken from skin samples. This was followed in June of 2010 by researchers at Jeju National University in Korea cloning a bull that had been dead for two years. Cloning methods are also being studied for use in bringing back Tasmanian tigers, woolly mammoths, and other extinct creatures, and in the March/April 2010 edition of the respected *Archaeology* magazine, a feature article by Zah Zorich ("Should We Clone Neanderthals?") called for the resurrection via cloning of what some consider to be man's closest extinct relative, the Neanderthals. *National Geographic* confirmed this possibility in its May 2009 special report, "Recipe for a Resurrection," quoting Hendrik Poinar of McMaster University, an authority on ancient DNA who served as a scientific consultant for the movie *Jurassic Park*, saying:

> I laughed when Steven Spielberg said that cloning extinct animals was inevitable. But I'm not laughing anymore.... This is going to happen. It's just a matter of working out the details.[393]

The ramifications of using science to revive extinct animals or Nephilim could extend beyond cloning to include a mysterious germline connection with the armies of Armageddon and the kingdom of Antichrist. This is because, as interbreeding begins between transgenic animals, genetically modified humans, and species as God made them, the altered DNA will quickly migrate into the natural environment. When that happens (as is already occurring among genetically modified plants and animals), "alien" and/or animal characteristics will be introduced to the human gene pool and spread through intermarriage, altering the human genetic code and eventually eliminating humanity as we know it. According to many theologians, this is what happened before the Great Flood, allowing for Nephilim incarnation, and perhaps it has been the whole idea for the end times as well—to create a generation of genetically altered "fit extensions" for the resurrection of underworld Nephilim hordes in preparation of Armageddon.

If, as we believe, the Antichrist is the reincarnation of the ancient demon deity Apollo (the Old Testament Nimrod) as prophesied by the apostles Paul in 2 Thessalonians 2:3 and John in Revelation 17:8, not only will he be the exact opposite of Jesus (Son of God), but he will be the forerunner of the return of the Nephilim. The prophet Isaiah (chapters 13 and 14) spoke of the return of these beings and tied the advent to the destruction of the city of Babylon in the final age (which should give us pause in light of the ongoing presence of US armed forces in Iraq/Babylon and the powder keg surrounding it). From the Septuagint, we read:

> The vision which Esaias son of Amos saw against Babylon. Lift up a standard on the mountain of the plain, exalt the voice to them, beckon with the hand, open the gates, ye ruler. I give command and I bring them: giants are coming to fulfill my wrath.... For behold! The day of the Lord is coming which cannot be escaped, a day of wrath and anger, to make the world desolate.... And Babylon...shall be as when God overthrew Sodom and Gomorrah.... It shall never be inhabited... and monsters shall rest there, and devils shall dance there and satyrs shall dwell there. (Isaiah 13:1–3, 9, 19–22)

One can only speculate if something more than casually perceived is meant by Isaiah when he says, "open the gates, ye ruler," but whoever this ruler is, he opens "gates" in Iraq/Babylon through which end-times giants (*gibborim*) return to the surface of earth as agents of God's wrath. Noting that Isaiah ties the destruction of Iraq/Babylon with the reappearance of *gibborim* in this way, we recall how thousands of US troops, upon invading Iraq during the Bush administration, admittedly filled US containers with archeological materials, including what some have speculated to be cuneiform tablets pointing to the location of pure-blooded Nephilim buried in underground caves. This is exactly where Enoch said the dead antediluvian Nephilim are, and it raises fascinating questions: Would agencies like DARPA have an interest in studying or cloning the extinct beings if they were, or have been, found? Could man in his arrogance revive ancient DNA, revitalizing or blending it with other living organisms in a way similar to what the Watchers did in making the first Nephilim? Is the factual reappearance on earth of such legendary beings verified by Isaiah, who also foresaw transhuman creatures such as *satyrs* (transgenic half-men, half-goats) accompanying the return of giants in the end times, or why other apocryphal books like 2 Esdras 5:8 prophesy the birth of "monsters" for the same period of time? Some may be shocked to learn that, in addition to the citations above, the Bible actually describes an ultimate end-times spiritual warfare between the "mythological gods" and Christ. "The LORD will be terrible unto them: for he will famish all the gods of the earth" says Zephaniah 2:11. "The LORD of hosts, the God of Israel, saith; 'Behold, I will punish the...gods'" (Jeremiah 46:25). Human followers of the pagan deities will join the conflict, calling upon their idols (Revelation 9:20) to convene their powers against the Christian God, uniting with "the spirits of devils working miracles, which go forth unto the kings of the earth... to gather them to the battle of that great day...[to] a place called in the Hebrew tongue Armageddon [Megiddo]" (Revelation 16:13–14, 16). The ancient Book of Jubilees—another apocryphal text—considers the same time frame and verifies contemporaneous Nephilim resurrection. The familiar word "corruption" turns up again in association with these beings, insinuating an end-times repeat of what the

Watchers did by corrupting human DNA and blending it with animals to retrofit human bodies for Nephilim incarnation. Note that this happens just before Satan is judged:

> The malignant evil ones [spirits of Nephilim destroyed in the Flood] were bound in the place of condemnation, but a tenth part of them were left that they might be subject before Satan on the earth. These are for corruption [corruption of DNA as in days of old?] and leading astray men before Satan's judgment. (Jubilees 10:7–12)

The well-known prophecy in the second chapter of the book of Joel also includes reference to returning *gibborim* (giants, Nephilim offspring). Though expositors tend to view Joel describing an army of locusts, he includes *gibborim* in his descriptions in the phrase "they shall run like *mighty men* [*gibborim*]." Does this mean something besides the fact that grasshoppers will be involved in Joel's end-times army?

> [They are] a great people and a strong; there hath not been ever the like, neither shall be any more after it...and nothing shall escape them. The appearance of them is as the appearance of horses; and as horsemen, so shall they run.... They shall run like mighty men [*gibbowr, gibborim*]; they shall climb the wall like men of war.... They shall run to and fro in the city; they shall run upon the wall, they shall climb up upon the houses; they shall enter in at the windows like a thief. The earth shall quake before them.... And the LORD shall utter His voice before His army: for His camp is very great: for He is strong that executeth His word: for the day of the LORD is great and very terrible; and who can abide it? (Joel 2:2–11)

Another expression Joel uses—"the appearance of them is as the appearance of horses; and as horsemen, so shall they run"—sounds like the last-days locusts and transgenic horse-men mutations in Revelation 9:7–19. When all such texts are added up, there is persuasive evidence that the massive *gibborim* army that runs upon the wall from which nobody can escape could be the result of man's willingness to play "god" in reviving forbidden science and opening "gates" to *gibborim* lurking in the beyond.

Does a curious verse in the book of Daniel also hint at this? Speaking of the last days of human government, the prophet said:

> They shall mingle themselves with the seed of men: but they shall not cleave one to another, even as iron is not mixed with clay. (Daniel 2:43)

While Daniel does not explain who "they" that "mingle themselves with the seed of men" are, the personal pronoun "they" caused Chuck Missler and Mark Eastman, in their book, *Alien Encounters,* to remark:

> Just what (or who) are 'mingling with the seed of men?' Who are these non-seed? It staggers the mind to contemplate the potential significance of Daniel's passage and its implications for the future global governance.[394]

Daniel's verse also troubled Missler and Eastman because it seemed to indicate that the same phenomenon that occurred in Genesis chapter 6, where nonhuman species or "nonseed" mingled with human seed and produced Nephilim, would happen again in the end times. When this verse from Daniel is coupled with Genesis 3:15, which says, "And I will put enmity between thee and the woman, and between thy *seed* [*zera*, meaning "offspring," "descendants," or "children"] and her *seed,*" an incredible tenet emerges: Satan has seed, and it has enmity for Christ.

To "mingle" nonhuman seed with Homo sapiens by altering human DNA while simultaneously returning Nephilim to earth has been the inspiration of the spirit of Antichrist ever since God halted the practice during the Great Flood. According to Louis Pauwells and Jacques Bergier in *The Dawn of Magic* (first published in France in 1960 under the title *Le Matin des Magiciens*), this was certainly the goal of the antichrist Adolf Hitler:

> Hitler's aim was neither the founding of a race of supermen, nor the conquest of the world; these were only means towards the realization of the great work he dreamed of. His real aim was to perform an act of creation, a divine operation, the goal of a biological mutation which would result in an unprecedented exaltation of the human race and the "apparition of a new race of heroes and demigods and god-men."[395]

One cannot read the conclusion by Pauwells and Bergier regarding Hitler's antichrist ambition without seeing how it corresponds perfectly with the goals of transhumanism, even to the connection of creating posthuman bodies fit for deity incarnation through genetic engineering.

BIBLICAL EXAMPLE OF NEPHILIM RESURRECTION?

We believe an example of such Nephilim "resurrection" may exist in the Bible, which evolved as a result of human genetic alteration. The story is doubly important to our book because it centers around Nimrod, the original character who later was mythologized as the god Apollo prophesied by the apostle Paul in the New Testament (and by the occult elite on the Great Seal of the United States as detailed in *Apollyon Rising 2012*) as the ancient spirit that will return to earth to rule the *novus ordo seclorum*. The story of Nimrod in the book of Genesis may illustrate how this could happen through genetic engineering or a retrovirus of demonic design that integrates with a host's genome and rewrites the living specimen's DNA, thus making it a "fit extension" or host for infection by the entity. Note what Genesis 10:8 says about Nimrod:

And Cush begat Nimrod: he began to be a mighty one in the earth.

Three sections in this unprecedented verse indicate something very peculiar happened to Nimrod. First, note where the text says, "he *began* to be." In Hebrew, this is *chalal,* which means "to become profaned, defiled, polluted, or desecrated ritually, sexually or genetically." Second, this verse tells us exactly *what* Nimrod began to be as he changed genetically—"a mighty one" (*gibbowr, gibborim*), one of the offspring of Nephilim. As Annette Yoshiko Reed says in the Cambridge University book, *Fallen Angels and the History of Judaism and Christianity*, "The Nephilim of Genesis 6:4 are always... grouped together with the gibborim as the progeny of the Watchers and human women."[396] And the third part of this text says the change to Nimrod started while he was on "earth." Therefore, in modern language, this text could accurately be translated to say: "And Nimrod began to change genetically, becoming a *gibborim*, the offspring of watchers on earth."

To understand how, as a mature, living specimen, Nimrod could have "begun to be a gibborim," it is helpful to imagine this in terms of biology as we know it. For instance, at one point, Tom "began to be" a diabetic. Because of poor choices of food, diet, and exercise, his doctor said he triggered a genetic inherent and that it began changing him genetically. Yet just because he had the heritable, disease-related genotype that can lead to diabetes, this didn't necessarily mean he would develop the medical condition. It is entirely possible to be a carrier of a genetic mutation that increases the risk of developing a particular disease without ever actually becoming afflicted with the disorder in the course of a lifetime. Due to his earlier lifestyle, or maybe even certain environmental conditions he was unaware of, the gene mutation involved in the action of insulin "turned on," and he "began to be" a diabetic.

We've often wondered if the record of Nimrod that says he "began to be" a "gibborim" indicated something similar about his genetics,

310

DNA, or bloodline that "turned on" as a result of his decisions, triggering a change in him from one type of being to another. It is also a possibility, we suppose, that Nimrod became afflicted with a retrovirus that integrated with his genome and, in essence, "rewrote" his genetic makeup, fashioning him into a transhuman or posthuman "fit extension" for an underworldly spirit. When we asked Sharon Gilbert, author of *The Armageddon Strain,* whose formal education includes theology, molecular biology, and genetics, if she thought this was possible, she said:

> Absolutely! Retroviruses essentially inject single-stranded RNA strands into somatic (body) cells during "infection." These ssRNA strands access nucleotide pools in the host cell and form a double-stranded DNA copy. This dsDNA can then incorporate itself into the host chromosome using a viral enzyme called "integrase." The new "fake gene" then orders the cell to make more mRNA copies of the original virus RNA. These then travel out of the cell and infect the next cell, and so on.

Perhaps this type of genetic rewriting is implied in Genesis 10:8, which says, "And Cush begat Nimrod: he began to be a mighty one [*gibborim*] in the earth."

In addition to such scientific deduction, another reason we believe this story is suspicious is because of what Nimrod did immediately following Genesis chapter 10. As soon as he "began to be a mighty one," he set out to build a tower whose top would "reach unto heaven" (Genesis 11:4). This was the infamous Tower of Babel, and Nimrod was designing it so that the top of it would extend into *Shamayim* ("Heaven"), the abode of God. The *Jewish Encyclopedia* confirms several historical records that Nimrod, whom it establishes was also identified by various ancient cultures alternatively as the god Apollo, built the Tower of Babel in an attempt to defiantly ascend into the presence of God. Jehovah Himself came down and said of the structure's design:

Nothing will be restrained from them, which they have imagined to do. (Genesis 11:6)

In other words, according to the Lord, Nimrod would have accomplished what he "imagined" to do—to build a tower whose top would reach into the abode of God.

That this section of Scripture could be viewed as a secondary support for the concept of Nimrod having become "revived Watcher offspring" is supported by Nimrod seeming to be abruptly aware of *where* and *how tall* to build a tower so that the top of it would penetrate the dwelling place of God. Were his eyes suddenly opened to realities that are outside a person's normal mode of perception? Did he become Professor Nick Bostrom and the Arizona State University's SOPHIA Project dream come true, capable of seeing into the spirit world as a result of transhuman or posthuman alteration? If Nimrod was genetically modified according to the original Watcher formula, he would have inherited animal characteristics (Bostrom's method) within his new material makeup, and, according to the biblical story of Balaam's donkey, animals can, like angels, perceive "domains" that humans cannot. This includes obvious things, such as wavelengths of the electromagnetic spectrum, but evidently something even more substantial, like the spirit realm. Additionally, as Nimrod/Apollo became *gibborim*, he would have taken on Watchers' propensities, which, as angels, could see into the supernatural realm including where Heaven is located and possibly where to enter it. Even the name "Babylon" implies this, meaning the "gate of God" or "gateway *to* God." Sacred locations where beings that can see into the supernatural realm could literally walk up onto a high place and enter Heaven is not as far-fetched as it sounds. Numerous examples from the Bible may substantiate the idea that Heaven could be attained on high towers or mountainous locations. Consider Moses meeting with God on Sinai, Jesus returning atop the Mount of Olives, the two hundred Watchers that "descended in the days of Jared on the summit of Mount

Hermon" (from the Apocryphal Book of Enoch 6:6), and other examples, including Jacob's ladder. This could also explain why, in the deep recesses of our psyche, people tend to believe they can draw closer to God when going up onto mountains.

The big question is this: Could a modern form of a genetically altered Nimrod/Apollo returning as the Antichrist with an army of revived Nephilim reopen these gateways (Isaiah 13:2–3) and fulfill the sign of "the days of Noah," which Jesus said would mark the time just prior to His return? A growing body of theologians believes so, and we make no argument against it, but we are happy in the next and final section of this book to share "other" signs of the days of Noah, ones we believe could be manifested in these troubling times as well—signs wherein true believers become the only power on earth against which this *spirit of transhumanism* cannot prevail.

THE TRANSHUMAN
NEW FACE OF
SPIRITUAL WARFARE

If the U.S. [today] has a national religion,
the closest thing to it is faith in technology.
—Scott Keeter, director of survey research
for the Pew Research Center

Yet again humankind seems ready to plunge headlong into
another human, or demonic, contrivance promising salvation
and eternal happiness for all. This time the Faustian bargain
is being struck with technology, what John McDermott
referred to as the "opiate of the intellectuals."
—C. Christopher Hook, MD

When the stars align, Cthulhu will rise again to resume
His dominion over the Earth, ushering in an age
of frenzied abandon. Humankind will be "free and wild
and beyond good and evil, with laws and morals thrown aside
and all men shouting and killing and reveling in joy."
—Transhumanist Mark Dery, celebrating the rise
of H. P. Lovecraft's cosmic monster

On July 20, 2010, the *New York Times* ran a feature introducing a new nonprofit organization called the Lifeboat Foundation.[397] The concept behind the group is simple yet disturbing. Protecting people from threats posed by potentially catastrophic technology—ranging from artificial intelligence running amok to self-replicating nanobots—represents an emerging opportunity for designing high-tech "shields," and lots of them, to protect humankind this century. The article states:

> For example, there's talk of a Neuroethics Shield to prevent abuse in the areas of neuropharmaceuticals, neurodevices, and neurodiagnostics. Worse cases include enslaving the world's population or causing everyone to commit suicide.
>
> And then there's a Personality Preserver that would help people keep their personalities intact and a Nano Shield to protect against overly aggressive nanocreatures.

If the Lifeboat Foundation sounds like a storehouse for overreacting geeks or even outright nut jobs, consider that their donors involve Google, Hewlett-Packard, Sun Microsystems, and an impressive list of industry and technology executives, including names on their advisory boards like Nobel laureate and Princeton University Professor Eric Maskin.

What the development of such enterprising research groups illustrates is that even if one doesn't believe speculation from the previous chapters suggesting mind-bending concepts like Nephilim being resurrected into posthuman bodies via GRIN technology, all of society—regardless of religious or secular worldviews—should consider that what we are doing now through genetic modification of living organisms and the wholesale creation of new synthetic life-forms is either a violation of the divine order (biblical Creation, such as the authors of this book believe) or chaos upon natural evolution, or both. The road we have started down is thus wrought with unknown perils, and the Lifeboat Foundation is correct to discern how the transhuman era may abruptly result in the need for "shields" to protect earth species from designer viruses, nanobugs, prion contamination, and a host of other clear and present dangers. Part of the obvious reasons behind this is, in addition to the known shortcomings of biotechnology corporations and research facilities to remain impartial in their safety reviews (they have a vested interest in protecting approval and distribution of their products), futurist think tanks such as the Lifeboat Foundation understand that the phrase, "those who fail to learn from history are doomed to repeat it," is axiomatic for a reason. Human nature has a clear track record of developing defense mechanisms only after natural or manufactured threats have led to catastrophe. We humans seem doomed to learn from our mistakes far more often than from prevention. Consider how nuclear reactors were forced to become safer only after the Chernobyl disaster, or how a tsunami warning system was developed by the United Nations following 230,000 people being killed by a titanic wave in the Indian Ocean. This fact of human nature portends an especially ill wind for humankind when viewed against the existential threats of biological creations, artificial intelligence systems, or the geoengineering of nature, which carry the potential not only of backfiring but of permanently altering the course of humanity. "Our attitude throughout human history has been to experience events like these and then to put safeguards in place," writes Professor Nick Bostrom. "That strategy is completely futile with existential risks [as represented in GRINtech]. By definition, you don't get to learn from experience. You only have one chance to get it right."[398] Because of the truly catastrophic threat thus posed by mostly unregulated GRIN advances this century, Richard Posner, a US appeals court judge and author of the book *Catastrophe: Risk and Response*, wants "an Office of Risk and Catastrophe set up in the White House. The office would be charged with identifying potentially dangerous technologies and calling in experts to inform its own risk assessment." The problem right now, Posner adds, "is that no single government department takes responsibility for these kinds of situations."[399] Not surprisingly, many transhumanists contest Posner's idea, saying it represents just another unnecessary bureaucracy that would stand in the way of scientific progress.

Yet of greater significance and repeatedly missing from such secular considerations is what the authors of this book believe to be the more important element: supernaturalism and spirituality. Beyond the material ramifications of those threats posed by the genetics revolution is something most scientists, engineers, and bioethicists fail to comprehend—that humans are not just a series of biological functions. We are spirit and soul and vulnerable to spiritual, not just environmental, dangers. Thus the "shields" the Lifeboat Foundation is working on will only protect us so far. We will need *spiritual shields,* too, as GRIN raises those bigger issues of how human-transforming enhancements may alter our very souls (says Joel Garreau) as well as hundreds of immediate new challenges that Christians, families, and ministries will be facing.

It's an understatement to say technology often works hand in hand with unseen forces to challenge our faith or open new channels for spiritual warfare. This has been illustrated in thousands of ways down through time—from the creation of Ouija boards for contacting the spirit world to online pornography gateways. But the current course upon which GRIN technology and transhumanist philosophy is taking humanity threatens to elevate the reality of these dangers to quantitatively higher levels. Some of the spiritual hazards already surfacing as a result of modern technology include unfamiliar terms like "i-dosing," in which teens get "digitally high" by playing specific Internet videos through headphones that use repetitive tones to create binaural beats, which have been shown in clinical studies to induce particular brainwave states that make the sounds appear to come from the center of the head. Shamans have used variations of such repetitive tones and drumming to stimulate and focus the "center mind" for centuries to make contact with the spirit world and to achieve altered states of consciousness.

More broadly, the Internet itself, together with increasing forms of electronic information-driven technology, is creating a new kind of addiction by "rewiring our brains," says Nora Volkow, world-renowned brain scientist and director of the National Institute of Drug Abuse. The lure of "digital stimulation" can actually produce dopamine releases in the brain that affect the heart rate and blood pressure and lead to drug-like highs and lows. As bad, the addictive craving for digital stimulation is leading to the electronic equivalent of attention deficit disorder (ADD) among an increasing population in which constant bursts of information and digital stimulation undermine one's ability to focus—especially in children, whose brains are still developing and who naturally struggle to resist impulses or to neglect priorities. A growing body of literature is verifying this e-connection to personality fragmentation, cyber-relationships over personal ones, and other psychosocial issues. Volkow and other researchers see these antisocial trends leading to widespread diminished empathy between people—which is essential to the human condition—as a result of humans paying more and more attention to iPads, cell phones, and computer screens than to each other, even when sitting in the same room. New research shows this situation becoming an electronic pandemic as people escalate their detachment from traditional family relationships while consuming three times as much digital information today as they did in 2008, checking e-mails, texting thirty-seven times per hour, and spending twelve hours per day on average taking in other e-media.

How brain-machine interfacing will multiply this divide between human-to-human relationships versus human-machine integration should be of substantial concern to readers for several reasons, including how 1) the Borgification of humans will naturally exasperate the decline of the family unit and interpersonal relationships upon which society has historically depended; 2) the increase of euphoric cybernetic addiction will multiply as cerebral stimulation of the brain's pleasure centers is added to existing natural senses—sight, hearing, taste, smell, and touch; and 3) the threat of computer viruses or hijackers disrupting enhanced human neural or cognitive pathways will develop as cyber-enhanced individuals evolve. To illustrate the latter, Dr. Mark Gasson, from the School of Systems Engineering at the University of Reading in the United Kingdom, intentionally contaminated an implanted microchip in his hand that allows him biometric entry through security doors and that also communicates with his cell phone and other external devices. In the experiment, Dr. Gasson (who agrees that the next step in human evolution is the trans-human vision of altered human biology integrated with machines) was able to show how the computer virus he infected himself with spread to external computer systems in communication with his microchip. He told BBC News:

> With the benefits of this type of technology come risks. We [will] improve ourselves…but much like the improvements with other technologies, mobile phones for example, they become vulnerable to risks, such as security problems and computer viruses.[400]

Such threats—computer viruses passing from enhanced humans to enhanced humans via future cybernetic systems—are the tip of the iceberg. The real danger, though it may be entirely unavoidable for some, will be the loss of individuality, anonymity, privacy, and even free will as a result of cybernetic integration. Dr. Christopher Hook contends that "if implanted devices allow the exchange of information between the biological substrate and the cybernetic device," such a device in the hippocampus (the part of the brain involved in forming, storing, and processing memory) for augmenting memory, for instance, "would be intimately associated with the creation and recall of memories as well as with all the emotions inherent in that process."

Dr. Hook continues:

> If this device were…to allow the importation of information from the Internet, could the device also allow the memories and thoughts of the individual to be downloaded or read by

others? In essence, what is to prevent the brain itself from being hacked [or externally monitored]? The last bastion of human privacy, the brain, will have been breached.[401]

Despite these significant ethical and social dangers, industry and government interest in the technological dream of posthumanism, as documented earlier in this book, is more than *laissez-faire*. The steady migration toward the fulfillment of biologically and cybernetically modified humans, combined with corporate and national investments, will predictably fuse this century, ultimately leading to strong cultural forces compelling all individuals to get "plugged in" to the grid. Whoever resists will be left behind as inferior Luddites, or worse, considered enemies of the collectives' progress, as in de Garis' nightmarish vision in the *Artilect War* or former counterterrorism czar Richard Clark's *Breakpoint,* which depicts those who refuse technological enhancement as "terrorists."

According to the work *Human Dignity in the Biotech Century,* this pressure to become enhanced will be dramatic upon people in all social strata, including those in the middle class, law, engineering, finance, professional fields, and the military, regardless of personal or religious views:

Consider...whether the military, after investing billions in the development of technologies to create the cyborg soldier... would allow individual soldiers to decline the enhancements because of religious or personal qualms. It is not likely. Individuals may indeed dissent and decline technological augmentation, but such dissenters will find job options increasingly scarce.

Because the network of cyborgs will require increasing levels of cooperation and harmonious coordination to further improve efficiency, the prostheses will continue to introduce means of controlling or modulating emotion to promote these values. Meanwhile, the network is increasingly controlled by central planning structures to facilitate harmony and efficiency. While everyone still considers themselves fully autonomous, in reality behavior is more and more tightly controlled. Each step moves those who are cybernetically augmented toward becoming like the Borg, the race of cybernetic organisms that inhabit the twenty-sixth century of the *Star Trek* mythology. The Borg, once fully human, become "assimilated" by the greater collective mind, losing individuality for the good of the whole.[402]

Lest anyone think the writers of *Human Dignity in the Biotech Century* are overly paranoid, consider that NBIC (nanotechnology, biotechnology, information technology, and cognitive science) director Mihail Roco, in the US government report, *Converging Technologies for Improving Human Performance*, wrote:

> Humanity would become like a single, distributed and interconnected "brain" based in new core pathways in society.... A networked society of billions of human beings could be as complex compared to an individual being as a human being is to a single nerve cell. From local groups of linked enhanced individuals to a global collective intelligence, key new capacities would arise from relationships arising from NBIC technologies.... Far from unnatural, such a collective social system may be compared to a larger form of biological organism.... We envision the bond of humanity driven by an *interconnected virtual brain* of the Earth's communities searching for intellectual comprehension and conquest of nature.[403]

Nowhere will the struggle to resist this human biological alteration and machine integration be more immediate than in religious homes where transhumanism is seen as an assault on God's creative genius, and where, as a result, people of faith seek to maintain their humanity. Yet the war against such believers is poised to emerge over the next decade as much from inside these homes and families as it will from external social influences.

As a simple example, flash forward to the near future when much of the technology previously discussed—factually based on emerging technologies and anticipated time frames—is common. Your tenth-grade daughter, Michelle, walks in from a first day at a new school.

"Well, how did it go, honey?" you ask with a smile.

"It was okay," she says, "though the kids here are even smarter than at the last school." But then she pauses. She knows begging to be enhanced like most of her classmates will only lead to more arguing—common between you two on this subject. How can she make you understand what it's like even trying to compete with the transhumans? The fact that most of the student body, students who are half her age, will graduate from college *summa cum laude* with IQs higher than Einstein's by the time she even enters is a ridiculous and unnecessary impediment, she feels. She can't understand it. You've seen the news, the advertising, the *H+* magazines articles and television specials outlining the advantages of enhancement. Even the family doctor tried to convince you. But it will probably take a visit from Child Welfare Services, which in the US is soon to follow the European model where, in 2019, activists were trying to enforce policies that stated that parents whose children went without basic modifications were charged with neglect and had their kids put in foster homes. She just wishes it wouldn't come to that. If only you could be like those Emergent Christians 2.0 whose techno-theology arose during the early enhancement craze of 2016–2018, based on a universalist imperative for "perfectionist morality" and the Christian duty to be "healers and perfecters" as opposed to the "bio-Luddite theology" of your outdated religious "divine order" concept, which only keeps people like her at a disadvantage. That's why she gave you the school report compiled by Professor Garreau describing the average high school pupil today, so you could understand how her classmates:

- Have amazing thinking abilities. They're not only faster and more creative than anyone she's ever met, but faster and more creative than anyone she's ever imagined.
- They have photographic memories and total recall. They can devour books in minutes.
- They're beautiful, physically. Although they don't put much of a premium on exercise, their bodies are remarkably ripped.
- They talk casually about living a long time, perhaps being immortal. They're always discussing their "next lives." One fellow mentions how, after he makes his pile as a lawyer, he plans to be a glassblower, after which he wants to become a nanosurgeon.
- One of her new friends fell while jogging, opening up a nasty gash on her knee. Your daughter freaked, ready to rush her to the hospital. But her friend just stared at the gaping wound, focusing her mind on it. Within minutes, it simply stopped bleeding.
- This same friend has been vaccinated against pain. She never feels acute pain for long.
- These new friends are always connected to each other, sharing their thoughts no matter how far apart, with no apparent gear. They call it "silent messaging." It seems like telepathy.
- They have this odd habit of cocking their head in a certain way whenever they want to access information they don't yet have in their own skulls—as if waiting for a delivery to arrive wirelessly...which it does.
- For a week or more at a time, they don't sleep. They joke about getting rid of their beds, since they use them so rarely.[404]

Even though these enhanced students treat her with compassion and know she is biologically and mentally handicapped by no fault of her own, she hates it when they call her a "Natural." It feels so condescending. And then, at the last school, there was that boy she wanted to date, only to discover it was against the informed-consent regulations passed by the Department of Education restricting romantic relationships between "Naturals" and the "Enhanced." She could have crawled into a hole she was so embarrassed. But she's decided not to fight you anymore about it. Next year she will be eighteen years old and has been saving her money. With the federal Unenhanced Student Aid programs administered by the US Department of Education and the United Naturals Student Fund (UNSF) that provides financial assistance and support for "Disaugmented American Students," grades pre-kindergarten to twelve, whose motto is, "An augmented mind is a terrible thing to waste," she'll have enough for Level 1 Genetic Improvement plus a couple of toys like Bluetooth's new extracranial cybernetic communicator. It's not much, but it's a start, and though you will tell her that her brain-machine interface, and especially her genetic upgrade, makes her—as well as any kids she has in the future—inhuman, according to the school's genetic guidance counselor, there will be nothing you can do to legally stop her.

THE DEVIL IS IN THE DETAILS

As transhumanist philosophy and GRIN technology become integrated within society and national and private laboratories with their corporate allies provide increasingly sophisticated arguments for its widest adoption, those of us who treasure the meaning of life and human nature as defined by Judeo-Christian values will progressively find ourselves engaged in deepening spiritual conflicts over maintaining our humanity in the midst of what we believe is fundamentally a supernatural conflict.

Just as the fictional exercise with the seventeen-year-old "Michelle" above illustrates, intensifying techno-spiritual issues Christian families will face this century will escalate simultaneously at both spiritual and scientific levels. This material/immaterial struggle, which philosopher and theologian Francis Schaeffer once described as always at war "in the thought-world," is difficult for some to grasp. The idea that human-transforming technology that mingles the DNA of natural and synthetic beings and merges human with machine could somehow be used or even inspired by *evil supernaturalism* to foment destruction within the material world is for some people so exotic as to be inconceivable. Yet nothing should be more fundamentally clear, as students of spiritual warfare will understand. We are body (physical form), mind (soul, will, emotions), and spirit, thus everything in the material and immaterial world has potential to influence our psychosomatic existence and decisions. "There is no conflict in our lives that is strictly a spiritual issue," writes Robert Jeffress in his book, *The Divine Defense*. This is because "there is never a time when the spirit is divorced from the body. Likewise, there is no turmoil in our lives that is solely psychological or physical, because our spirit, along with God's Spirit within us and demonic spirits around us, is always present as well."[405] Jeffress' point that material stimuli cannot be divorced from spiritual conditions conveys why the Bible is so concerned with the antitheses of transhumanism—the integrity of our bodies and minds. The goal is to bring both into obedience to Christ (2 Chronicles 10:5), because this is where the battle is first fought and won. No marriage breakup ever transpired that did not start there—no murder, no theft, no idolatry—but that the contest was staged in the imagination, then married to the senses, and the decision to act given to the victor.

How technology is now poised to raise this mind-body-spirit game is hidden in the shadows of the National Institute of Health and DARPA, which for more than three decades have invested hundreds of millions of dollars not only designing new DNA constructs but crafting arrays of microelectrodes, supercomputers, and algorithms to analyze and decipher the brain's neural code, the complex "syntax" and communication rules that transform electrical neuron pulses in the brain into specific digital and analog information we ultimately perceive as decisions, memories, and emotions. Understanding how this secret brain language functions, then parsing it down into digital computer code (strings of ones and zeros), where it can be reassembled into words and commands and then manipulated, is at the center of military neurobiology, artificial intelligence research, and cybernetics.

While significant studies in neurosciences have been conducted with "neuro-prostheses" in mind to help the handicapped—for instance, the artificial cochlear implant that approximately 188,000 people worldwide have received thus far—DARPA "is less interested in treating the disabled than in enhancing the cognitive capacities of soldiers," says former senior writer at *Scientific American*, John Horgan. "DARPA officials have breached the prospect of cyborg warriors downloading complex fighting procedures directly into their brains, like the heroes of the Matrix," and has "interest in the development of techniques that can survey and possibly manipulate the mental processes of potential enemies [by] recording signals from the brains of enemy personnel at a distance, in order to 'read their minds and to control them.'"[406] Because what develops within military technology eventually migrates into the broader culture, where it is quickly embraced for competitive or mutual advantages, the ramifications of neurobiology have not escaped international interests in both public and private agencies. Entire fields of research are now under development worldwide based on the notion that breakthroughs will provide unprecedented opportunities for reading, influencing, and even controlling human minds this century. The implications from this field are so staggering that France, in 2010, became the first nation to establish a behavioral research unit specifically designed to study and set "neuropolicy" to govern how such things as "neuromarketing" (a field of marketing that analyzes consumers' sensorimotor and cognitive responses to stimuli in order to decode what part of the brain is telling consumers to make certain buying decisions) may be used in the future to access unconscious decision-making elements of the brain to produce desired responses. This precedent for government neuropolicy comes not a second too soon, as the world's largest semiconductor chip maker, Intel Corp., has wanted brain communicators on the market and "in its customers' heads" since before the year 2020. In what can only be described as *Matrix* creep, researchers at Intel Labs Pittsburgh are designing what it bets will be "the next big thing"—brain chips that allow consumers to control a host of new electronic and communication gadgets by way of neural commands. Developers at Toyota and the University of Utah are also working on brain transmitters, which they hope will contribute to building a global "hive mind."

From these developments comes the distant groaning of a "fearful unknown" in which the architecture of the human brain—as transformed by current and future cybernetic inventions—begins to act in ways that borderline the supernatural. Consider experimental telepathy, which involves mind-to-mind thought transference that allows people to communicate without the use of speaking audibly. Most do not know that Hans Berger, the inventor of electroencephalography (EEG, the recording of electrical activity along the scalp produced by the firing of neurons within the brain) was a strong believer in psychic phenomena and wanted to decode brain signals to establish nonverbal transmission between people. GRIN technology proposes to fulfill his dream.

Another example is telekinesis (psychokinesis), which involves the movement or manipulation of physical matter via direct influence of the mind. As incredible as it may seem, both this idea and the one above are under research by DARPA and other national laboratories as no pipe dream. Such brain-to-brain transmission between distant persons as well as mind-to-computer communication was demonstrated recently at the University of Southampton's Institute of Sound and Vibration Research using electrodes and an Internet connection. The experiment at the institute went farther than most brain-to-machine interfacing (BMI) technology thus far, actually demonstrating brain-to-brain (B2B) communication between persons at a distance. Dr. Christopher James, who oversaw the experiment, commented:

> Whilst BCI [brain-computer interface] is no longer a new
> thing and person-to-person communication via the nervous

THE TRANSHUMAN NEW FACE OF SPIRITUAL WARFARE

system was shown previously in work by Prof. Kevin Warwick from the University of Reading, here we show, for the first time, true brain to brain interfacing. We have yet to grasp the full implications of this.

The experiment allowed one person using BCI to transmit thoughts, translated as a series of binary digits, over the Internet to another person whose computer received the digits and transmitted them to the second user's brain.[407]

The real danger is how these accomplishments within human-mind-to-synthetic intelligence may take the proverbial "ghost in the machine" where no *modern human* has gone before, bridging a gap between unknown entities (both virtual and real), perhaps even inviting takeover of our species by malevolent intelligence. Is that what will be behind the living image of the Beast in Revelation, chapter 13?

Note that the experiments above are being conducted at Southampton's Institute of Sound and Vibration Research. Some years ago, scientist Vic Tandy's research into sound, vibration frequencies, and eyeball resonation led to a thesis (actually titled "Ghosts in the Machine") that was published in the *Journal of the Society for Psychical Research*. Tandy's findings outlined what he thought were "natural causes" for particular cases of specter materialization. Tandy found that 19-Hz standing air waves could, under some circumstances, create sensory phenomena in an open environment suggestive of a ghost. He actually produced a frightening manifested entity resembling contemporary descriptions of "alien grays." A similar phenomenon was discovered in 2006 by neurologist Olaf Blanke of the Brain Mind Institute in Lausanne, Switzerland, while working with a team to discover the source of epileptic seizures in a young woman. They were applying electrical currents through surgically implanted electrodes to various regions of her brain, when, upon reaching her left temporoparietal junction (TPJ, located roughly above the left ear), she suddenly reported feeling the presence of a shadow person standing behind her. The phantom started imitating her body posture, lying down beneath her when she was on the bed, sitting behind her, and later even attempting to take a test card away from her during a language exercise. While the scientists interpreted the activity as a natural, though mysterious, biological function of the brain, is it possible they were actually discovering gateways of perception into the spirit world that were closed by God following the Fall of man? Were Tandy's "ghost" and Blanke's "shadow person" *living unknowns?* If so, is it not troubling that advocates of human-mind-to-machine intelligence may produce permanent conditions similar to Tandy and Blanke's findings, giving rise to simulated or real relationships between humans and "entities"? At the thirteenth European Meeting on Cybernetics and Systems Research at the University of Vienna in Austria, an original paper submitted by Charles Ostman seemed to echo this possibility:

> As this threshold of development is crossed, as an index of our human /Internet symbiosis becoming more pronounced, and irreversible, we begin to develop communication modalities which are quite "nonhuman" by nature, but are "socio-operative" norms of the near future. Our collective development and deployment of complex metasystems of artificial entities and synthetic life-forms, and acceptance of them as an integral component of the operational "culture norm" of the near future, is in fact the precursory developmental increment, as an enabling procedure, to gain effective communicative access to *a contiguous collection of myriad "species" and entity types (synthetic and "real") functioning as process brokeraging agents.*[408]

A similar issue that "pinged" in our memories from past experience with exorcism and the connection between *sound resonance* and contact with supernaturalism has to do with people who claim to have become possessed or "demonized" after attempting to open mind gateways through vibratory chanting at New Age vortices or "Mother

Earth" energy sites such as Sedona, Arizona. When we queried www.
RaidersNewsNetwork.com resident expert Sue Bradley on this subject, asking if she believed a connection could exist between acoustics,
harmonics, sound resonance, and spirit gateways, she emailed this
lengthy and shocking response:

> From the ancients to the New Age, resonance and harmon-
> ics have long been recognized as vehicles of communication
> and manifestation. Ancient rock outcroppings, sacred temples,
> and monuments have for millennia been used as gathering
> places for the so-called spiritually enlightened. Through recent
> understanding of quantum entanglement and the high energy
> physics of sound and light, both with adaptable vibratory char-
> acteristics, these popular sites for gatherings with ritual chants
> and offerings, often employing ancient spells and mathemati-
> cal harmonic codes in various sets of tandem frequencies, may
> well have measurable and far greater esoteric effects than even
> recently believed.[409]

Note what New Ager and modern shaman Zacciah Blackburn of
Sacred Sound, Sound the Codes says he came in contact with at such
sites:

> It is not mere coincidence many of the ancient stone temples
> of the world were made with crystalline embedded stones, such
> as granite, which are known for their properties to pass or store
> energy.... Through Sacred Sound and awareness practices, the
> unseen "wisdom keepers" and guardians of these sacred temples
> have communed with me, and showed me how to hold fre-
> quency of awareness in the heart and mind, and combine them
> into sound codes to create a "key" which opens the "libraries"
> of these temples of ancient star beings and wisdom keepers to
> the modern way traveler whom comes with pure intent.[410]

With this in mind, also consider how the word "ear" appears 120 times in Scripture, "ears" 151 times, and is important with regard to *sound connected to spiritual hearing*. First used in Exodus 15:26, the ear is linked to a covenant relationship for those that *hearken* to the voice of the Lord and keep His statutes. The *right ear* is repeatedly described in the Levitical instructions: "Then shalt thou kill the ram, and take of his blood, and put it upon the tip of the right ear of Aaron, and upon the tip of the right ear of his sons" (Exodus 29:20; [Leviticus 8:23 and 24; 14:14, 17, 25, and 28].

Subsequent references to the ear and hearing are presented as petitions *to* God from His servants as well as *from* God as counsel, forewarning and rebukes.

The ear as a spiritual gateway termed "Ear-Gate" first appeared in English usage through an allegory penned by John Bunyan in 1682. Bunyan's classic, *The Pilgrim's Progress,* was the most widely read and translated book in the English language apart from the Bible: it was also an educational staple and considered to be required reading in the U.S. from colonial times through World War II. While *The Pilgrim's Progress* allegorizes the encounters and obstacles of a man seeking salvation, Bunyan's *The Holy War* or *The Losing and Taking Again of the Town of Mansoul* recounts the cosmic conflict for the souls of mankind with Peretti-like descriptions and precision.

The town of Mansoul, designed in the image of the almighty, *Shaddai,* is the target of the deceptive and malevolent giant, *Diabolus.* Mansoul is a city of five gates: the Ear-Gate, Eye-Gate, Mouth-Gate, Nose-Gate and Feel-Gate. The first and most strategic gate is the first gate breached: the Ear-Gate.

Nineteenth-century theologian, Rev. Robert Maguire, comments on the importance of the Ear-Gate:

> This was the gate of audience, and through this gate the words
> of the tempter must penetrate, if the temptation is to be suc-
> cessful. Into the ears of our first mother did the wily serpent

whisper the glozing words of his seductive wiles and through the Ear-Gate, he assailed her heart and won it. To give audience to the tempter is the next step to yielding up obedience to his will.[411]

One of the two principal powers in Mansoul, *Resistance*, quickly succumbs to an arrow from the army of Diabolus. The promises of Diabolus are familiar: to *enlarge the town* of man-soul, *to augment their freedom* and in the subtlety of pattern identical to Eden, *challenging the prohibition of the Tree of Knowledge* itself.

Dr. Maguire continues to describe this initial incursion at the Ear-Gate with the introduction of Mr. Ill-Pause, another of the diabolical army that visits Mansoul:

> Satan has many mysterious angels who are ready to second their master's temptations and to commend his wily overtures. Thus Ill-Pause persuades the men of Mansoul; and, lo! to the temptation from without (which was utterly powerless in itself), there answers the yielding from within. This is the fatal act; and is straightaway followed by another grave disaster— the death of Innocency, one of the chiefest and most honorable townsmen. His sensitive soul was poisoned by the contact of the breath of the lost[412]

The Holy War continues with civil war raging within Mansoul and the defeat of the giant Diabolus and his demonic army by the son of Shaddai, Emmanuel, but the allegory perhaps finds more direct application in the twenty-first century than earlier. This is because, more than any other time in history, the seduction of high-tech has taken firm root—and among the most vulnerable of the population. Culturally adrift, this high risk generation, most of whom have never heard the exquisite truths of John Bunyan, has been denied spiritual cultivation through an educational system which values tolerance above absolutes and through social training that elevates technology above heritage.

FULL-FLEDGED EAR-GATE ASSAULT

With the advent of cell phones, iPods, and other personal devices, the ear-gates of an entire generation have been dangerously compromised. In addition to the obvious physical risks that associate cell phone use and texting while driving, effects have been measured on teenage language abilities and a markedly increased incidence of tinnitus, a chronic ringing in the ears.

A 2005 ChildWise study found that one in four children under the age of eight had a mobile phone, a figure which increased to 89 percent by the time the child reaches eleven years.

"Teenagers: A Generation Unplugged" is a 2008 study that determined four out of five teens carry a wireless device (an increase of 40 percent from 2004) and found that their cell phones rank second, only to clothing, in communicating personal social status and popularity, "outranking jewelry, watches and shoes." Additionally, over half (52 percent) view cell phones as a form of entertainment and 80 percent feel that a cell phone provides a sense of security while 36 percent dislike the idea of others knowing their exact location.

While a recent World Health Organization study determined that a cell phone-cancer link is inconclusive, the United Nations did acknowledge that a 2010 examination of thirteen thousand participants found up to 40 percent higher incidence of glioma, a cancerous brain tumor, among the 10 percent that used the mobile phone most. While there is near-unanimous agreement within the scientific community that it is simply too early to accurately project damage caused by radiation, even the most modest estimates acknowledge minimal consequences; the estimated 4.6 billion cell phone users "appear prepared to take the risk" without "firm assurances" that they are safe.[413]

As dire as these possibilities for physical damage appear, the psychological and spiritual implications are significantly more profound—and sinister.

"Thought reading" has come of age. First published in January 2009, CBS revealed technology conducted at Carnegie Mellon University that makes it possible to see what is happening within the brain while people are thinking. Using specialized magnetic resonance, neuro-activity can be recorded by analyzing brain activity.[414]

While mainstream media carefully smudges the science fiction-actual science line, both government and private research groups charge the fields of neuro-fingerprinting, neuro-databases, and abject control neuro-control.

Following the Human Genome Project's mapping of human DNA, the Human Brain Project, HPB, was launched. The international research group hopes to provide a "blueprint of normal brain activity" to the goal of understanding brain function for improved healthcare, but inherent in the study is the very real possibility of threatening autonomous and unrestricted thought. If in 2002 the BBC was touting wireless sensors that record and generate brain waves and anatomical functions remotely,[415] and in 2008, *Scientific American* reported that scientists can "selectively control brain function by transcranial magnetic stimulation (TMS)" via the pulsing of powerful electromagnetic fields into the brain or a subject's brain circuits,[416] what might be a more current—and sinister—application?

UNBOUNDED EVIL

A March 2010 study published in the *Proceedings of the National Academy of Sciences* reported that electromagnetic currents directed at the right TPJ, located just above and behind the right ear (the same location mentioned above from Exodus 29:20 where the priests were to be anointed that they might hear from God), can impair a person's ability to make moral judgments by inducing a current that disrupts this region of the brain.

By producing "striking evidence" that the right TPJ is "critical for making moral judgments," the lead author, Liane Young, also noted that, "under normal circumstances, people are very confident and consistent in these kinds of moral judgments." The researchers believe that transmagnetic stimulation, TMS, interfered with the subject's ability to interpret the intentions of others, suggesting that they are believed to be "morally blameworthy."[417] Subsequent publications have proposed an interest by the US military to use transmagnetic stimulation to enhance soldiers' battle duration by reducing the need to stop for sleep.[418]

With the acknowledged identification, documentation, and cataloging of "brain-printing" via wireless devices, and the comparatively recent release of the morally consequential findings of transmagnetic stimulation, the premise of Stephen King's 2006 novel, *Cell*, evokes a frighteningly possible scenario:

> Mobile phones deliver the apocalypse to millions of unsuspecting humans by wiping their brains of any humanity, leaving only aggressive and destructive impulses behind....
> What if cell phones didn't cause cancer? What if they did something much worse? What if they turned the user into a zombie killing machine?[419]

Or perhaps just a glance at a keyboard before powering down: The message is clear: CONTROL...ALTER...DELETE.

MIND GATES:
FROM NIGHTMARES TO INCEPTION

From Sue Bradley's chilling e-mail above discussing how the area of the right ear (which was to be anointed for priestly hearing of God in the Old Testament) is now being targeted by electromagnetic currents to illustrate how a person's moral judgment could be impaired, to the work of neurologist Olaf Blanke that produced a "shadow person" by stimulating the left TPJ at the left ear, serious questions arrive about the mysteries of the mind and what God knows that we don't (and therefore why the priests were anointed there) about spiritual gateways existing in these regions. Once again, by interfacing with or manipulating the brain in this way, are we approaching a forbidden unknown?

Another example of how near-horizon neurosciences and human-machine integration may reconfigure human brains to allow borderline (or more than borderline) supernatural activity involves certain video games played before bedtime, which are being shown to allow people to take control of their dreams, to shape the alternate reality of dream worlds in a way that reflects spiritual warfare. According to *LiveScience* senior writer Jeremy Hsu, published studies on the dreams of hard-core gamers by Jayne Gackenbach, a psychologist at Grant MacEwan University in Canada, found that gamers experienced reversed-threat simulation in nightmares, which allowed the dreamer *to become the threatener instead of the threatened.* In other words, a scary nightmare scenario turned into something "fun" for a gamer, allowing the player to assume the role of the aggressor or demon attacker. "They don't run away; they turn and fight back. They're more aggressive than the norms," Gackenbach explained. "Levels of aggression in gamer dreams also included hyper-violence not unlike that of an R-rated movie," and when these dreaming gamers became aggressive, "oh boy, they go off the top."[420]

From learning to influence our private dreams via game-tech to having our dreams infiltrated and manipulated by outside forces, disquieting ideas deepen. In the 2010 movie *Inception* starring Leonardo DiCaprio, industrial spies use a dream machine called PASIV to steal corporate secrets by means of invasion and "extraction" of private information through a victim's dreams. In a second scenario, the film depicts ideas planted in the person's mind (inception) so that the individual perceives them as his or her own, thus allowing the victim to be steered toward particular decisions or actions—a modern upgrade on brainwashing a la the *Manchurian Candidate.* While the film *Inception* is fantasy, it is based in part on near-future technology.

Electroencephalograms, functional magnetic resonance imaging (fMRIS), and computed tomography (CT) scans are already being used to "read and even influence the brain," points out Aaron Saenz at the Singularity Hub. But could the fundamental science *Inception* examines actually be setting the stage for making it a reality? "We're certainly working towards it," Saenz adds, continuing:

> In the next few decades we could have the means to understand, perhaps in rather detailed terms, what a person is thinking. Once that barrier is passed, we may develop the means to influence what someone thinks by directly stimulating their brain. [So] while the mind is still a very mysterious place, it may not remain that way forever.[421]

This trend toward technological mind invasion and mind control is or should be a frightening proposal for most people, especially those who value the concept of *free will*. That is because most secular neuroscientists view free will as an outdated religious notion related to "a fictional omnipotent divinity" (God) who chooses not to interfere with the choices of individuals, thus leaving them morally accountable for their actions and future judgment. There is even a concerted effort on the part of some neuroscientists to find proof against free will to illustrate that humans are little more than automatons whose decisions are predetermined by a complex mixture of chemical reactions, past events, and even nature, which work together to determine one's course of action. In the 1970s, Professor Benjamin Libet of the University of California in San Francisco claimed to have discovered proof of this theory through a series of tests in which a "time gap" between a brain's decision to act and the person's awareness of this decision led to the activity being carried out by the individual. His findings ignited a stormy debate regarding the ancient philosophical question of free will, says Naomi Darom for the online edition of *Haaretz* newspaper in Israel:

Are our decisions, the basis for our ostensible free activities, made before we are aware of them? In other words, does the brain ostensibly decide for us? And to what extent do we actually make our decisions consciously?

Professor Hezi Yeshurun explained how those engaged in the brain research concluded that "the question of free will is meaningless, because…the fact that your brain has actually decided in your absence and that I can know what you've decided before you do, paints a picture of an automaton."[422]

To insinuate that a section of the human brain makes decisions ahead of a human's independent awareness of them opens a wellspring of opportunity for civil or military arms technology to target that aspect of the brain and develop methods for "inserting" ideas into minds. DARPA, American Technology Corp., Holosonic Research Labs, and others are working on methods to adapt this science, where thoughts and ideas can be projected or "implanted" in the brain and perceived by the individual as his or her own. A while back, *Wired* magazine reported on DARPA's "sonic projector" as well as troops studying the Long Range Acoustic Device (LRAD) as a modified "Voice of God" weapon:

It appears that some of the troops in Iraq are using "spoken" (as opposed to "screeching") LRAD to mess with enemy fighters. Islamic terrorists tend to be superstitious and, of course, very religious. LRAD can put the "word of God" into their heads. If God, in the form of a voice that only you can hear, tells you to surrender, or run away, what are you gonna do?[423]

Wired went on to acknowledge how, beyond directed sound:

It's long been known that microwaves at certain frequencies can produce an auditory effect that sounds like it's coming from within someone's head (and there's the nagging question of classified microwave work at Brooks Air Force Base that the Air Force stubbornly refuses to talk about).

It is also reported that the Pentagon tested similar research during the Gulf War of 1991 using a technology called silent sound spread spectrum (SSSS), which evidently led to the surrender of thousands of Iraqi soldiers who began "hearing voices."

People of faith, including church theologians and philosophers, should find the idea of using technology to read the minds and manipulate the thoughts of individuals indefensible, as the vanguard of free will is fundamental to our religious and philosophical ethic. To humans, autonomy of thought is the most basic of doctrines in which we are unrestrained by causality or preordained by mystical powers. Yet how these issues—neurosciences, brain-machine interfacing, cybernetics, mind control, and even free will—could actually represent a prophetic confluence of events that soon will combine in an ultimate showdown over human liberty may be an unavoidable and *beastly* aspect of end-times prophecy.

WILL YOU GRIN FOR
THE MARK OF THE BEAST?

*Can a microscopic tag be implanted in a person's body to track
his every movement? There's actual discussion about that. You will
rule on that—mark my words—before your tenure is over.*

—US SEN. JOSEPH BIDEN, ASKED DURING SENATE JUDICIARY
COMMITTEE HEARINGS ON THE NOMINATION OF JOHN ROBERTS
TO BE CHIEF JUSTICE OF THE SUPREME COURT

*Although microchip implantation might be introduced as
a voluntary procedure, in time, there will be pressure to make it
mandatory. A national identification system via microchip implants
could be achieved in two stages. Upon introduction as a voluntary
system, the microchip implantation will appear to be palatable.
After there is a familiarity with the procedure and a knowledge
of its benefits, implantation would be mandatory.*

—DR. ELAINE M. RAMESH, PATENT ATTORNEY
FOR FRANKLIN PIERCE LAW CENTER

*Now imagine a world in which every newborn baby immediately
has a little capsule implanted under his armpit. Inside are monitors,
tiny amounts of hormones, a wireless transmitter and receiver....
From birth, no moment in a person's life will go unmonitored.*

—JOSEPH FARAH, *WHISTLEBLOWER* MAGAZINE

Unless you've been hidden under a rock for the past twenty years,
you're probably familiar with the development of radio-frequency

identification (RFID) technology that, under certain applications, is forecast to be connected to future GRIN technologies, especially neurosciences, brain-machine interfacing, and cybernetics.

RFID chips employ tiny integrated circuits for storing and processing information using an antenna for receiving and transmitting the related data. This technology is most commonly applied as a "tag" for tracking inventory with radio waves at companies like Walmart, where consumer goods are embedded with "smart tags" that are read by hand-held scanners for supply-chain management.

But, in recent years, RFID technology has been expanding within public and private firms as a method for verifying and tracking people as well. While we personally believe it is more likely that the so-called nark of the Beast will emerge from an exotic "vaccine," there are those who imagine the Beast's number coalescing around implantable microchips. We first became aware of this trend a while back when chief of police Jack Schmidig of Bergen County, New Jersey, a member of the police force for more than thirty years, received an RFID chip implant as part of a tech company's strategy of enlisting key regional leaders to accelerate adoption of its product.

Kevin H. McLaughlin, VeriChip Corp.'s chief executive officer at the time, said of the event that "high-profile regional leaders are accepting the VeriChip, representing an excellent example of our approach to gaining adoption of the technology" (note that VeriChip Corp. was renamed to PositiveID Corp. on November 10, 2009, through the merger of VeriChip Corp. and Steel Vault Corp.). Through a new and aggressive indoctrination program called "Thought and Opinion Leaders to Play Key Role in Adoption of VeriChip," the company set out to create exponential adoption of its FDA-cleared, human-implantable RFID tag. According to information released by the company, the implantable transceiver "sends and receives data and can be continuously tracked by GPS (global positioning satellite) technology." The transceiver's power supply and actuation system are unlike anything ever created. When implanted within a body, the device is powered electromechanically through the movement of muscles and can be activated either by the "wearer" or by the monitoring facility. In the wake of the terrorist attacks in New York and Washington, an information technology report highlighted the company's additional plans to study implantable chips as a method of tracking terrorists. "We've changed our thinking since September 11 [2001]," a company spokesman said. "Now there's more of a need to monitor evil activities." As a result, PositiveID has been offering the company's current incarnation of implantable RFID as "a tamper-proof means of identification for enhanced e-business security…tracking, locating lost or missing individuals, tracking the location of valuable property [this includes humans], and monitoring the medical conditions of at-risk patients." While PositiveID offers testimony that safeguards have been implemented to ensure privacy in connection with its implantable microchips, some believe privacy is the last thing internal radio transmitters will protect—that, in fact, the plan to microchip humanity smacks of the biblical mark of the Beast. Has an end-times spirit indeed been pushing for adoption of this technology this generation?

Consider the following:

- In the year 1973, *Senior Scholastics* began introducing school kids to the idea of buying and selling in the future using numbers inserted in their foreheads. In the September 20, 1973, feature "Who Is Watching You?" the secular high school journal speculated:

  All buying and selling in the program will be done by computer. No currency, no change, no checks. In the program, people would receive a number that had been assigned them tattooed in their wrist or forehead. The number is put on by laser beam and cannot be felt. The number in the body is not seen with the naked eye and is as permanent as your fingerprints. All items of consumer goods will be marked with a computer mark. The computer outlet in the store which picks up the number on the items at the checkstand will also pick up the number in the person's body and automatically total the price and deduct the amount from the person's "Special Drawing Rights" account.

- The following year, the 1974 article, "The Specter of Eugenics," had Charles Frankel documenting Nobel Prize winner Linus Pauling's suggestions that a mark be tattooed on the foot or forehead of every young person. Pauling envisioned a mark denoting genotype.

- In 1980, *U.S. News and World Report* revealed how the federal government was plotting "National Identity Cards" without which no one could work or conduct business.

- The *Denver Post Sun* followed up in 1981, claiming that chip implants would replace the identification cards. The June 21, 1981, story read, in part:

The chip is placed in a needle which is affixed to a simple syringe containing an anti-bacterial solution. The needle is capped and ready to forever identify something—or somebody.

- The May 7, 1996, *Chicago Tribune* questioned the technology, wondering aloud if we would be able to trust "Big Brother under our skin?"

- Then, in 1997, applications for patents of subcutaneous implant devices for "a person or an animal" were filed.

- In August 1998, the BBC covered the first-known human microchip implantation.

- That same month, the Sunday Portland *Oregonian* warned that proposed medical identifiers might erode privacy rights by tracking individuals through alphanumeric health-identifier technologies. The startling *Oregonian* feature depicted humans with bar codes in their foreheads.

- Millions of *Today Show* viewers then watched in 2002 when an American family got "chipped" with Applied Digital Solution's VeriChip live from a doctor's office in Boca Raton, Florida.

- In November of the same year, IBM's patent application for "identification and tracking of persons using RFID-tagged items" was recorded.

- Three years later, former secretary of the Health and Human Services department, Tommy Thompson, formed a lucrative partnership with VeriChip Corp. and began encouraging Americans "to get chipped" so their medical records would be "inside them" in case of emergencies.

- The state of Wisconsin—where Thompson was governor before coming to Washington—promptly drew a line in the sand, passing a law prohibiting employers from mandating that their employees get "chipped." Other states since have passed or are considering similar legislation.

- Despite this, in the last two decades, an expanding number of companies and government agencies have started requiring the use of RFID for people identification. Unity Infraprojects, for example, one of the largest civil contractors in India, tracks its employees with RFID, as does the US Department of Homeland Security for workers involved in baggage handling at airports.

- Since September 11, 2001, the US government has proposed several versions of a national identification card that would use RFID technology.

- Starting in 2006, the US government began requiring passports to include RFID chips.

- Hundreds of Alzheimer's patients have been injected with implantable versions of RFID tags in recent years.

- RFID bracelets are now being placed on newborns at a growing list of hospitals.

- Students are being required in some schools and universities to use biometric ID employing RFID for electronic monitoring.
- Thousands of celebrities and government officials around the world have had RFID radio chips implanted in them so that they can be identified—either for entry at secure sites or for identification if they are kidnapped or killed.
- Others, like Professor Kevin Warwick (discussed earlier), have been microchipped for purposes of controlling keypads and external devices with the wave of a hand.
- Besides providing internal storage for individual-specific information like health records, banking and industry envisions a cashless society in the near future where all buying and selling could transpire using a version of the subdermal chips and wireless authentication. As mentioned above, in 1973, *Senior Scholastics* magazine introduced school-age children to the concept of buying and selling using numbers inserted in their forehead. But, more recently, *Time* magazine, in its feature story, "The Big Bank Theory and What It Says about the Future of Money," recognized how this type of banking and currency exchange would not require a laser tattoo. Rather, the writer said, "Your daughter can store the money any way she wants—on her laptop, on a debit card, even (in the not-too-distant future) on a chip implanted under her skin."[424]
- In 2007, PositiveID, which owns the Food and Drug Administration-approved VeriChip that electronically transmits patients' health information whenever a scanner is passed over the body, ominously launched "Xmark" as its corporate identity for implantable healthcare products.
- Fast forward to 2023 and the World Economic Forum (WEF) just published "Solid" reasons to microchip kids. An article on the institution's website makes the case that

"human implant technologies will soon become a commodity and that there are 'solid, rational' reasons for microchipping children with location trackers."[425]

- And now, at the time this book is going to the printer, the Department of Homeland Security has begun working out how to implement codifying an international biometric ID system.

The list above continues to accumulate, causing a growing number to wonder if RFID adoption will, for all practical purposes, result in every man, woman, boy, and girl in the developed world having an ID chip inside them (like animals worldwide already do) sometime this century. Students of eschatology (the study of end-times events) find it increasingly difficult to dismiss how this all looks and feels like movement toward fulfilling Revelation 13:16–17:

And he causeth all, both small and great, rich and poor, free and bond, to receive a mark in their right hand, or in their foreheads: And that no man might buy or sell, save he that had the mark, or the name of the beast, or the number of his name.

As newer versions of RFID-like transmitters become even more sophisticated—adding other "prophetic" components such as merging human biological matter with transistors to create living, implantable machines—the authors of this book believe the possibility that the mark of the Beast could arrive through a version of this technology is plausible. That is one reason we found the *Discovery News* report, "Part-Human, Part Machine Transistor Devised," particularly disturbing:

Man and machine can now be linked more intimately than ever. Scientists have embedded a nano-sized transistor inside a cell-like membrane and powered it using the cell's own fuel.

The research could lead to new types of man-machine interactions where embedded devices could relay information about the inner workings of proteins inside the cell membrane, and eventually lead to new ways to *read, and even influence, brain or nerve cells.*

"This device is as close to the seamless marriage of biological and electronic structures as anything else that people did before," said Aleksandr Noy, a scientist at the University of California, Merced, who is a co-author on the recent ACS Nano Letters. "We can take proteins, real biological machines, and make them part of a working microelectronic circuit."[426]

A similar story ("DNA Logic Gates Herald Injectable Computers") was published by *New Scientist* magazine the same month as the story above, and a few weeks earlier, an article by the *Daily Mail* ("Meet the Nano-Spiders: The DNA Robots That Could One Day Be Walking through Your Body") reported the creation by scientists of microscopic robots made of DNA molecules that can walk, turn, and even create tiny products of their own on a nano-scale assembly line. This is important because, a while back, Tom Horn's wife, Nita Horn, brought up a point we had never considered. She asked if the biblical mark of the Beast might be a conspiracy employing specific implantable technology only now available. Her theory was gripping. An occult elite operating behind the US government devises a virus that is a crossover between human and animal disease—let's say, an entirely new and highly contagious influenza mutation—and intentionally releases it into the public. A pandemic ensues, and the period between when a person contracts the virus and death is something like ten days. With tens of thousands dead in a few weeks and the rate of death increasing hourly around the globe, a universal cry for a cure goes out. Seemingly miraculously, the government then steps forward with a vaccine. The only catch, the government explains, is that, given the nature of the animal-human flu, the "cure" uses animal

DNA and nanobots to rewrite one's genetics so the person is no longer entirely human. The point made was that those who receive this antidote would become part "beast," and perhaps thus the title, "mark of the Beast." No longer "entirely human" would also mean—according to this outline—that the individual could no longer be "saved" or go to Heaven, explaining why the book of Revelation says "whosoever receiveth the mark" is damned forever (while also explaining why the Nephilim, whose DNA was part human and part animal, could not be redeemed). If one imagines the global chaos of such a pandemic, the concept of how the Antichrist "causes all," both small and great, to receive this mark becomes clearer. When looking into the eyes of dying children, parents, or a spouse, it would be incredibly difficult to allow oneself to die or to encourage others to do the same when a "cure" was readily available. Lastly, this scenario would mean that nobody would be allowed to "buy or sell" in the marketplace without the mark-cure due to the need to quarantine all but the inoculated, thus fulfilling all aspects of the mark-of-the-Beast prophecy.

To find out if the science behind this abstract would be as reasonable as it appeared on the surface, we again contacted Sharon Gilbert. This was her troubling response:

What is human? Until recently, most of us would readily respond that *we* are humans. You and I, we might argue, are *Homo sapiens*: erect, bipedal hominids with twenty-three pairs of matched chromosomes and nifty little thumbs capable of apposition to the palm that enable us to grasp the fine tools that our highly developed, bi-lobed brains devise.

Humans, we might argue, sit as rulers of the earth, gazing down from the pinnacle of a pyramid consisting of all plant and animal species. We would remind the listener that natural selection and evolution have developed mankind into a superior thinker and doer, thereby granting us royal privilege, if not infinite responsibility. The Bible would take this definition much farther, of course, adding that mankind is the only part of God's creation formed by His hands, rather than spoken into existence, and that you and I bear God's unique signature as having been created "in His image" (Genesis 1:27).

Many members of the "illuminated brotherhood of science" would likely demur to the previous statement. These have, in point of fact, redefined *human*. Like Shelley's *Modern Prometheus*, Victor Frankenstein, today's molecular magicians play "god" not by stitching together rotting corpses, but by reforming the very essence of our beings: our DNA.

So-called "postmodern man" began as a literary reference but has evolved into an iconic metaphor representing a collective image of perfected humanity beyond the confines of genetic constraints. Transhumanism, also known as the H+ movement (see www.HPlusMagazine.com, for example) envisions a higher life-form yet, surpassing *Homo sapiens* in favor of *Homo sapiens 2.0*, a bioengineered construct that fuses man's original genome with animal and/or synthetic DNA.

While such claims ring of science fiction, they are indeed science fact. For decades, laboratories have created chimeric combinations of animal, plant, and even human DNA under the guise of medical research. The stated goal is to better man's lot by curing disease, but this benign mask hides an inner, sardonic grin that follows an ancient blueprint to blend God's perfect creature with the seed of fallen angels: "You shall be as gods."

You two speak to the heart of the matter when you warn of a day when true humans may receive transhuman instructions via an implant or injection. A seemingly innocuous vaccine or identification "chip" can initiate intracellular changes, not only in somatic or "body" cells but also in germ-line cells such as ova and sperm. The former alters the recipient only; the latter alters the recipient's doomed descendants as well.

In my second novel, *The Armageddon Strain*, I present a device called the "BioStrain Chip" that employs nanotechnology to induce genetic changes inside the carrier's body. This miracle chip is advertised as a cure for the H5N1/ebola chimera that is released in the prologue to the book. Of course, if you've read the novel, then you know the BioStrain chip does far more than "cure"—it also kills.

Though a work of fiction, *The Armageddon Strain* raises a chilling question: What limitations lie within the payload of a biochip? Can such a tiny device do more than carry digitized information? Could it actually serve as the *mark of the Beast?*

The answer is yes.

DNA (deoxyribonucleic acid) has become the darling of researchers who specialize in synthetic constructs. The "sticky-end" design of the DNA double-helix makes it ideal for use in computing. Though an infinite number of polyhedra are possible, the most robust and stable of these "building blocks" is called the double crossover (DX). An intriguing name, is it not? The double-cross.

Picture an injectible chip comprised of DNA-DX, containing instructions for a super-soldier. Picture, too, how this DNA framework, if transcribed, might also serve a second, *sinister,* purpose—not only to instruct, but also to *alter.*

Mankind has come perilously far in his search for perfection through chemistry. Although millennia passed with little progress beyond roots, herbs, and alchemical quests for gold from lead, the twentieth century ushered science into the rosy dawn of breathless discovery. Electricity, lighter than air travel, wireless communication, and computing transformed the ponderous pace of the scientific method into a light speed race toward self-destruction.

By the mid-1950s, Watson and Crick had solved the structure of the DNA molecule and the double helix became all the rage. Early gene splicing, and thus transgenics, began in 1952 as a crude, cut-and-paste sort of science cooked up in kitchen blenders and petri dishes—as much accident as inspiration. As knowledge has increased (Daniel 12:4), genetic scientists learned to utilize microbiological "vectors" and sophisticated methods to insert animal or plant genes from one species into another. It's the ultimate "Mr. Potato Head" game, where interchangeable plastic pieces give rise to an infinite number of combinations; only, in genetic splicing, humanity is the unhappy potato.

Vectors provide the means of transport and integration for this brave new science. Think of these vectors as biological trucks that carry genetic building materials and workers into your body's cells. Such "trucks" could be a microsyringe, a bacterium, or a virion (a virus particle). Any entity that can carry genetic information (the larger the load capacity, the better) and then surreptitiously gain entry into the cell is a potential vector. Viruses, for example, can be stripped of certain innate genes that might harm the cell. Not only does this (supposedly) render the viral delivery truck "harmless," it also clears out space for the cargo.

Once inside the cell, the "workers" take over. Some of these "workers" are enzymes that cut human genes at specific sites, while others integrate—or load—the "cargo" into appropriate reading frames—like microscopic librarians. Once the payload is stored in the cell's nuclear "library stacks," the new genes can be translated, copied, and "read" to produce altered or brand-new, "alien" polymers and proteins.

The resulting hybrid cell is no longer purely human. If a hybridized skin cell, it may now glow, or perhaps form scales rather than hair, claws rather than fingernails. If a brain cell, the new genetic instructions could produce an altered neurotransmitter that reduces or even eliminates the body's need for sleep. Muscle cells may grow larger and more efficient at using low levels of calcium and oxygen. Retina cells may encode for receptors that enable the "posthuman being" to perceive infrared or ultraviolet light frequencies. The hybrid ears may now sense a wider range of sounds, taste buds a greater range of chemicals. Altered brains might even attune to metaphysics and "unseen" gateways, allowing communication with supernatural realms.

Germ-line alterations, mentioned earlier, form a terrifying picture of generational development and may very well already be a reality. Genetic "enhancement" of sperm-producing cells would change human sperm into tiny infiltrators, and any fertilized ovum a living chimera. Science routinely conducts experiments with transgenic mice, rats, chickens, pigs, cows, horses, and many other species. It is naïve to believe humans have been left out of this transgenic equation.

If so many scientists (funded by government entities) believe in the "promise" of genetic alteration and transgenic "enhancement," how then can humanity remain human? We cannot. We will not. Perhaps, *some have not.*

Spiritually, the enemy has ever sought to corrupt God's plan. Originally, fallen angels lay with human women to corrupt the original base pair arrangements. Our genome is filled with "junk DNA" that seemingly encodes for nothing. These "introns" may be the remains of the corrupted genes, and God Himself may have switched them off when fallen angels continued their program, post-Flood. If so, today's scientists might need only to "switch them back on" to resurrect old forms such as Gibborim and Nephilim.

I should point out that not all "trucks" (vectors) deliver their payload immediately. Some operate on a time delay. Cytomegalovirus (CMV) is a common infective agent resident in the cells of many humans today. It "sleeps" in our systems, waiting for a window of opportunity to strike. Recently, genetic specialists began utilizing CMV vectors in transgenic experiments. In 1997, the Fox television program *Millennium* featured an episode in the second season called "Sense and Antisense" (referring to the two sides of the DNA molecule). In this chilling story, a scientist named Lacuna reveals a genetic truth to Frank Black: "They have the map, the map, they can make us go down any street they want to. Streets that we would never even dream of going down. They flip a switch, we go east. They flip another switch, we go north. And we never know we have been flipped, let alone know how."

In the final days of this current age, humanity may indeed "flip." Paul tells us that Christians will be transformed in a moment (1 Corinthians 15:51–53). Is it possible that the enemy also plans an instantaneous "flip"? Are genetic sleeper agents (idling "trucks") already at work in humanity's DNA, waiting and ready to deploy at the appropriate moment?

Science is ready. Knowledge has been increased. The spiritual players have taken the stage.

All we need is the signal. The sign. The injection. The mark. The moment.

We shall ALL be changed. Some to incorruptible bodies ready to meet the Lord. Others to corrupted genomes ready to serve the Beast.

FROM ANTICHRIST'S MARK TO HIS TRANSHUMAN CHURCH

Perhaps related to the rise of Antichrist and his human-transforming mark of the Beast technology is an intriguing aspect of transhumanism that is only now developing into what could be an end-times universalist religion. Is it a coincidence that this comes during the same epoch in which the United States Supreme Court, for the first time in its history, became devoid of Protestant representation with the confirmation of Elena Kagan; a time also in which the Claremont School of Theology analyzing the future of American religion concluded at its 2010 Theology After Google Conference that "technology must be embraced" for Christianity to survive?

Although most transhumanists, especially early on, were secular atheists and would have had little resemblance to prototypical "people of faith," in the last few years, the exclusion of supernaturalism in favor of rational empiricism has softened as the movement's exponential popularity has swelled to include a growing number of Gnostic Christians, Buddhists, Mormons, Islam, Raelianism, and other religious traditions among its devotees. From among these groups, new tentative "churches" arose—the Church of Virus, the Society for Universal Immortalism, Transtopianism, the Church of Mez, the Society for Venturism, the Church of the Fulfillment, Singularitarianism, and others. Today, with somewhere between 25 and 30 percent of transhumanists considering themselves religious, these separate sects or early "denominations" within transhumanism are coalescing their various religious worldviews around generally fixed creeds involving *spiritual transcendence* as a result of human enhancement. Leaders within the movement, whom we refer to here as *transevangelists,* have been providing religion-specific lectures during conferences to guide these disciples toward a collective (hive) understanding of the mystical compatibility between faith and transhumanism. At Trinity College in Toronto, Canada, for instance, transhumanist Peter Addy lectured on the fantastic "Mutant Religious Impulses of the Future" during the Faith, Transhumanism, and Hope symposium. At the same meeting, Prof. Mark Walker spoke on "Becoming Godlike," James Hughes offered "Buddhism and Transhumanism: The Technologies of Self-Perfection," Michael LaTorra gave a "Trans-Spirit" speech, nanotechnologist and lay Catholic Tihamer Toth-Fejel presented "Is Catholic Transhumanism Possible?" and Nick Bostrom spoke on "Transhumanism and Religion."

The *New York Times* picked up this meme (contagious idea) in its feature titled *Merely Human? That's So Yesterday*, speaking of transhumanism and the Singularity as offering "a modern-day, quasi-religious answer to the Fountain of Youth by affirming the notion that, yes indeed, humans—or at least something derived from them—can have it all."[427] In commenting on the *Times* article at his blog, one of our favorite writers, bioethicist Wesley J. Smith, observed the following:

> Here's an interesting irony: Most transhumanists are materialists. But they desire eternal life as much as the religionists that so many materialists disdain. So they invent a material substitute that offers the benefits of faith, without the burden of sin, as they forge a new eschatology that allows them to maintain their über-rationalist credentials as they try to escape the nihilistic despair that raw materialism often engenders. So they tout a corporeal New Jerusalem and prophesy the coming of the Singularity—roughly equivalent of the Second Coming for Christians—that will…begin a New Age of peace, harmony, and eternal life right here on Terra firma.[428]

In the peer-reviewed *Journal of Evolution and Technology* published by the Institute for Ethics and Emerging Technologies (founded in 2004 by transhumanists Nick Bostrom and James Hughes), the "Apologia for Transhumanist Religion" by Professor Gregory Jordan lists the many ways transhumanism is emerging as either a new form of religion or a mirror of fundamental human ambitions, desires, longings, shared hopes, and dreams traditional religions hold in common. In spite of denial by some of its advocates, Jordan concludes that transhumanism may be considered a rising religion because of its numerous parallels to religious themes and values involving godlike beings, the plan for eternal life, the religious sense of awe surrounding its promises, symbolic rituals among its members, an inspirational worldview based on faith, and technology that promises to heal the wounded, restore sight to the blind, and give hearing back to the deaf.

Of the technological Singularity in particular, Jordan writes how some transhumanists especially view it as a religious event, "a time when human consciousness will expand beyond itself and throughout the universe." Quoting Kurzweil's "The Singularity Is Near: When Humans Transcend Biology," Jordan provides:

> The matter and energy in our vicinity will become infused with the intelligence, knowledge, creativity, beauty, and emotional intelligence (the ability to love, for example) of our human-machine civilization. Our civilization will expand outward, turning all the dumb matter [normal humans] and energy we encounter into sublimely intelligent—transcendent—matter and energy. So in a sense, we can say that the Singularity will ultimately infuse the world with spirit.

According to these Singularitarians, this expansion of consciousness after the Singularity will also be an approach to the divine:

> Evolution moves toward greater complexity, greater elegance, greater knowledge, greater intelligence, greater beauty, greater creativity, and greater levels of subtle attributes such as love. In every monotheistic tradition God is likewise described as all of these qualities, only without any limitation: infinite knowledge, infinite intelligence, infinite beauty, infinite creativity, infinite love, and so on…. So evolution moves inexorably toward this conception of God…. We can regard, therefore, the freeing of our thinking from the severe limitations of its biological form to be an essentially spiritual undertaking.[429]

Yet while development of a *new* universalist religion appears to be forming among members of transhumanism's enlightenment, conservative scholars will taste the *ancient* origin of its heresy as the incarnation of Gnosticism and its disdain for the human body as basically an evil design that is far inferior to what we can make it. "Despite all their rhetoric about enhancing the performance of bodily functions," says Brent Waters, director of the Jerre L. and Mary Joy Stead Center for Ethics and Values, "the posthuman project is nevertheless driven by a hatred and loathing of the body."[430] Transhumanist Kevin Warwick put it this way: "I was born human. But this was an accident of fate—a condition merely of time and place."

Conversely, in Judeo-Christian faith, the human body is not an ill-designed "meat sack," as transhumans so often deride. We were made in God's image to be temples of His Holy Spirit. The incarnation of God in the person of Jesus Christ and His bodily resurrection are the centerpieces of the Gospel and attest to this magnificent fact. While in our fallen condition human suffering is reality, most traditional Christians believe this struggle makes us stronger and that healing and improvements to the human condition are also to be desired. Throughout history, the Church has therefore been at the forefront of disease treatment discovery, institutions for healthcare, hospitals, and other medical schools and research centers. In other words, we do not champion a philosophy toward techno-dystopianism. *Indeed, what a day it will be when cancer is cured and we all shout "Hallelujah!"*

But in the soulless posthuman, where DNA is recombined in mockery of the Creator and no one is made in God's image, "there are no essential differences, or absolute demarcations, between bodily existence and computer simulation, cybernetic mechanism and biological organism, robot technology and human goals," says Katherine Hayles, professor of English at the University of California, in her book *How We Became Posthuman.* "Humans can either go gently into that good night, joining the dinosaurs as a species that once ruled the earth but is now obsolete," she says in transhuman contempt of—or outright hostility to—intrinsic human dignity, "or hang on for a while longer by becoming machines themselves. In either case…the age of the human is drawing to a close."[431]

Thus the gauntlet is thrown down and a holy war declared by the new and ungodly apostles of a transhuman faith! We who were created in His image will either adapt and be assimilated to posthuman, or be replaced by Nephilim 2.0 and the revival of their ancient mystery religion. This solidifies how, the more one probes into the ramifications of merging unnatural creations and non-biological inventions according to the transhumanist scheme of seamlessly recalibrating humanity, a deeper malaise emerges, one that suggests those startling "parallels" between modern technology and ancient Watchers activity may be no coincidence at all—that, in fact, a dark conspiracy is truly unfolding as it did "in the days of Noah."

Consider, in conclusion of this chapter, the thoughtful commentary by Dr. C. Christopher Hook:

There are several key questions that our churches and theologians will have to address. Is it appropriate for members of the body of Christ to engage in alterations that go beyond therapy and are irreversible? Is it just to do so in a world already deeply marked by inequities? What does it mean that our Lord healed and restored in His ministry—never enhanced? Is it significant that the gifts of the Holy Spirit—wisdom, love, patience, kindness—cannot be manufactured by technology?[432]

THOSE "OTHER" SIGNS OF THE DAYS OF NOAH

As laboratories incubate new blends of man and machine....
The path of progress cuts through the four-way intersection of
the moral, medical, religious and political—and whichever way
you turn, you are likely to run over someone's deeply held beliefs.
Venter's bombshell [the creation of the synthetic life "Synthia"]
revived the oldest of ethical debates, over whether scientists were
playing God or proving he does not exist because
someone re-enacted Genesis in suburban Maryland.

—Nancy Gibbs, *Time* magazine

If Christians are to help shape contemporary culture—particularly
in a setting in which I fear the posthuman message will prove
attractive, if not seductive—then they must offer an alternative and
compelling vision; a counter theological discourse so to speak.

—Brent Waters, director of
the Jerre L. and Mary Joy Stead Center for Ethics and Values

Earlier in this book, we pointed out how English theologian George
Hawkins Pember, in his 1876 masterpiece, *Earth's Earliest Ages*,
studied the book of Matthew—where Jesus, in answering His disciples' questions concerning the signs of His coming and of the end
of the world, said it would be "as the days of Noah were"—and concluded from it that the most fearful sign of the end times would be the
reappearance upon earth "of beings from the Principality of the Air,
and their unlawful intercourse with the human race."

We have built on this concept as well, suggesting that parallels between human-modifying technology and what the ancient Watchers did in creating Nephilim may be no coincidence at all; a dark conspiracy could be unfolding by way of GRIN sciences and transhumanist philosophy that specifically allows fulfillment of the prophecy, "as it was in the days of Noah."

But if, indeed, Satan has initiated an extraordinary conspiracy to revive species-altering supernaturalism as existed in Noah's day, and assuming there is a gap between that sign and when God removes His own from this planet, the Church as the Body of Christ and God's representation on earth could play a unique role as the instrument through which the Almighty, on behalf of His creation, will engage this evil. True believers are the salt of the earth and the only social influence identified in Scripture as the power against which the gates of Hell cannot prevail. This, friends, unveils good news, because while Nephilim were on earth during (and after) the antediluvian age, this was not the only "sign" related to ancient days. There were other signs too, as illustrated in the Bible, having to do with God's covenant people and their unequaled ability through faith to turn back Nephilim plans. "As it was in the days of Noah" points to this fact as well.

Consider how King Saul in 1063 BC stared across his tent into the eyes of the unproven and youngest son of Jesse. By chance, the teenager named David had come on a mission for his father to deliver food and gather information regarding the welfare of his brothers. On his arrival, Goliath, the champion of the Philistines, stood up at his camp across the Valley of Elah and once again challenged the armies of Israel to send a warrior out against him. Two times per day for the past forty days the fearsome giant had terrified Saul's army, crying over the steep basin to the ranks of Israel.

"Why set the battle in array? Am I not a Philistine and you servants of Saul? Choose a man from among yourselves and let him come down to me." Goliath challenged. "If he is able to fight with me and to kill me, then we will become your servants; but if I prevail against him and kill him, then you shall become our servants. I defy the ranks of Israel; give me a man that we may decide the outcome of this conflict in a single fight!"

On seeing and hearing this spectacle, David learned that Saul was promising a rich reward to any man who could defeat the nine-foot-tall menace. David's response was one of dismay at the lack of Israel's faith. "Who is this uncircumcised Philistine, that he should defy the armies of the living God?" he asked among the soldiers (1 Samuel 17:26). When Saul heard of this, he sent for the lad. But standing in front of the king, unable to fill his armor, the ruddy kid didn't look like much of a killer. Then David told Saul about slaying a lion and later a bear in defense of his father's sheep, and Saul relented.

With nothing but a staff, a sling, and five smooth stones, David emerged on the battlefield and ran toward Goliath. When the chiseled Philistine saw the fair-skinned youth approaching, he looked around, scoffed, then thundered, "Am I a dog, that you send a boy at me with a stick!?" Cursing in the name of his gods, he sneered, "Come on then, and I will give your flesh as supper to the birds of the air and the beasts of the field."

David shocked everybody with his retort. "You come at me with a sword and a shield, but I am coming in the name of the LORD of Hosts, the God of the armies of Israel, whom you have defied," he cried. "This day the Lord will deliver you into my hand; and I will smite you, and take your head off, and *your* carcass is the one the birds of the air and the beasts of the field will dine on!" With that, David rushed forward, let the stone go from his sling, and the rest, as they say, is history.

Why is that story important to this book? Because Goliath was a Nephilim, and was defeated by a young servant of God. If the arrival of these beings or the spirit of their sins is the preeminent sign of the end times, David defeating one is germane as well. This, too, is an important prophetic symbol.

From a youth to an old man, consider another example. Four

hundred twenty-seven years before David slew Goliath, the people of Israel were camped along the southern border of Canaan, the "Promised Land" God had said He would give them. Twelve spies—one from each tribe of Israel—went in to survey the land and found walled cities inhabited by giant Nephilim offspring. Psalm 78:41 records what happened at this discovery: "Yea, they turned back and tempted God, and limited the Holy One of Israel." In other words, like Saul's army later did, the children of Israel trembled at the sight of the sons of Anak, the giants of Nephilim descent. "And there we saw the giants, the sons of Anak, which come of the giants," they uttered in hopeless despair before adding, "and we were in our own sight as grasshoppers, and so we were in their sight" (Numbers 13:32–33). Only two of the spies, Joshua and Caleb, believed in the promises of God. They encouraged the people not to be afraid, to trust in the Lord who would give them victory over the Nephilim. But that generation disagreed, wanted to have Joshua and Caleb stoned, cursed God, and died in the wilderness never having received their inheritance in Canaan. Joshua and Caleb, on the other hand, waited for God's further orders, which came in 1451 BC:

> Now therefore arise, go over this Jordan, thou, and all this people, unto the land which I do give to them, even to the children of Israel. Every place that the sole of your foot shall tread upon, that have I given unto you, as I said unto Moses.... There shall not any man be able to stand before thee. (Joshua 1:2–3, 5)

Joshua and Caleb trusted God as usual, and this time, at the age of eighty-five, no less, Caleb drove out the sons of Anak that had so terrified the unbelieving spies.

The fact that God's people could prevail over the spirit of the Nephilim in these ways is an ageless reality. It suggests that believers today not only could survive, but could triumph over the inhuman threat represented by GRIN technology and the transhumanist agenda. This will occur as believers recall specific Bible knowledge and engage in dynamic activity, what we title *those other two signs of the days of Noah.*

THE DAYS OF NOAH: PREACHING RIGHTEOUSNESS

While it could certainly be possible to be discouraged by focusing on the Nephilim and the prediction of their return at the end of time, a wonderful portion of Scripture from the same days of Noah adds, "But Noah found grace in the eyes of the Lord." Think about what a marvelous revelation this is: At the darkest time in earth's history, when the sins of the Watchers had spread like a cancer across continents, infecting all of humanity both genetically and philosophically, "Noah walked with God" (Genesis 6:9). At a time when all flesh was tainted by transhuman genes and every imagination was only focused on evil continually (Genesis 6:5), one man had not forgotten where to glory, one man walked with God, one man found grace.

Today, as we move into the uncharted waters of a resurrected technological and human-transforming era, the keys to victory for believers will be the same as they were for David, Joshua, Caleb, and Noah—knowing where to glory, what to keep one's focus on, where to place one's faith, and whose champion we can be.

On this point, it is clear that Noah didn't buy into the transhuman lies of his day. While the immortals known as Watchers were promising advanced technology to the world in exchange for use of human DNA (Book of Enoch, chapter 8), it must have been obvious to Noah how reminiscent this was of the serpent in the Garden who made similar promises of godlike abilities for those who partook forbidden fruit. Noah assumed leadership instead, independently maintaining his faith and focus in God, not willing to compromise his flesh or that of his family for any temporal therapeutic benefit (lie). Furthermore, Noah did not sit idly by keeping these opinions to himself. In 2 Peter 2:5, we learn he became a "preacher of righteousness" (Greek *kerux*: a herald or "one who announces"). This was true in his use of technology as an "illustrative sermon" while building the ark (contrasted to the misuse of technology by Watchers), but some scholars believe it was more than this, that he preached audibly, facing the transhuman movement of his day with boldness, publicly warning of the dangers of grievous sins related to genetic manipulation incited by invisible agents.

In the letter to the church at Ephesus, Paul states the responsibility of the Church in this regard for today, concluding this was by divine intention:

> His intent was that now, through the church, the manifold wisdom of God should be made known to the rulers and authorities in the heavenly realms. (Ephesians 3:10)

Imagine that. It is our duty as believers to follow Noah's example and make known the manifold wisdom of God until even the angelic powers are aware of it. Was this behind what Brent Waters, whom we quote at the beginning of this chapter, had in mind when he said the following?

> If Christians are to help shape contemporary culture—particularly in a setting in which I fear the posthuman message will prove attractive, if not seductive—then they must offer an alternative and compelling vision; a counter theological discourse so to speak?

While "a counter theological discourse" reflective of the everlasting Gospel of human redemption through the person of Jesus Christ will be antithetical to the salvation plan of transhumanism, it must address the difficult philosophical and ethical questions raised by modern technology and the portentous move by governments and powers to use biological sciences to remanufacture humankind. The message needs to be relevant and must appeal to the questions and style of a generation raised during the Digital Revolution, an age of personal computing and information-sharing technology that, for many of us, represents a shift away from the Industrial Revolution's outdated methods of communicating. Although the Vatican in 2008 issued a limited set of instructions on bioethics primarily dealing with in vitro fertilization and stem cell research (*Dignitas Personae* or "the Dignity of the Person") and a handful of Christian scientists, policymakers, and conservative academics have hinted in public commentary on the need for a broader, manifesto-like document on the subject, the Church as an institution has failed at any concerted effort to focus on the genetics revolution, the government's interest in human enhancement, the viral transhumanist philosophy capturing the mind of a generation at colleges and universities (not to mention via popular media), and the significant moral and ethical issues raised by these trends.

While the Vatican's *Dignitas Personae* likewise failed to provide instructions on the greater issue of biological enhancement (as envisioned by transhumans and espoused by agencies of the US and other federal governments as the next step in human evolution), its positional paper did provide an important bird's-eye view on the clash developing between traditional morality and *the quiet adoption of transhumanist philosophy by Christian apologists, who likewise have begun to question what it means to be human and whose competing moral vision could ultimately shape the future of society.*

Immediately following the release of *Dignitas Personae*, Catholic scientist William B. Neaves, in an essay for the *National Catholic Reporter*, reflected the new biblical exegesis, causing reporter Rod Dreher to describe it as clearly illustrating "the type of Christianity that is eager to jettison the old morality and embrace the new." The subtleties behind Neaves' comments included:

An alternative point of view to the Vatican's, embraced by many Christians, is that personhood [a transhumanist concept] occurs after successful implantation in the mother's uterus, when individual ontological identity is finally established....

If one accepts the viewpoint that personhood begins after implantation, the moral framework guiding the development and application of medical technology to human reproduction and treatment of disease looks very different from that described in *Dignitas Personae*.

In the alternative moral framework, taking a pill to prevent the products of fertilization from implanting in a uterus is morally acceptable. Using IVF [in vitro fertilization] to complete the family circle of couples otherwise unable to have children is an unmitigated good. Encouraging infertile couples with defective gametes to adopt already-produced IVF embryos that will otherwise be discarded is a laudable objective. And using embryonic stem cells to seek cures [creating human embryos for research "parts"] becomes a worthy means of fulfilling the biblical mandate to heal the sick.[433]

Notwithstanding that the discussion by Neaves was limited to the Vatican's position on embryos, his introduction of memes involving personhood and "ensoulment" represents worrisome Christian theological entanglement with transhumanist philosophy, further illustrating the need for a solid manifesto providing a conservative vision for public policy with regard to human experimentation and enhancement.

From Noah to the present hour, making known this "righteous" and manifold wisdom of God in hopes of persuading an age to appreciate the human-affirming virtues of Christian morality can be intrinsic to the Great Commission. There is no middle ground for preachers of righteousness in these matters. Believers are either asleep at the wheel or actively engaged in spiritual warfare for the souls of a generation whose members today are desperately seeking reasons to believe, despite everything they are being told, that the Church remains relevant. To fail in this responsibility will be to abdicate to a frightening transhuman vision of the future such as was predicted by theologian and Christian apologist C. S. Lewis in *The Abolition of Man*. Lewis foresaw the day when transhumanist and scientific reasoning would win out, permanently undoing humankind through altering the species, ultimately reducing Homo sapiens to utilitarian products. Here is part of what he said:

In order to understand fully what Man's power over Nature, and therefore the power of some men over other men, really means, we must picture the race extended in time from the date of its emergence to that of its extinction. Each generation exercises power over its successors: and each, in so far as it modifies the environment bequeathed to it and rebels against tradition, resists and limits the power of its predecessors. This modifies the picture which is sometimes painted of a progressive emancipation from tradition and a progressive control of natural processes resulting in a continual increase of human power. In reality, of course, if any one age really attains, by eugenics and scientific education, the power to make its descendants what it pleases [transhuman/posthuman], all men who live after it are the patients of that power. They are weaker, not stronger: for though we may have put wonderful machines in their hands we have pre-ordained how they are to use them. And if, as is almost certain, the age which had thus attained maximum power over posterity were also the age most emancipated from tradition, it would be engaged in reducing the power of its predecessors almost as drastically as that of its successors.... The last men, far from being the heirs of power, will be of all men most subject to the dead hand of the great planners and conditioners and will themselves exercise least power upon the future.... The final stage [will have] come when Man by eugenics, by pre-natal conditioning, and by an education and propaganda based on a perfect applied psychology...shall have "taken the thread of life out of the hand of Clotho" [one of the

Three Fates in mythology responsible for spinning the thread of human life] and be henceforth free to make our species whatever we wish it to be. The battle will indeed be won. But who, precisely, will have won it?[434]

Lewis foresaw the progressive abandonment of what we would call "moral law" based on Judeo-Christian values giving way to "the dead hand of the great planners and conditioners" who would decide what people should biologically become. The term "great planners and conditioners" corresponds perfectly with modern advocates of transhumanism who esteem their blueprint for the future of the species as the one that will ultimately decide the fate of humanity. A recent step toward establishing this goal (in addition to all the other "steps" we've documented) occurred when the US National Science Foundation (NSF) and the Human Enhancement Ethics Group (based at California Polytechnic State University, whose advisory board is a wish list of transhumanist academics and institutions worldwide) released its fifty-page report entitled "Ethics of Human Enhancement: 25 Questions & Answers." This government-funded report addressed the definitions, scenarios, anticipated societal disruptions, and policy and law issues that need to be considered en route to becoming posthuman. Some of the topics covered in the study include:

- What are the policy implications of human enhancement?
- Is the natural-artificial distinction of human enhancement morally significant?
- Does human enhancement raise issues of fairness, access, and equity?
- Will it matter if there is an "enhanced divide" between "new" people classifications?
- How would such a divide make communication difficult between "normals" and the "enhanced"?
- How should the enhancement of children be approached?

- What kind of societal disruptions might arise from human enhancement?
- Should there be any limits on enhancement for military purposes?
- Might enhanced humans count as someone's intellectual property?
- Will we need to rethink the very meaning of "ethics," given the dawn of enhancement?

The "Ethics of Human Enhancement" report was authored by the NSF-funded research team of Dr. Fritz Allhoff (Western Michigan University), Dr. Patrick Lin (California Polytechnic State University), Professor James Moor (Dartmouth College), and Professor John Weckert (Center for Applied Philosophy and Public Ethics/Charles Sturt University, Australia) as part of a three-year ethics study on human enhancement and emerging technologies. "No matter where one is aligned on this issue, it is clear that the human enhancement debate is a deeply passionate and personal one, striking at the heart of what it means to be human," explained Dr. Lin in the report. Then, with surprising candor, he added, "Some see it as a way to fulfill or even transcend our potential; others see it as a darker path towards becoming Frankenstein's monster."[435]

Given that the impending human-enhancement revolution raises such profound questions concerning the meaning of life—not to mention threatening to unleash unknown environmental and health-related dangers—the authors of this book hope that by making this information available to the widest possible audience, thinking ministers, policy makers, academics, and the general public will weigh in on this issue while there is still time, get involved in the public debate over human-enhancement technology and transhumanist desires, and make their concerns known. If we fail our generation in this respect (to be, as it were, Noah-like preachers of righteousness), the guidelines for public policy toward morphological human enhancement will be determined in our absence, and we and our children will be forced to live with the decisions made by "the dead hand of the great planners and conditioners." Thank God we still have time to act, if we do so now.

THE DAYS OF NOAH:
NOT ALL OF THE ANGELS FELL

According to many Bible scholars, integral to the "signs of the days of Noah" was the fall of the first transhuman technicians—the Watcher angels who altered human genetics through angelic and animal integration. When this mutated DNA began rapidly spreading throughout nature, God instructed Noah, whose family was evidently the last on earth not yet genetically corrupted, to build an ark and to prepare for a Flood that would destroy every living thing. Worldwide extrabiblical texts consistently agree with this Bible story, detailing how the cause of the historic deluge (Great Flood) was in response to "all flesh" having become "corrupted, both man and beast" (see Genesis 6:12). When this Scripture is compared with other ancient texts, it unfolds that the giants of the Old Testament—such as Goliath, whom David slew—were the part-human, part-animal, part-angelic offspring of a supernatural interruption into the divine order of species. The book that contains the clearest historical account of this event is not widely regarded as part of the canon of Scripture (though it is included in the Ethiopian Orthodox Church's canon and the Beta Israel canon). The authorship of this apocryphal text, known as the Book of Enoch, is ascribed to the biblical figure Enoch, the son of Jared, father of Methuselah, and great-grandfather of Noah. While not in most modern versions of the Bible, the Book of Enoch was clearly familiar to the writers of the New Testament and, according to the critically acclaimed 1899 *Encyclopedia Biblica*, influenced their theology. It is quoted as canon or as historical fact by Jude in the New Testament (Jude 1:14–15) and as canon or as fact by Peter in 1 Peter 3. During the discovery of the Dead Sea Scrolls, pre-Maccabean fragments of the Book of Enoch were found, helping scholars verify its antiquity while also illustrating that the ancients held it to be inspired. Many of the early Church fathers likewise considered the Book of Enoch to be part of sacred Scriptures, including Justin Martyr, Irenaeus, Origen, Athenagoras, Clement of Alexandria, and Quintus Septimius Florens Tertullianus, (Anglicized *Tertullian*), who offered an explanation in AD 200 for its absence from the Jewish canon, saying it was removed by the Jews because of its prophecies pertaining to Jesus Christ. As the case may be, this ancient book provides the most detailed account of the fall of the Watchers, the angels who fathered the infamous Nephilim. From the sixth chapter of Enoch we read:

And it came to pass when the children of men had multiplied that in those days were born unto them beautiful and comely daughters. And the angels, the children of the heaven, saw and lusted after them, and said to one another: "Come, let us choose us wives from among the children of men and beget us children." And Semjaza, who was their leader, said unto them: "I fear ye will not indeed agree to do this deed, and I alone shall have to pay the penalty of a great sin." And they all answered him and said: "Let us all swear an oath, and all bind ourselves by mutual imprecations not to abandon this plan but to do this thing." Then sware they all together and bound themselves by mutual imprecations upon it. *And they were in all two hundred; who descended in the days of Jared* on the summit of Mount Hermon, and they called it Mount Hermon, because they had sworn and bound themselves by mutual imprecations upon it. And these are the names of their leaders: Samlazaz, their leader, Araklba, Rameel, Kokablel, Tamlel, Ramlel, Danel, Ezeqeel, Baraqijal, Asael, Armaros, Batarel, Ananel, Zaq1el, Samsapeel, Satarel, Turel, Jomjael, Sariel. These are their chiefs of tens.[436]

We raise the record of the Book of Enoch in particular because, if it is an accurate account, only two hundred of the powerful angel class known as the "Watchers" fell. When added to Revelation 12:3–4, which says, "And there appeared another wonder in heaven; and behold a great red dragon [whose] tail drew the third part of the stars of heaven, and did cast them to the earth," a reference some scholars believe represents one-third of the angels following Lucifer in his fall, the record becomes clear: most angels—including the powerful ones—did not fall. In other words, the third sign "of the days of Noah" is that far more angels remain on our side than those against us. Why is this important to this book? Because angels play an active and historic role in assisting preachers of righteousness in making known the manifold wisdom of God to the world. Thus if "evil angels" or the spirits of Nephilim are at work behind transhumanism, as we believe they are, unfallen and more powerful ones can assist in our counter-mission as emissaries of God. We have supernatural "secret agents" on our side who can go where we cannot and "whisper" ideas and suggestions into the ears of policy makers and legislators at the highest levels of geopolitical influence.

From the Old and New Testament accounts, the responsibility of angels as it relates to such message delivering is obvious. The New Testament word *angelos*, like the Old Testament word *malak*, simply means "messenger." This definition not only implies angels carry dispatches for God, but that they deliver tangible actions. This includes "guidance" to nations, help for the body of Christ, and protection of individuals. Their ministry in this capacity is according to the will of God, not the church's (meaning we do not give them direct orders, God does), and is defined in Scriptures according to four main categories, each of which is important to this book and to our involvement in the revival of targeted spiritual warfare.

1. **Angels deliver messages of guidance to nations.** Angels, both good and evil, take part in the spiritual battle for civilization. Throughout the Bible there is clear evidence that angels regularly participate in influencing world governments and in shaping human history, especially as it relates to God's covenant people and prophetic fulfillment.

In Exodus 23:20, we read, "Behold, I send an angel before thee, to keep thee in the way, and to bring thee into the place which I have prepared." When God brought Israel out of Egypt, He promised that His angel would go before them and assist them in the development of their nation. In Daniel 12:1, we discover the archangel Michael will continue this relationship with Israel during the Great Tribulation period:

> And at that time shall Michael stand up, the great prince which standeth for the children of thy people: and there shall be a time of trouble, such as never was since there was a nation even to that same time.

Throughout this seven years of Jacob's trouble, the book of Revelation depicts angels serving God in shaping the future of nations by dispensing His will and judgments through pouring out vials, sounding trumpets, carrying out functions related to wars, and affecting "natural" phenomena such as earthquakes and storms. This latter role is especially interesting, given how, simultaneous to GRIN advances and humanity's current fascination with becoming creation-altering technology gods, we are witnessing in America and around the world the most bizarre and destructive weather patterns in hundreds of years; in some cases, we've seen the most devastating storms on record. When we understand how angels strive with nations by controlling natural phenomena (such as weather), it emerges that God may be saying something to this generation about the message of 2 Chronicles 7:14:

> If my people…will humble themselves, and pray, and seek my face, and turn from their wicked ways; then will I hear from heaven…and will heal their land.

Does this suggest that if we, as preachers of righteousness, participate in repentance and spiritual warfare, God will send forth the "heavenly host" to assist in guiding the world toward moral clarity on the issues described in this book?

2. Angels deliver messages of direction to individuals. This first and most recurrent function of angels, message bearing, includes delivery of special instructions from God to individuals concerning the best courses of action. It was an angel that brought God's prophetic message to Mary concerning the immaculate conception of her Son, Jesus (Luke 1:26–38). Earlier, a similar message was delivered by an angel to Zechariah about the birth of his son, John the Baptist (Luke 1:5–25). But, after Jesus was born, angels delivered a specific warning to Joseph, instructing him to flee with Mary and Jesus into Egypt. The angel added, "Be thou there until I bring thee word: for Herod will seek the young child to destroy him" (Matthew 2:13).

Another example of a message from an angel to an individual giving instructions on timing and movement is found in the book of Acts. Satan had filled Herod's heart with hatred for the Church. James was killed and Peter was imprisoned for preaching the Gospel. When the believers understood that Herod was also planning to kill Peter, "prayer was made without ceasing of the church unto God for him" (Acts 12:5).

Peter was in strict confinement, sleeping between two Roman soldiers in chains. During the night, an angel entered the prison and hit Peter on the side. "Arise up quickly," the angel said. "Gird thyself, and bind on thy sandals...and follow me" (Acts 12:7–8). Peter thought he was dreaming as he followed the angel outside past the guards. It wasn't until he was standing on the street that he realized the *angelos*, the messenger of God, had pronounced God's instructions and delivered him from the Roman prison.

Each of these examples reveals that, as we pray, divine prompting will help in determining the timing and correct course of action each of us will need in the days ahead. A peculiar additional fact to keep in mind concerning angels delivering such messages is how often they are perceived as "heavenly beings" only after their departure.

This was the case in Judges 6:11–24, with the angel that appeared to Gideon; in Hebrews 13:2, an important caveat is added: "Be not forgetful to entertain strangers: for thereby some have entertained angels unawares." Entertaining angels without being aware that's what they are is possible, because while angels can appear brilliant or even frightening, they usually manifest in simple human form. As we move toward a dystopian future, it would be interesting to know how many times we may encounter these mysterious "strangers" and how often the "person" who delivers God's special words of counsel at just the right moment might actually be an *angel on assignment.*

3. **Angels deliver messages of strength and encouragement.** In the tenth chapter of the book of Daniel, the prophet had been praying and fasting for three weeks—conducting spiritual warfare for the future of Israel—when, as he stood on the banks of the Tigris River, the angel Gabriel appeared before him. Daniel fell on his face trembling, overcome by the extent of his fast and by the glorious presence of the angel. He said:

How can the servant of this my lord talk with this my lord? for as for me, straightway there remained no strength in me, neither is there breath left in me. (Daniel 10:17)

Then the angel touched him, saying, "O man greatly beloved, fear not: peace be unto thee, be strong, yea, be strong" (Daniel 10:19), and Daniel immediately received strength and energy to continue supernatural combat.

Psalm 34:7 is a beautiful verse about this, written from the warrior's perspective. It says, "The angel of the LORD encampeth round about them that fear him, and delivereth them." It was an angel that ministered such strength and deliverance to Elijah in 1 Kings, chapter 19, when he was running for his life and trying to escape the wicked queen Jezebel. In the New Testament, we find angels ministering to Jesus in similar fashion following His wilderness experience (Mark

1:13). Thankfully, such ministry is not limited to great prophets or to Jesus exclusively, for as Paul taught, these are ministering spirits sent to deliver messages of strength and encouragement to all of God's children (Hebrews 1:14). In other words, they will be there for us, too, as we advance in our mission.

4. Angels deliver messages of protection for preachers of righteousness. In the Scriptures, we read how angels were sent to protect Jesus:

> For He shall give His angels charge over thee, to keep thee in all thy ways. They shall bear thee up in their hands, lest thou dash thy foot against a stone. (Psalm 91:11–12)

Such verses reflect the ancient (and we believe accurate) Jewish belief that God assigns protective angels to those who belong to Him.

The writers of the Early Church, including Origen and Eusebius, believed every person is accompanied by a personal guardian angel. The followers of Christ evidently held this view as well, for when Peter stood outside knocking on the door at Mary's house, they said, "It is his angel" (Acts 12:15). Angels watching over children is depicted in Matthew 18:10, and in Daniel 6:1–23, it appears this is also true for adults. After a sleepless night of fasting, King Darius ran to the lion's den where Daniel had been thrown. "O Daniel, servant of the living God," he cried, "is thy God, whom thou servest continually, able to deliver thee from the lions?" Daniel answered, "O king, live for ever. My God has sent His angel, and hath shut the lions' mouths" (Daniel 6:20–22).

Another example of angels protecting the servant of God is found in 2 Kings 6:13–17. The king of Aram hated Elisha and sent spies to track him down. When they found Elisha in the city of Dothan, they surrounded him with a great army:

> And when the servant of the man of God was risen early, and gone forth, behold, an host compassed the city both with horses and chariots. (2 Kings 6:15)

On seeing this multitude, the servant of Elisha cried out in panic, "Alas, my master! How shall we do?" and Elisha answered, "Fear not: for they that be with us are more than they that be with them" (2 Kings 6:15–16). Elisha prayed God would open his servant's eyes and allow him to see the angelic realm:

> And the LORD opened the eyes of the young man; and he saw;
> and, behold, the mountain was full of horses and chariots of
> fire round about Elisha. (2 Kings 6:17)

During spiritual warfare, we can thus pray for God to surround our homes in this way and provide our families with angelic shelter. Volumes of testimonies have been given about the verity of such requests.

RELATIONSHIP BETWEEN PRAYER AND PRINCIPALITIES

While the Church doesn't give direct orders to angels, it is obvious from the biblical examples above that both good and evil supernaturalism respond to effective intercession by saints. Robert E. Lee (general of the Army of Northern Virginia and famed southern preacher) once wrote of this, saying, "Intercessory prayer is our mightiest weapon and the supreme call for all Christians today."[437] Lee found this important, because in 2 Chronicles 7:14, the intercessory role of God's people is directly tied to the "healing" of the nation. This is partly due to interdiction of enemy angels on behalf of persons, cities, states, nations, and even generations that can occur during intercessory prayer. John Knox was so well known for this type of prayer that the queen of Scotland, "Bloody Mary" (who burned Protestant reformers at the stake during the Marian Exile), confessed she feared his prayers more than an army of soldiers. It is this kind of spiritual activity, when issued from a sincere and repentant heart, that radiates God's authority and turns back evil supernaturalism. Every verse in the Bible dealing with spiritual warfare confirms this divine symmetry between God's authority and overcoming evil as predicated upon the Church's responsiveness as evangelists of human-kind. Jesus commissioned Paul to preach to the Gentiles and "turn them from darkness to light, and from the power of Satan unto God" (Acts 26:18a). The Bible subsequently reveals that it is the believer's responsibility to "ask" before God will respond, to bind and release on earth for Heaven to do the same, and that part and parcel of the Great Commission is the duty of the Church to cast out demons and tread over the power of the enemy. Apparently when we do, we send shock waves through the heavenlies! Note that in Nehemiah 9:6, the prophet spoke of more than one heaven: he saw the heavens and the "heaven of heavens." These were not peripheral heavens as taught in Mormonism, but heavenly divisions as Paul referred to in 2 Corinthians 12:2, saying, "I knew a man in Christ above fourteen years ago, (whether in the body, I cannot tell; or whether out of the body, I cannot tell: God knoweth;) such an one [was] caught up to the third heaven." Some scholars believe when Paul referred to this third heaven, he was echoing his formal education as a Pharisee concerning three heavens that included a domain of air (the *kosmos*) or height, controlled by Satan—Beelzeboul, "lord of the height." In pharisaical thought, the first heaven was simply the place where the birds fly, anything removed from and not attached to the surface of the earth. On the other end of the spectrum and of a different substance was the third heaven—the dwelling place of God. This was the place from which angelic spheres spread outward. Between this third heaven, "where dwells the throne room of God," and the first heaven, where the birds fly, was a war zone called the "second heaven." This was the *kosmos*—the Hebrew equivalent of the Persian *Ahriman-abad*—the place where Satan abides as the prince of the power of the "air" (Greek *aer*: the lower air, circumambient; see Ephesians 2:2), a sort of gasket heaven, the domain of Satan encompassing the surface of the earth. From here, *kosmokrators* could overshadow the ages of men and intrude upon and attempt to influence their philosophy and affairs.

A particularly interesting mystery about the *kosmos* has to do with the ancient belief that Satan's minions could close this space above specific areas (strongholds) so prayers from the saints wouldn't be able to penetrate through to God. Some say this concept is allegorical, but that it illustrates how, when believers pray, their intercession is literally opposed—both the prayers going to God and the answers returning from Him. The effectual, fervent prayers of the righteous (James 5:16) are the battering rams that push through all such demonic opposition en route to and from the third heaven. Was this illustrated in the tenth chapter of Daniel, when the prophet prayed for twenty-one days until the angel broke through and delivered God's answer? It would seem so, as the persistence of our prayers, when they are prayed "according to His will," creates activity within the second and third heavens. In turn, the heavenly responses affect every level of spiritual and physical society. Daniel prayed until he pushed a hole through walls of demonic opposition and the heavens opened with spiritual revelations. In 1 Kings 18, Elijah continued in prayer until the heavens opened and the rains fell. The disciples interceded until their prayers penetrated the heavens and the glory of Pentecost came rushing down from the throne of God. Jacob prayed and the heavens opened. Angels ascended and descended. Elisha prayed and his servant beheld the heavens opening and the angelic host standing upon the mountains to help them.

If modern believers pray as eagerly, can we expect similar supernatural authority over the looming threat of Nephilimism via GRIN technology and the transhuman agenda?

A HAUNTING LESSON FROM THE YALU RIVER

As one considers the role of prayer in spiritual warfare, there is what we call the Yalu River Dilemma. From 1950–1953, America fought one of its most bloody and forgotten battles, the Korean War, a conflict in which the dictator of North Korea, Kim Il Sung, obtained military help from USSR dictator Joseph Stalin. During this time, the Chinese army, on November 26, 1950, surprised Gen. Douglas MacArthur by crossing the Yalu River in great force. Hitting the exposed flanks of MacArthur's forces, the Chinese stunned the allies and forced them back. By Christmas of the same year, the United Nations forces were once again fighting below the thirty-eighth parallel.

It was this point that would lead to irreconcilable differences between President Harry S. Truman and General MacArthur. Truman—thoroughly frightened by China's action and fearing the possibility of a world war—moved to limit the confrontation, while MacArthur pressed to bomb the bridges at Yalu and expand the war into China proper. Truman refused and decided to allow only the Korean halves of the Yalu bridges to be bombed. By March of 1951, Truman announced his "limited war" policy. The compromise so infuriated MacArthur that he released his "Military Appraisal," an amazing document that amounted to an ultimatum to the Chinese and to President Truman. This led to Truman firing MacArthur. "By this act," the president said, "MacArthur left me no choice—I could no longer tolerate his insubordination." MacArthur was ordered to return home, relieved of duty. Afterward, MacArthur famously addressed the Congress, saying, "There is no substitute for victory!"

Douglas MacArthur wanted to end the Korean War by total military victory in Asia. Truman chose to continue a limited engagement. In the spirit realm, we face this same type of dilemma. As a local church or as individuals, we pray. When short-term victories come, we may slack off, only to later discover the same problems resurfacing. This principle is critical for believers to understand. A limited war policy or passive approach to prayer can only result in the enemy simply retreating behind its own Yalu River, there to regroup, strategize, and attack again when prayer has ceased. But here is the good news: Whether it is the issue of transhumanism and the deepening challenge to maintain our humanity as God made us, or private issues we currently face, God has given the Church what the US government refused to give MacArthur during the Korean War: the power to move beyond the protective bridges of our enemy's stronghold. God allows the contrite believer to invade the opponent's headquarters through the power of prayer, to identify and bind the ruling prince through the authority of Jesus' name, and to permanently destroy the fortress walls of nefarious warlords—or, as the military would say, "to offer them no quarter."

Of course, some will argue this is easier said than done. When looking at the awesome scope of government and academic interests in GRIN technology and the planned rollout of industrialized techno-sapiens, we as individuals may feel small or powerless, as though our single prayers or input will be of little effect. The Tea Party movement in the United States illustrates that this is not true. A nation is simply a multitude of people. Each time an individual takes a righteous stand, we move one person closer to victory. In fact, every notable spiritual awakening began with an individual. The Reformation started with the convictions of Martin Luther. Paul stood alone at Ephesus, a city ruled by an unsurpassed religious and political machine, yet he started a church there that ultimately released the minds of men and women from the deception of Diana worship and brought the downfall of a cult that had flourished for centuries. When Charles Finney launched his evangelism effort, he took onto his team a man named Nash, who made prayer his only activity. When Finney preached, Nash stayed behind and prayed, and guess what? As many as fifty thousand people per week accepted Jesus as Lord. Jonathan Edwards, George Whitefield, Catherine Booth, Gilbert Tennent, Shubal Stearns, Fanny Crosby, Daniel Marshall, Billy Sunday, Maria Woodworth-Etter, and numerous others proved one cannot underestimate the power of a single dedicated believer.

Having said that, the past also reveals what happens when individuals do nothing, or worse, when they become corrupt and tyrannical. Students of history have looked with interest at the French Revolution, which was marked by death and torture under Maximilien Robespierre, and have compared it to the Revolutionary War in America that eventually resulted in unprecedented cultural and monetary success. While citizens after the war in America were rejoicing in newfound freedoms, in Paris, more than twenty thousand people died in the guillotine. The years to follow in France witnessed a reign of terror leading to totalitarianism and the rise of an Antichrist figure, Napoleon. Why were the American and French Revolutions followed by such contrasting conclusions? The difference was that in America the pilgrim influence had created strong Christian sentiments, while in France the movement was anti-God. The forces behind the French Revolution were out to eliminate God as the enemy of France. They placed a statue of a nude woman upon the altar in the church of Notre Dame and proclaimed the God of Christianity dead. Soon after, the French government collapsed.

Conversely, when we understand how, during the American Revolution, a small number of mostly agrarian Americans stood up for something that mattered and held tightly to a Christian faith that could not be stamped out by the fires of revolution, we comprehend where the strength of those generations that followed came from, including the so-called Greatest Generation, the children of the pioneers who overcame the Great Depression, who won World War II and outperformed their competitors during the Industrial Revolution. Those who followed them built on the same success until finally the United States emerged as "a shining city on a hill," a beacon of hope and inspiration to the rest of the world—what President Ronald Reagan in his January 11, 1989, farewell speech called "a tall, proud city built on rocks stronger than oceans, windswept, God-blessed, and teeming with people of all kinds living in harmony and peace, a city with free ports that hummed with commerce and creativity, and if there had to be city walls, the walls had doors and the doors were open to anyone with the will and the heart to get here."[438]

WHOSE VISION WILL PREVAIL?

Ronald Reagan's depiction of America is sweet, but (as we have documented) a worrying trend is darkening the horizon and threatening to undo this dream and similar big ideas in countries around the world.

Recent polling shows a generation disinterested in the faith of their fathers and even less attracted to Judeo-Christian definitions about sin and repentance. Society now wants a God that makes them happy and who only comes around when needed. This new widespread movement even has a name: "Moralistic Therapeutic Deism" (dubbed so by researchers during a National Study of Youth and Religion at the University of North Carolina). It defines what has become the "Christianity" of choice among modern teens and their parents. Like the deistic God of the Freemasons and eighteenth-century philosophers, "this undemanding deity is more interested in solving our problems and in making people happy," concludes Dr. Albert Mohler Jr. for the *Christian Post*. He said:

> In short, [this] God is something like a combination Divine Butler and Cosmic Therapist: he is always on call, takes care of any problems that arise, professionally helps his people to feel better about themselves, and does not become too personally involved in the process.

In continuing his troubling dissertation, Mohler unknowingly describes elements of transhumanism:

> This radical transformation of Christian theology and Christian belief replaces the sovereignty of God with the sovereignty of the self [a central transhumanist value]. In this therapeutic age, human problems are reduced to pathologies in need of a treatment plan. Sin is simply excluded from the picture, and doctrines as central as the wrath and justice of God are discarded as out of step with the times and unhelpful to the project of self-actualization.

All this means is that teenagers have been listening carefully. They have been observing their parents in the larger culture with diligence and insight. They understand just how little their parents really believe and just how much many of their churches and Christian institutions have accommodated themselves to the dominant culture. They sense the degree to which theological conviction has been sacrificed on the altar of individualism and a relativistic understanding of truth. They have learned from their elders that self-improvement [another important theme of transhumanism] is the one great moral imperative to which all are accountable, and they have observed the fact that the highest aspiration of those who shape this culture is to find happiness, security, and meaning in life. [We thus] face a succession of generations who have transformed Christianity into something that bears no resemblance to the faith revealed in the Bible. The faith "once delivered to the saints" is no longer even known, not only by American teenagers, but by most of their parents.[439]

Thus, like a ship adrift at sea, a gilded age arises in which intellectual achievements and human-transforming technologies are valued as supreme. And no wonder. For more than five decades, hundreds of millions of dollars in public funds have poured into transhumanist goals; media outlets have denigrated traditional values; the highest courts in the land have ruled with imperious decree against the free expression of Christianity; evangelicals have been disinvited to the National Day of Prayer at the Pentagon; and finally, according to former president of the United States, Barack Hussein Obama, America is no longer a Christian nation.

The net result is the dawn of a generation without sacred moorings, an era in which people are sufficiently prepared to accept the nightmarish transhuman vision unfolding around us. The question is: Is it too late to reverse these trends and set this age on track toward moral and spiritual recovery? We must believe it's not too late—that if, like Noah, David, Joshua, and Caleb, we stand up to the infernal power operating just beyond the range of normal vision, it will yet be possible to illustrate the living dynamic against which the gates of hell cannot prevail.

But make no mistake about it: The gods of chaos are coming. They are poised to redefine what it means to be human and remove anyone or anything that stands in their way. The Church must prepare for this now, both physically and spiritually, as the threat is real and spreading like cancer.

While *Summoning the Demon: Artificial Intelligence and the Image of the Beast* includes fresh insights for traditional, tried-and-true methods of overcoming darkness, it also unveils for the first time how breakthrough advances in science, technology, and philosophy—including cybernetics, bioengineering, nanotechnology, machine intelligence, synthetic biology, and transhumanism—will combine to create mind-boggling game-changes to everything you have ever known about spiritual warfare.

How so?

As a result of GRINS tech, new modes of perception between things visible and invisible are on the near horizon and expected to challenge the Church in ways that are historically and theologically unprecedented. Without comprehending what is quickly approaching in related disciplines of research and development, vast numbers of believers could be paralyzed by the most fantastic—and most far-reaching—supernatural implications. The destiny of each individual—as well as the future of their families—will depend on knowledge of the new paradigm and the preparedness to face it head on.

As outlined in this book, the power operating behind this scheme to integrate human-animal-machine interfaces in order to reengineer humanity is not new. The ancient, malevolent force is simply repackaging itself these days as the forward-thinking and enlightened progress needed for the next step in human evolution.

Facing godlike machines and humanity's willingness to cross over species and extradimensional barriers put in place by God, traditional methods of spiritual warfare—which Christian institutions have relied on for the last century—will soon be monumentally impacted in non-traditional ways and insufficient when approaching this threshold.

YOUR HIDDEN ENEMY

There is always subtle danger when writers who attempt to discuss evil supernaturalism focus too much on unnecessary and often wildly exaggerated and biblically unsupported characteristics. We've shuddered more than once at so-called authorities on spiritual warfare using their works to fascinate people with everything from the particular names of demons to their size, shape, skin color, hair color, number of digits, and even thickness of saliva dripping from their lips. While such details may seem innocuous enough, or even entertaining in a Stephen King-ish sort of way, this practice can become unbalanced and antithetical to New Testament instructions, even opening doors into the imagination for mental and spiritual danger. It is therefore the goal of this work to help the Body of Christ with only the material we believe is necessary to recognize the battle all believers are engaged in, and to comprehend the nature of the tactics employed by our hidden enemy. As Theoden learned in the *Lord of the Rings*, we are in this war whether we want to be or not, so we need to be equipped and informed.

We shall never forget some years ago, when Dr. David Yonggi Cho described in vivid detail how he learned the truth about such unseen intelligence, which, among other things, operates behind the scenes to obstruct the work of the ministry.

As a young preacher, Cho had gone into a small Korean community to pioneer a church. Soon he discovered, as is common throughout much of Korea, a temple dedicated to the city's "guardian god" atop the highest local mountain. When the priests of the shrine learned that he was planning to start a mission outreach, they came to him infuriated, demanding that he leave the village. When he refused, they vowed to return and put to death him and any converts he won in the meantime.

A few days later, the priests were back—this time with a mob. The head priest, making sure the crowd was watching, called out, "Cho!

Do you really believe that Jesus Christ is the same yesterday, today, and forever, and that He can still work miracles?"

Cho replied, "Yes, I do."

"Then we have a challenge," the priest yelled. "Down in the village is a woman who has been bedridden for seven years. She and her child are dying now of disease. If Jesus can heal this woman in the next thirty days, we will go away and you can have your church. But if she is not healed, you must abandon your work or we will return and kill you and your followers."

Cho explained how in the United States, most Americans would never respond to such a dare, but that in those days and in that culture, his failure to do so would have been (in his opinion) to imply that his God was inferior to the temple deity, and it would have closed the community's willingness to consider the Gospel message.

As a result, Cho accepted the contest, and the following day he traveled with his mother-in-law to the village where he found the dying woman. He suggested to the infirmed lady that if she would pray the sinner's prayer and accept Jesus as her Savior, the Lord might choose to heal her. Instead, he found the woman to be very angry with any god (including Cho's) who would allow her to suffer the way she had. After several unsuccessful visits to convince her otherwise, Cho decided prayer alone would be his best alternative for her and her child.

Over the next few weeks, he prayed earnestly for a miracle. He made regular visits to the village and sent messengers to report back any change. To his disappointment, the woman's condition only seemed to worsen.

As the weeks passed and the deadline loomed, Cho grew very concerned. Finally, on the evening of the thirtieth day, he entered his prayer room and reminded God that unless a miracle occurred, people from the temple of the guardian deity would arrive within hours to kill him and his followers. Cho said he prayed throughout that night and into the next morning "with the most passion ever."

Then, at 2 a.m., he experienced a powerful vision.

He thought he saw a shadow by the front door, and a strange sound spread along the wall.

Fixing his gaze on the opening, he felt primal fear, black and mindless, roll over him.

His intuition screamed. Something dreadful was coming his way.

Another *thump*, and the front door to his home began slowly opening.

Gooseflesh crawled over his arms as "eerie Oriental music" swept in through the entrance, barely discernable at first, then growing in intensity.

Against his better judgment, he turned his body toward the door.

He held his breath, looked harder, squinted.

The shadow slowed, became defined, an enormous silhouette of something *alive* creeping stealthily toward him.

Remaining very still, a moment passed, then *it* emerged from the darkness: huge, snakelike, an agathodemon from ancient times bearing the body of a serpent and the head of a man. Swaying to the melodious rhythm, the horrendous archfiend appeared wicked and menacing as it slunk along the opening into the room where Cho was. It made eye contact with him, and in heavy modulation that sounded as if each gurgling syllable started somewhere deep underground and passed through boiling magma on its way to his mouth, said, "Cho, if you don't leave this town, you are a dead man. I have been ruling this area all of these years, and who are you to come here and disturb my nest!?"

With that, the being lunged across the room lightning fast, landing on top of Cho and wrapping its body around him like prey, contracting its muscles to quickly constrict the air from his lungs. A baleful laughter, malignant and terrible, tittered from the monster's lips as from pebbled sockets its zenithal eyes glared mockingly down at him.

Grotesque and enraged, the thing opened its mouth wider, exposing a hideous, forked tongue inside a nightmarish cavity lined with jagged molars and angled razor fangs. A phlegmy gurgle more dragon-like than reptilian disgorged a sulfurous stench that distilled through the room, filling the air all around them.

A chill radiated through Cho as seconds passed and the undulating fiend's hide, crusty and wart-covered, tightened around him like a garrote. He could feel his ribs bending toward the breaking point as the sheer force of the brutal creature's strength sent his own tongue curling to the roof of his mouth in pain. His body began reacting to the lack of blood flow, his hands and feet started going numb, and his thoughts raced: *Jesus! I'm dying!*

But at that, something caught his attention. The creature's eyes had seemed to dart wildly about the very moment the name of Jesus passed through his mind. He thought it again—*Jesus*—and this time he was sure. The serpent had cringed, and its grip had weakened *at the very moment he had imagined that name!*

With all the strength he could muster, Cho gasped for a breath of air and opened his mouth in a whisper: "Jesus."

The effect was immediate and dramatic. The sound of the name of Jesus discharged from his lips as tangibly as if a two-edged sword had been thrown into the heart of the being.

He spoke the name again, louder this time, and the demon jerked back, its expression filling with terror, its grip unwinding from his waist.

Slipping from the coil, Cho quickly jumped to his feet and shouted, "JESUS…JESUS…*JESUS!*"

Now the creature reeled, first one way then the other, flailing about as if punch drunk, wailing an otherworldly moan; then abruptly it fell to the floor. Before it could gather its strength and raise up to attack him again, Cho lifted his leg and crushed the humanlike head beneath his foot. Studying it to make sure it wasn't moving, he picked up the front part of the carcass and dragged it toward the entry to toss it outside. As he moved to the opening and pushed the door fully out of the way, he noticed a large crowd of villagers gathering in front of his home. Cautiously, he surveyed his surroundings, then lifted the agathodemon's face above him and exclaimed, "This is the god you have been serving all of these years, but now you must turn and serve the true and living God!"

With that, Cho awoke to find the serpent-man visitation had been a compelling vision or dream. It was 4 a.m., time for early morning prayer at his tent church. With the memory of the threats made against him thirty days earlier still fresh in his mind, he rushed out the door and up the path to meet his tiny congregation. He knew the priests from the guardian temple would not be long in coming, and no sooner had he arrived than a Korean layman started shouting, "Pastor! Come quickly!" Glancing out the tent door, he saw over the hill in the rising dawn what appeared to be the entire city marching up the valley walls.

Cho's palms were sweating and his heart was racing as he stepped outside and watched the throng approach. *Jesus*, he thought, *what should we do? Run? Hide?* Then he noticed something curious. The people looked happy, as if they were rejoicing about something. A moment of silence passed as he considered them, and he thought, *It can't be!* But it was. Leading the crowd, baby in arms, was the dying woman from the village. She ran up to him and said, "Oh, Brother Cho, thank you so much for coming and praying for me last night. The Lord heard your prayer and I am healed!"

Cho stared at her in amazement. "I did not come to your house and pray for you last night," he replied.

"Oh yes," the woman insisted, "You came at 2 o'clock this morning and stood outside my window. You said loudly, 'Woman! Be healed in the name of Jesus Christ!' And I arose and found that I was healed, and my baby is healed!"

Then Cho remembered that it had been 2 a.m. when he had seen the vision and the agathodemon had been destroyed.

With very few exceptions, the entire community converted to Christianity within forty-eight hours. Today, Cho pastors the largest evangelical church in the world, with nearly a million members. It all started in a city delivered from demonic siege.

"THEY'RE HERE"

Undoubtedly when reading the story above, some people will feel hard-pressed to interpret the narrative in any way other than as somebody's overactive imagination. Nevertheless, as Carol Anne so ominously expressed in the 1982 film *Poltergeist*, "They're here." Demons and their militaristic interest in people and geography are ontological facts, according to the Bible. In the Old Testament, demons are seen as the living dynamic behind idolatry (i.e., Deuteronomy 32:17), and in the New Testament, every writer refers to their influence. Extrabiblical texts including ancient pseudepigraphical works like the first Book of Enoch and post-New Testament writings such as the Didache, Ignatius' Epistle to the Ephesians, and the Shepherd of Hermas agree with this concern. Early Church fathers also reinforced the belief that evil spirits seek to thwart the will of God on earth through attacks on the body of Christ in particular and against society in general. Spiritual Warfare 101 begins by taking these facts into account by asserting that not only do visible agents exist everywhere around us, but unseen intermediaries—both good and evil—interlope between spiritual and human personalities at home, in church, in government, and in society. On rare occasions, the general public may catch a glimpse of this ethereal existence. For instance, on April 5, 1991, ABC's *20/20* broadcast the first televised Catholic exorcism. We watched this historic event twenty years ago and thought that, regardless of one's denominational affiliation, it illustrated contemporary demonism.

While deliverance ministry such as exorcism should be carefully administered within the church, demons play an even wider role in society—a role that includes controlling or influencing not only individuals and small groups, but institutions and governments as well. Understanding how and why this is true is defined in demonological studies such as the *divine council* (a term used by Hebrew and Semitic scholars to describe the pantheon of divine beings or angels who administer the affairs of Heaven and earth), where experts typically agree that, beginning at the Tower of Babel, the world and its inhabitants were disinherited by the sovereign God of Israel and placed under the authority of lesser divine beings that became corrupt and disloyal to God in their administration of those nations (Psalm 82). Following Babel, these beings quickly became idolized on earth as gods, giving birth to the worship of "demons" (see Acts 7:41–42; Psalms 96:5; and 1 Corinthians 10:20) and the quest by fallen angels to draw humankind away from God. While the dominion of these entities and their goals are frequently overlooked, close collaboration between *evil ones* and unregenerate social architects operates on a regular basis outside the purview of the countless multitudes who are blinded to their reality. Behind governors, legislators, presidents, dictators, and even religious leaders, these wicked spiritual powers move about unrestricted, controlling the machine of ecclesiastical and civil governments as freely as they are allowed. Whenever such principalities recognize a religious or political body that has become a force for moral good, they set about—through a sophisticated labyrinth of visible and invisible representatives—to bring that organization down, one righteous soul at a time.

It is within this concealed arena of evil supernaturalism that unregenerate people are organized. Under demonic influence, they are orchestrated within a great evil system (or empire) described in various scriptural passages as a satanic order. In more than thirty important biblical texts, the Greek New Testament employs the term *kosmos*, describing this "government behind government." It is here that human ego, separated from God, becomes hostile to the service of humankind while viewing people as commodities to be manipulated in the ministration of fiendish ambition. Some expositors believe the origins of this phenomenon began in the distant past, when a fire in the minds of angels caused Lucifer to exalt himself above the good of God's creation. The once-glorified spirit, driven mad by an unequivocal thirst to rule, conquer, and dominate, spawned similar lust between his followers, which continues today among agents of dark power who guard a privileged, "cause-and-effect" symmetry between visible and invisible personalities.

394

At Satan's desire, archons command this supernatural, geopolitical sphere, dominating *kosmokrators* (rulers of darkness who work in and through human counterparts), who in turn command spirits of lesser rank until every level of earthly government, secular and religious, can be touched by this influence. If we could see through the veil into this domain, we would find a world alive with good against evil, a place where the ultimate prize is human souls and where legions battle for control of its cities and people. With vivid testimony to this, Satan offered Jesus all the power and the glory of the governments of this world:

All this power [control] will I give thee, and the glory of them [earthly cities]: for that is delivered unto me: and to whomsoever I will I give it. If thou therefore wilt worship me, all shall be thine. (Luke 4:6–7)

According to the epistle of the Ephesians, it is this dominion, not flesh and blood, where opposition to God's will on earth is initiated. Whereas people and institutions often provide the "faces" on our problems, the conflict originates beyond them, in this place where unseen forces scheme.

THAT DOMAIN BETWEEN LIGHT AND SHADOW

Although the hidden region described above represents otherdimensional existence within the *supernatural realm*, the dark strategies fomented there manifest destructive fallout throughout the material world—wars, genocide, terrorism, Christian persecution, broken marriages, juvenile delinquency, occultism, and hundreds of other tangible demonstrations of the infernal influence. Whereas the average person may never understand this assault on his or her corporeal interests as being fundamentally supernatural, Gregory Boyd, in his book, *God at War: The Bible and Spiritual Conflict*, explains:

God's good creation has in fact been seized by hostile, evil cosmic forces that are seeking to destroy God's beneficent plan for the cosmos.... The general assumption of both the Old and New Testaments is that the earth is virtually engulfed by cosmic forces of destruction, and that evil and suffering are ultimately due to this diabolical siege.[440]

It is therefore the responsibility of every believer to understand the need to put on:

...the whole armour of God, that ye may be able to stand against the wiles of the devil. For we wrestle not against flesh and blood, but against principalities, against powers, against the rulers of the darkness of this world, against spiritual wickedness in high places. Wherefore take unto you the whole armour of God, that ye may be able to withstand in the evil day, and having done all, to stand. (Ephesians 6:11–13)

In the tenth chapter of the book of Daniel, the Bible lifts the curtain on this interdimensional activity in what is considered to be one of the most important Scriptures having to do with spiritual warfare. This is where the prophet Daniel is found fasting and praying for twenty-one days. He had set out to chasten himself before the Lord in hopes that God would bless him with a revelation of Israel's future. On the twenty-first day of his fast, while he was standing on the bank of the Tigris River, an angel suddenly appeared to him and said:

From the first day that thou didst set thine heart to understand, and to chasten thyself before thy God, thy words were heard, and I am come for thy words. (Daniel 10:12)

If a messenger was dispatched from Heaven "from the first day," why did it take three weeks before he arrived? The angel provided the answer by explaining that a powerful Persian demon had opposed him for twenty-one days. Not until the archangel Michael came to assist in the battle was he free to continue his journey. The book of Daniel also describes similar powers at work behind Babylon, Greece, and Rome, revealing an incredible tenet: Demons can control not only individuals, but entire societies, on a territorial scale.

In Persian theology, the spirit that opposed Daniel and his angel would have been identified as Ahriman, whose legend closely parallels the biblical fall of Lucifer. According to Persian religion, Ahriman was the death dealer—the powerful and self-existing evil spirit from whom war and all other evils had their origin. He was the chief of the cacodemons, or fallen angels, expelled from Heaven for their sins. After being kicked out of Heaven, the cacodemons endeavored to settle down in various parts of the earth, but were always rejected, and out of revenge found pleasure in tormenting the planet's inhabitants. Ahriman and his followers finally took up their abode in the space between Heaven and the earth and there established their domain, called *Ahriman-abad*—"the abode of Ahriman." From this location, the cacodemons could intrude into and attempt to corrupt human governments

Besides Persian Zoroastrianism and the mythos of Ahriman (and a host of other ancient origin myths for demons), scholars in the field of demonology offer various hypotheses they believe explain the genesis and motivation of these malevolent spirits.

ANOTHER EXAMPLE OF SUPERNATURAL WARFARE

During our formative years in ministry, few people more profoundly influenced our theology and practical Christianity than pastor and theologian Dr. Robert Cornwall. Bob—or simply "Cornwall," as his friends knew him—had a photographic memory, and in order to pay his way through Bible college as a young man, he had gotten a job proofreading books for a publisher of scholarly works. As a result of maintaining this job for years and having an uncanny propensity for recalling facts, Cornwall retained the majority of material he read and became one of the most well informed and brilliant thinkers we ever had the privilege of knowing or being mentored under. Cornwall was also a great storyteller and could thrill audiences at churches and in conferences by weaving details of true-life events with deep theological propositions. A particular story that raised profound spiritual-warfare implications revolved around one of the first churches he pastored as a young minister in a sleepy little town near the Oregon coast. As described by Cornwall himself at Redwood Family Camp meeting in the 1970s, he had barely settled into leadership at the church when strange things began to happen for which he had no explanation. Objects in the building seemed to move around on their own, especially overnight when the building was supposed to be unoccupied. He would hear the piano playing and go into the sanctuary to find nobody there. Doors would slam, pews would be discovered positioned backward against the wall, and his notes would disappear—then reappear. Members of the church reported similar phenomena, and Cornwall eventually learned that the activity had been going on for years.

One night, hours after he had gone home to bed, Cornwall's telephone rang and the police chief was on the other end of the line. He wanted to know what kind of party Cornwall was sponsoring at the church.

"What do you mean, a party?" Cornwall asked.

"Neighbors are calling. They say it's so loud they can't sleep. We thought maybe the youth group was having an overnight event that was getting out of hand."

Assuring the officer that nobody was supposed to be in the building, Cornwall agreed to meet him at the church. On arrival, they noticed the lights inside the auditorium were going off and on, the piano was banging loudly, and what sounded like shouting of some kind could be heard throughout the edifice. The officer drew his sidearm while Cornwall unlocked the front door. As they pushed the entrance open, all activity inside the facility abruptly ceased. The lights were still on, but the noises had suddenly gone silent. Cornwall moved through the building with the officer and found every entryway locked, with no signs of break in. This experience was documented in the police report—which, at the time, Cornwall was happy to let us confirm with the chief along with other unexplained events.

Together with his board members and ministry leaders, Cornwall began a series of special prayers over the building in what today some might call a "cleansing" ceremony to purge the house of worship of malevolent spirits mimicking trickster ghosts or poltergeists (German *poltern*, "to rumble or make a noise," and *geist*, meaning "spirit"— invisible entities that manifest by creating noises or by moving objects around). But the results of these prayers were mixed, and Cornwall couldn't understand why. Whenever members of the church were inside the building and prayed, the activity stopped. As soon as they would leave the facility, it would start up again. This went on sporadically for some time, until one day the chief—now a member of the church—called Cornwall and asked if he could meet him downtown at the police department, saying he had found something important and wanted the pastor to see it. Arriving on schedule, Cornwall was handed an envelope that contained a copy of the original deed to the church property and other interesting documents. One of these records was very enlightening. It revealed that the structure—which was nearly one hundred years old and had been boarded up for over a decade before the organization Cornwall was a member of purchased it and turned it into a church—had originally been constructed by an occult group as a meeting place for their "order." It had been dedicated as a residence "for spirits of Lucifer as they move to and fro upon the earth."

Cornwall was shocked. Legalese existing within the building's first title and deed provided lodging for satanic spirits. Equally disturbing, the experiences at the church suggested demons were operating under some legal claim to be there.

As soon as possible, a new church was erected across the street from the old one, and subsequently the original building was torn down and an asphalt parking lot was poured over the plot of land on which it had sat for nearly a century. From that day forward, all paranormal activity on the property ceased, and a powerful and important theological proposition was born in Cornwall's mind—that, under certain conditions, Satan and his spirits have legal rights to property and people.

While some may step back at this point and ask what comparable authority over earth Satan continues to hold following the redemptive work of Christ, most scholars agree that until the Second Coming of Jesus and the final judgment of people and angels, this planet remains under limited jurisdiction of Satan as "the god of this world" (2 Corinthians 4:4) and under the influence of "the rulers of the darkness of this world" (Ephesians 6:12). During this time, contracts and covenants with such spirits allowing access or entry into one's property or life do not have to be officially recorded as in the story of Cornwall's church above. They can be oral or assumed agreements, not to mention "adverse possession," or what laymen call "squatter's rights." In the physical world, this is when a person openly uses somebody else's property without permission over such a long period that eventually the "squatter" gains legal claim to the land, due to the original owner not taking legal action against him or her. These are ancient statutory principles that pertain equally to material and spiritual dynamics. They imply that wherever activity favorable to malevolent spirits occurs by consent, is tolerated, or action is not taken to force the "squatter" to cease and desist, footholds and even personal rights can be surrendered to hostile forces over people and locations.

This is what has been happening in America for the past fifty years. It is up to the Body of Christ to change this course, and now that you're aware of some of the enemy's historic and future tactics, you can armor up, speak out, and pray down the towers of principalities and powers while there is still time.

USE THE QR-CODE BELOW TO ACCESS MANY
SPECIAL DEALS AND PROMOTIONS
ON BOOKS AND FILMS FEATURING DISCOVERY,
PROPHECY, AND THE SUPERNATURAL!

NOTES

1   https://en.wikipedia.org/wiki/Technological_singularity
2   https://www.weforum.org/pages/the-fourth-industrial-revolution-by-klaus-schwab
3   https://theweek.com/artificial-intelligence/1024341/ai-the-worst-case-scenario
4   Ibid.
5   https://www.theepochtimes.com/godfather-of-ai-speaks-out-ai-capable-of-reason-may
    -seek-control_5365093.html?utm_source=partner&utm_campaign=ZeroHedge&src
    _src=partner&src_cmp=ZeroHedge
6   https://ifapray.org/blog/the-artificial-intelligence-movement-a-greater-threat-to
    -christianity-than-darwinism/
7   Ibid.
8   https://www.foxnews.com/tech/tech-experts-outline-four-ways-ai-could-spiral-world
    wide-catastrophes
9   https://www.israeltoday.co.il/read/will-ai-become-a-god-rabbis-express-concern/
10 https://www.israel365news.com/373086/25-major-rabbis-rule-its-forbidden-to-use-ai/
11 https://www.cgi.org/news-and-events/2022/8/1/ai-artificial-intelligence-and-the-beast
    -of-revelation?sapurl=LytxNWdtL2FwcD9lbWJlZD10cnVlJnJlY2VudFJvdXRlPWFFwc
    C53ZWltYXBwLnJlZGlyZWN0b3ImcmVjZW50Um91dGVbHVnPWFFw
12 https://harbingersdaily.com/artificial-intelligence-in-the-military-progress-or-the-spark
    -that-ignites-dangerous-ramifications/
13 https://harbingersdaily.com/leading-chruch-services-and-bringing-back-the-dead-how
    -ai-could-pave-the-way-for-deception-on-a-global-scale/
14 https://crisismagazine.com/opinion/in-the-age-of-ai-even-the-very-elect-will-be-deceived
15 John Milton, *Paradise Lost*, public domain, 301.
16 Max More, "Transhumanism Towards a Futurist Philosophy," *MaxMore.com*, 1990,
    accessed December 8, 2010, http://www.maxmore.com/transhum.htm.
17 Christopher Hook, "Transhumainism and Posthumanism," *Encyclopedia of Bioethics*
    3rd ed. Stephen G. Post, (New York, NY: MacMillan, 2007), 2519.
18 Carl Teichrib, "The Rise of the Techno-Gods: The Merging of Transhumanism and
    Spirituality," *Forcing Change* 4,10, October 2010, 2.
19 James Ledford, "Christian Transhumanism," *Hyper-Evolution.com*, accessed May 5,
    2011, http://www.hyper-evolution.com/Christian%20Transhumanism.pdf.
20 *Dialog: A Journal of Theology* 44, 4 (Winter 2005).
21 Thomas Horn, "An Open Letter to Christian Leaders on Biotechnology and the Future
    of Man," *Raiders News Update*, accessed December 16, 2010, http://www.raidersnews
    update.com/leadstory94.htm.

22 Francis J. Beckwith, "What Does It Mean to Be Human?" *Christian Research Journal* 26, 3 (2003): 1.

23 Michael McKenzie, "Genetics and Christianity: An Uneasy but Necessary Partnership," *Christian Research Journal* 18, 2 (1995): 2. Huntington's disease, as defined by the Alzheimer's Association, is "a progressive brain disorder caused by a defective gene."

24 McKenzie. "Genetics," 2.

25 "Gene Therapy" *Human Genome Project Information*, accessed May 6, 2011, http://www.ornl.gov/sci/techresources/Human_Genome/medicine/genetherapy.shtml.

26 Teichrib, "The Rise," 3.

27 McKenzie, "Genetics," 2.

28 https://www.realclearinvestigations.com/articles/2023/07/19/oh_the_humanity_anti-humanism_rising_and_now_along_comes_artificial_intelligence_966474.html

29 McKenzie, "Genetics," 2.

30 Richard Dawkins, "Afterword," In *What Is Your Dangerous Idea?* (New York: Harper Perennial, 2007), 300, by John Brockman.

31 Francis Fukuyama, *Our Posthuman Future* (New York: Picador, 2002), 7.

32 Jim Leffel, "Engineering Life: Human Rights in a Postmodern Age," pdf accessed May 6, 2011, http://www.equip.org/PDF/DE311.pdf.

33 Claudia Joseph, "Now Scientists Create a Sheep That's 15% Human," Daily Mail UK Online, March 2007, accessed December 11, 2010, http://www.dailymail.co.uk/news/article-444436/Now-scientists-create-sheep-thats-15-human.html.

34 Fukuyama, *Our Posthuman*, 43.

35 Nick Bostrom, *The Transhumanist FAQ Version 2.1.* (Oxford: World Transhumanist Association, 2003), 5.

36 Ray Kurzweil, *The Singularity Is Near: When Humans Transcend Biology* (New York: Viking Penguin, 2005), 25.

37 Richard Andersen, "Selecting the Signals for a Brain-Machine Interface," *Current Opinion in Neurobiology*, 14 (2004):1.

38 Mike Yamamoto, "Gaming by Brainwaves Alone," *Cnet News*, March 1, 2007, http://news.cnet.com/8301-17938_105-9692846-1.htm.

39 "Ray Kurzweil Bio," *Kurzweil Accelerating Intelligence*, accessed December 14, 2010, http://www.kurzweilai.net/ray-kurzweil-bio.

40 Ray Kurzweil, *The Age of Spiritual Machines: When Computers Exceed Human Intelligence* (New York, NY: Viking Penguin, 1999), 89.

41 Ibid., 62.

42 Ibid., 163.

43 Ibid.

44 Ibid., 212.

45 Hook, "Transhumanism," 2517.

46 Kurzweil, *The Singularity*, 282.

47 Ted Peters, "The Soul of Transhumanism," *Dialog: A Journal of Theology 44, no. 4*, (Winter 2005): 385.

48 Ibid., 393.

NOTES

49   Derek Parfit, "Divided Minds and the Nature of Persons," *Mindwaves* (1987): 19–28.

50   Kurzweil, *The Singularity*, 275.

51   Ibid.

52   Millard J. Erickson, *The Concise Dictionary of Christian Theology*, Rev. ed., 1st Crossway ed. (Wheaton, IL: Crossway, 2001), 201.

53   More, "Transhumanism."

54   Norman L. Geisler and Frank Turek, *I Don't Have Enough Faith to Be an Atheist* (Wheaton, IL: Crossway, 2004), 20.

55   David Nobel, "Secular Humanism," in Ed Hindson & Ergun Caner, *The Popular Encyclopedia of Apologetics* (Eugene, OR: Harvest House, 2008), 444.

56   R.J. Rummel, "20th Century Democide," *Freedom, Democracy, Peace; Power, Democide, and War*, November 23, 2002, http://www.hawaii.edu/powerkills/20TH.HTM.

57   Bostrom, The Transhumanist FAQ, 46.

58   Ibid.

59   Millard J. Erickson, *Christian Theology*, 2nd ed. (Grand Rapids, MI: Baker Book House, 1998), 501.

60   Phillip Hefner, *The Human Factor: Evolution, Culture and Religion* (Minneapolis, MN: Fortress Press, 1993), 32.

61   Ibid., 26.

62   Hubert Meisinger, "Created Co-Creator," *Encyclopedia of Science and Religion (Macmillan-Thomson Gale, eNotes.com, 2006)*, accessed May 6, 2011, http://www.enotes.com/science-religion-encyclopedia/created-co-creator.

63   Philip Hefner, "Biological Perspectives on Fall and Original Sin," *Zygon*, 28, 1 (March 1993): 77.

64   Paul Tillich, *The Shaking of the Foundations* (New York: Charles Scribner's Sons, 1948), 155, quoted in Hefner's "Biological Perspectives," 92.

65   Hefner, "Biological Perspectives," 98.

66   Erickson, *Christian Theology*, 505.

67   Ibid., 616.

68   Philip Hefner, "The Animal that Aspires to Be an Angel: The Challenge of Transhumanism," *Dialog: A Journal of Theology*, (Summer 2009): 166.

69   Ibid.

70   Ibid.

71   Ibid.

72   James Ledford, "Christian Transhumanism," 164–165.

73   Paul Tillich, *A History of Christian Thought from its Judaic and Hellenistic Origins to Existentialism* (New York: Harper and Row, 1967), 45.

74   Erickson, *Christian Theology*, 333.

75   Ledford, "Christian Transhumanism," 29.

76   Ibid., 58.

77   D. G. Bloesch, "Sin," in *The Evangelical Dictionary of Theology:* Walter A. Elwell (Grand Rapids, MI: Baker Academic, 2001), 1104.

78   Teichrib, "The Rise," 14.

79 Francis A. Schaeffer, *How Should We Then Live? The Rise and Decline of Western Thought and Culture* (Old Tappan, NJ: Revell, 1976): 228.

80 Hook, "Transhumanism," 2518.

81 Ledford, "Christian Transhumanism," 51.

82 Hugo de Garis, *The Artilect War: Cosmists vs. Terrans: A Bitter Controversy Concerning Whether Humanity Should Build Godlike Massively Intelligent Machines* (Palm Springs, CA: ETC, 2005) 11–12, 15, 84.

83 Theodore Kaczynski, "Industrial Society and Its Future," Wikisource, http://en.wiki source.org/wiki/Industrial_Society_and_Its_Future.

84 Joe Garreau, *Radical Evolution: The Promise and Peril of Enhancing Our Minds, Our Bodies—And What It Means to Be Human* (New York: Broadway, 2005) 71–72)

85 Ray Kurzweil, *The Singularity Is Near* (New York: Penguin, 2006) 7–8.

86 Abou Farman, "The Intelligent Universe," *Maison Neuve* (8/ 2/10) http://maisonneuve .org/pressroom/article/2010/aug/2/intelligent-universe/.

87 Kurzweil, 9.

88 "The Coming Technological Singularity," presented at the VISION-21 Symposium sponsored by NASA Lewis Research Center and the Ohio Aerospace Institute (3/30–31/93).

89 https://medium.datadriveninvestor.com/australian-team-wins-600-000-for-merging -ai-with-human-brain-cells-e14b2629aa64

90 Jerome C. Glenn, "The State of the Future" (7/14/10) www.kurzweilai.net/the-state -of-the-future; emphasis added.

91 Ibid.; emphasis added.

92 Case Western Reserve University, "Case Law School Receives $773,000 NIH Grant to Develop Guidelines for Genetic Enhancement Research: Professor Max Mehlman to Lead Team of Law Professors, Physicians, and Bioethicists in Two-Year Project," (April 28, 2006).

93 https://www.independentsciencenews.org/commentaries/children-from-gamete-like -cells-dishing-up-a-eugenic-future/

94 https://www.dailymail.co.uk/health/article-12124367/100-lab-grown-babies-FIVE -YEARS-Japanese-researchers-make-breakthrough.html

95 Jane Picken, "Medical Marvels," *The Evening Chronicle* (April 13, 2007).

96 Joseph Infranco, "President Barack Obama Warped and Twisted Science with Embryonic Stem Cell Order," *LifeNews* (4/13/09) http://www.lifenews.com/bio2823.html.

97 Nick Bostrom, "Transhumanist Values," www.nickbostrom.com.

98 "Facing the Challenges of Transhumanism: Religion, Science, Technology," *Arizona State University*, http://transhumanism.asu.edu/.

99 http://lach.web.arizona.edu/Sophia/

100 Leon R. Kass, *Life, Liberty, and the Defense of Dignity: The Challenge for Bioethics* (New York: Encounter, 10/25/02).

101 Rick Weiss, "Of Mice, Men, and In-Between," MSNBC (11/20/04) http://www.msnbc .msn.com/id/6534243/.

102 http://news.yahoo.com/s/cq/20090315/pl_cq_politics/politics3075228

103 *American Journal of Law and Medicine*, vol. 28, nos. 2 and 3 (2002), 162.

104 As quoted by Margaret McLean, PHD, "Redesigning Humans: The Final Frontier," http://www.elca.org/What-We-Believe/Social-Issues/Journal-of-Lutheran-Ethics/Book -Reviews/Redesigning-Humans-by-Gregory-Stock/Redesigning-Humans-The-Final -Frontier.aspx.

105 "The Coming Technological Singularity," presented at the VISION-21 Symposium sponsored by NASA Lewis Research Center and the Ohio Aerospace Institute (3/30–31/93).

106 Noah Shachtman, "Top Pentagon Scientists Fear Brain-Modified Foes," *Wired* (6/9/08) http://www.wired.com/dangerroom/2008/06/jason-warns-of/.

107 Nigel M. de S. Cameron, *Human Dignity in the Biotech Century* (Downers Grove, IL: InterVarsity, 2004) 75.

108 Ibid., 87; emphasis added.

109 Mihail Roco, *Converging Technologies for Improving Human Performance* (US National Science Foundation and Department of Commerce, 2002) 6.

110 http://www.newamerica.net/events/2010/warring_futures_a_future_tense_event

111 Chris Floyd, "Monsters, Inc.: The Pentagon Plan to Create Mutant 'Super-Soldiers,'" *CounterPunch* (1/13/03).

112 Garreau, *Radical Evolution:* 269–270.

113 Katie Drummond, "Holy Acronym, Darpa! 'Batman & Robin' to Master Biology, Outdo Evolution," *Wired* (7/6/10) http://www.wired.com/dangerroom/2010/07/holy -acronym-darpa-batman-robin-to-master-biology-outdo-evolution/.

114 Katie Drummond, "Darpa's News Plans: Crowdsource Intel, Edit DNA," *Wired* (2/2/10) http://www.wired.com/dangerroom/2010/02/darpas-new-plans-crowdsource -intel-immunize-nets-edit-dna/.

115 Katie Drummond, "Pentagon Looks to Breed Immortal 'Synthetic Organisms,' Molecular Kill-Switch Included," *Wired* (2/5/10) http://www.wired.com/dangerroom /2010/02/pentagon-looks-to-breed-immortal-synthetic-organisms-molecular-kill -switch-included/.

116 Catherine Muguira, "Why Frankenstein Still Sells 40,000 Copies a Year," *Jane Friedman Daily Blog*, last accessed September 2, 2023, https://janefriedman.com/why -frankenstein-still-sells-40000-copies-a-year/.

117 NewWorld Encyclopedia: "Golem," 2023. Last accessed September 2, 2023, https:// www.newworldencyclopedia.org/entry/Golem.

118 Daniel C. Matt, *The Essential Kabbalah: The Heart of Jewish Mysticism*, (New York: Harper Collins, 1995), 4.

119 Judisches Museum Berlin: "Golem," 2023. Last accessed September 2,2023, https:// www.jmberlin.de/en/topic-golem#:~:text=A%20golem%20is%20a%20creature,of%20 an%20imperiled%20Jewish%20community.

120 NewWorld Encyclopedia: "Golem."

121 Dan Joseph, *Kabbalah: A Very Short Introduction*, (Oxford University Press, 2006), 19.

122 Matt, *Essential Kabbalah*, 102.

123 Judisches Museum Berlin: "Golem."

NOTES

124 NewWorld Encyclopedia: "Golem," 2023. Last accessed September 2, 2023, https://www.newworldencyclopedia.org/entry/Golem.

125 Ibid.

126 Ibid.

127 Joseph, *Kabbalah*, 108.

128 NewWorld Encyclopedia: "Golem."

129 Katie, Balevic, "An AI Robot Gave a Side-Eye and Dodged the Question When Asked Whether It Would Rebel Against Its Human Creator," Business Insider Online, July 8, 2023, last accessed September 2, 2023, https://www.newsbreak.com/news/30838 04911613-an-ai-robot-gave-a-side-eye-and-dodged-the-question-when-asked-whether -it-would-rebel-against-its-human-creator?_f=app_share&s=a7&share_destination_id =MTIyODIzNDMxLTE2ODg4Njc4MjYzNzY%3D&pd=08JLz5lZ&hl=en_US&send _time=1688867826&actBtn=floatShareButton&trans_data%7B%22platform%22% 3A1%2C%22cv%22%3A%2223.6.0%22%2C%22languages%22%3A%22en%22%7D.

130 Ibid.

131 Ibid.

132 Brian Howell and Jenell Paris, *Introducing Cultural Anthropology: A Christian Perspective*, (Grand Rapids, MI: Baker Academic, 2019) 54.

133 William Shakespeare, *Romeo and Juliet*. (Mineola, NY: Dover Publications, 1993).

134 Ibid.

135 "Hodiernal", Merriam-Webster Dictionary. 2023. Last accessed September 2, 2023, https://www.merriam-webster.com/dictionary/hodiernal.

136 "Dasn't," Merriam-Webster Dictionary. 2023. Last accessed September 2, 2023, https://www.merriam-webster.com/dictionary/dasn't.

137 Amy Houston, "Lost in Translation: 10 Times Brands Got It Wrong When Going Global, The Drum Online, October 10, 2022, last accessed September 2, 2023, https://www.thedrum.com/news/2022/10/10/lost-translation-10-times-brands-got-it -wrong-when-going-global#:~:text=The%20Pepsi%20generation%20resurrected%20 dead%20ancestors&text=A%20mistranslation%20of%20Pepsi's%20iconic,from%20 the%20grave'%20in%20China.

138 Ibid.

139 Ibid.

140 Gordon Fee & Douglas Stuart, *How to Read the Bible for All Its Worth* (Grand Rapids, MI: Zondervan, 2014), 44.

141 Ibid.

142 Ibid.

143 Ibid.

144 Jason Nelson, "Researchers Are Breaking Ancient Language Barriers With AI," Decrypt Magazine Online, July 3, 2023, Last accessed September 2, 2023, https://decrypt.co/147176/ai-ancient-language-translation-cuneiform-akkadian.

145 Ibid.

146 Yordan Zhelyazkov, "8 of the Most Messed Up Stories from Greek Mythology," Symbolsage, July 12, 2022, Last accessed September 2, 2023, https://symbolsage.com /8-of-the-most-messed-up-stories-from-greek-mythology/.

NOTES

147 Andrew Gestalt, "Top 10 Accounts of Cannibalism That Will Freak You Out," Listverse, June 14, 2021, Last accessed September 2, 2023, https://listverse.com/2021/06/14/top-10-accounts-of-cannibalism-that-will-freak-you-out/.

148 Laura Conaway, "Military Robot Could Eat Corpses," NPR, July 15, 2009, Last accessed September 2, 2023, https://www.npr.org/sections/thetwo-way/2009/07/pentagon_dreaming_of_corpseeat.html#:~:text=I%20hope%20we're%20not,Could%20Feed%20on%20Dead%20Bodies.%22&text=%22whatever%20organic%20material%20it%20can,Tactical%20Robot%2C%20EATR%20for%20short.

149 Ibid.

150 Joe McKendrick and Andy Thurai, "AI Isn't Ready to Make Unsupervised Decisions," Harvard Business Review, September 15, 2022, Last accessed September 2, 2023, https://hbr.org/2022/09/ai-isnt-ready-to-make-unsupervised-decisions#:~:text=For%20the%20most%20part%2C%20AI,life%2C%20and%20society%20at%20large.

151 Ibid.

152 Xiang, Chloe, "'He Would Still Be Here': Man Dies by Suicide after Talking with AI Chatbot, Widow Says," Vice Online, March 30, 2023, Last accessed September 2, 2023, https://www.vice.com/en/article/pkadgm/man-dies-by-suicide-after-talking-with-ai-chatbot-widow-says.

153 Ibid.

154 Ibid.

155 Ibid.

156 Jacob Buckman, "We Aren't Close To Creating a Rapidly Self-Improving AI," As Clay Awakens, April 26, 2023, Last accessed September 2, 2023, https://jacobbuckman.substack.com/p/we-arent-close-to-creating-a-rapidly.

157 Ibid.

158 Ibid.

159 Ibid.

160 Ibid.

161 Ibid.

162 Ibid.

163 Ibid.

164 Future of Life Institute: Open Letter, "Pause Giant AI Experiments: An Open Letter," March 22, 2023, Last accessed September 2, 2023, https://futureoflife.org/open-letter/pause-giant-ai-experiments/.

165 Sawdah Bhaimiya, "An Asian MIT Student Asked AI to Turn an Image of Her Into a Professional Headshot. It Made Her White, with Lighter Skin and Blue Eyes," Newsbreak Business Insider, August 1, 2023, Last accessed September 2, 2023, https://www.newsbreak.com/news/3108074006845-an-asian-mit-student-asked-ai-to-turn-an-image-of-her-into-a-professional-headshot-it-made-her-white-with-lighter-skin-and-blue-eyes?_f=app_share&s=a7&share_destination_id=MTIyODIzNDMxLTE2OTEwMjcyMjIzMzY%3D&pd=08JLz5lZ&hl=en_US&send_time=1691027222&actBtn=floatShareButton&trans_data=%7B%22platform%22%3A1%2C%22cv%22%3A%2223.6.0%22%2C%22languages%22%3A%22en%22%7D.

166 Ibid.

167 Bernard Marr, "The Dangers of Not Aligning Artificial Intelligence with Human Values," Forbes Online, April 1, 2022, Last accessed September 2, 2023, https://www.forbes.com/sites/bernardmarr/2022/04/01/the-dangers-of-not-aligning-artificial-intelligence-with-human-values/?sh=d74818a751cf.

168 Ibid.

169 Matt McFarland, "Uber Self-Driving Car Operator Charged in Pedestrian Death," CNN Business Online, September 18, 2020, Last accessed September 2, 2023, https://www.cnn.com/2020/09/18/cars/uber-vasquez-charged/index.html#:~:text=Rafaela%20Vasquez%20was%20watching%20television,involving%20a%20fully%20autonomous%20vehicle.

170 Marr, "The Dangers of Not Aligning Artificial Intelligence With Human Values."

171 Ibid.

172 Scott Rosenburg, "In AI Arms Race, Ethics May Be the First Casualty," Anxios Online, January 31, 2023, Last accessed September 2, 2023, https://www.axios.com/2023/01/31/chatgpt-ai-arms-race-ethics-competition.

173 Ibid.

174 Ibid.

175 Indermit Gill, "Whoever Leads in Artificial Intelligence in 2023 Will Rule the World Until 2100," Brookings, January 17, 2020, Last accessed September 2, 2023, https://www.brookings.edu/articles/whoever-leads-in-artificial-intelligence-in-2030-will-rule-the-world-until-2100/.

176 Ibid.

177 Ibid.

178 David Autor and David Dorn, "How Technology Wrecks the Middle Class," The New York Times Opinionator Online, August 24, 2013, Last accessed September 2, 2023, https://archive.nytimes.com/opinionator.blogs.nytimes.com/2013/08/24/how-technology-wrecks-the-middle-class/.

179 Gill, "Whoever Leads in Artificial Intelligence."

180 This point has been covered at greater length in the book *Zeitgeist 2025: Countdown to the Secret Destiny of America…The Lost Prophecies of Qumran, and the Return of Old Saturn's Reign* (Crane, MO: Defender Publishing, 2021).

181 Nickie Louise, "These 6 Corporations Control 90% of the Media Outlets in America." *Tech Startups*, September 18, 2020. Last accessed February 18, 2021. https://techstartups.com/2020/09/18/6-corporations-control-90-media-america-illusion-choice-objectivity-2020/.

182 Emily Crane, "Amazon Shuts Down Customer's Smart Home Devices After Delivery Driver's False Racism Claim," New York Post, June 15, 2023, Last accessed September 2, 2023, https://nypost.com/2023/06/15/amazon-shuts-down-customers-smart-home-devices-over-false-racist-claim/.

183 Ibid.

184 Ibid.

185 Mark McLaughlin, "Hate Crime Bill: Hate Talk in Homes 'Must Be Prosecuted,'" The Sunday Times Online, October 28, 2020, Last accessed September 2, 2023, https://

www.thetimes.co.uk/article/hate-crime-bill-hate-talk-in-homes-must-be-prosecuted -6bcthrjdc.

186 Ibid.

187 Horn, *Zeitgeist 2025*, 63–64.

188 Jack Holmes, "Are We Ready for AI to Raise the Dead?" Esquire Magazine Online. Summer 2023. Accessed September 2, 2023, https://www.esquire.com/news-politics /a43774075/artificial-intelligence-digital-immortality/.

189 Ibid.

190 Ibid.

191 Ibid.

192 Kayleigh Donaldson, "Countess Elizabeth Bathory and the Dark Truth Behind Her Killer Legend," SYFY Magazine Online, September 30, 2020, last accessed September 2, 2023, https://www.syfy.com/syfy-wire/countess-elizabeth-bathory-and-the-dark-truth -behind-her-killer-legend.

193 Matthew Griffin, "DARPA Propose Creating an AI That Can Monitor the Whole World for Threats," Fanatical Futurist Online, January 25, 2019, last accessed September 2, 2023, https://www.fanaticalfuturist.com/2019/01/darpa-propose-creating-an-ai -that-can-monitor-the-whole-world-for-threats/.

194 https://www.dailymail.co.uk/sciencetech/article-11494731/How-does-Elon-Musks-Neuralink-brain-chip-actually-work.html#:~:text=muscles%20and%20nerves.-,The %20electrodes%20of%20the%20Neuralink%20chip%20are%20able%20to%20 read,smartwatch%2C'%20Musk%20has%20said

195 http://en.wikipedia.org/wiki/Plimpton_322

196 http://www.nazi.org.uk/eugenics%20pdfs/BloodOfTheNation.pdf, pp. 13–14.

197 http://dnapatents.georgetown.edu/resources/Bulletin10A.pdf

198 Ibid., p. 15.

199 http://www.youtube.com/watch?v=edikv0zbAlU

200 Edwin Black, "Eugenics and the Nazis—the California Connection," *San Francisco Chronicle*. November 9, 2003; viewable online, last accessed June 13, 2013: http://www.sfgate.com/opinion/article/Eugenics-and-the-Nazis-the-California-2549771.php.

201 Robert Proctor, *Racial Hygiene: Medicine Under the Nazis*, (Cambridge, MA: Harvard University Press, 1988, 108.

202 "Economic Impact of the Human Genome Project," http://www.battelle.org/publications/humangenomeproject.pdf(Battelle Technology Partnership Practice.

203 https://www.nytimes.com/1987/12/13/magazine/the-genome-project.html

204 https://www.nytimes.com/1987/12/13/magazine/the-genome-project.html#:~:text =There's%20more%20cooperation%20than%20friction,will%20eventually%20 get%20under%20way

205 https://bush41library.tamu.edu/archives/public-papers/2217#:~:text=This%20is%20 the%20vision%20that,and%20so%20are%20the%20stakes.

206 Theodore Roosevelt, "Society has no business to permit degenerates to reproduce their own kind" letter, *Letters of Note*, posted with image of original letter on March 25, 2011, http://www.lettersofnote.com/2011/03/society-has-no-business-to-permit.html.

207 http://www.theguardian.com/world/2004/sep/25/usa.secondworldwar(Ben Aris and Duncan Campbell, "How Bush's Grandfather Helped Hitler's Rise to Power," *The Guardian*, September 25, 2004

208 https://www.google.com/url?sa=t&rct=j&q=&esrc=s&source=web&cd=2&ved=0CD-QQFjAB&url=http%3A%2F%2Fwww.cdi.anu.edu.au%2FCDIwebsite_1998-2004%2Fphilippines%2Fphilippines_downloads%2FPhilJudgoba.rtf&ei=Z9X7UdzmHM3eyAGn-YDIDQ&usg=AFQjCNHdHuOC5jRN8G4hrzkgDrU-ZnO77A&sig2=nTF7Er4XNHji2TI-1EMBig

209 *Human Genome News*, Vol. 12, Nos. 1–2, http://web.ornl.gov/sci/techresources/Human_Genome/publicat/hgn/v12n1/HGN121_2.pdf US Department of Energy Office of Biological and Environmental Research, "Countering Bioterrorism: DOE-Funded DNA-Based Technologies Track Identity, Origin of Biological Agents,".

210 Ibid.

211 Nick Bostrom, "Are You Living in a Computer Simulation?" *Philosophical Quarterly*, 2003, Vol. 53, No. 211, 243–255, http://www.simulation-argument.com/simulation.html.

212 Mike Treder, "Top Ten Transhumanist Movies," *H + Magazine*, November 8, 2010, http://hplusmagazine.com/2010/11/08/top-ten-transhumanist-movies/.

213 Christopher Loring Knowles, "The Council of Nine and the *Star Trek* Pantheon," June 6, 2008, http://secretsun.blogspot.com/2008/06/council-of-nine-and-star-trek-pantheon.html.

214 http://runesoup.com/2012/05/the-seance-that-changed-america/#ixzz2aqB89N5l

215 Lawrence Gerald, "Surfing the E.L.F. Waves with Andrija Puharich," *Reality Hackers Magazine*, 1988, http://www.sirbacon.org/4membersonly/puharich.htm.

216 Andrija Puharich, *The Sacred Mushroom*, http://wiki.zimbra.com/images/archive/2/2b/20110603152623!13936.pdf.

217 Ibid.

218 Ibid.

219 Ibid.

220 Ibid.

221 Lynn Picknett and Clive Prince, *Stargate Conspiracy: Revealing the Truth behind Extraterrestrial Contact, Military Intelligence and the Mysteries of Ancient Egypt*, http://books.google.com/books?id=2P6DBTX3MXUC&pg=PT167&dq=puharich+round+table&hl=en&sa=X&ei=XikBUuyDMKGyAGFo4AY&ved=0CEAQ6AEwAQ#v=onepage&q=puharich%20round%20table&f=false..

222 Mark Russell Bell Blog, *Case Study: Uri*, by Andrija Puharich, http://metaphysicalarticles.blogspot.com/2012/06/uri-journal-of-mystery-of-uri-geller.html.

223 Ibid.

224 http://news21c.blog.fc2.com/blog-entry-6749.html

225 http://targetedindividualscanada.wordpress.com/2010/06/24/article-what-is-voice-to-skull/

226 Sharon Weinberger, "Army Yanks 'Voice-to-Skull Devices' Site," *Wired*, May 9, 2008, http://www.wired.com/dangerroom/2008/05/army-removes-pa/.

NOTES

227 https://neurophilosophy.wordpress.com/2007/12/11/hearing_voices/

228 http://techcrunch.com/2013/03/12/leap-motion-michael-buckwald-demo/

229 http://www.nist.gov/manuscript-publication-search.cfm?pub_id=914224

230 http://www.theguardian.com/technology/2010/jun/16/minority-report-technology
-comes-true

231 http://www.phorm.com/technologies

232 Mark Rockwell, "NIST Delivers Long-Sought Standards for Iris Recognition," http://
fcw.com/articles/2013/07/15/nist-iris-specifications-fingerprint.aspx.

233 Ibid.

234 "Police State: USPS, DOW, IRS, FEC, GSA, DEA, FBI, NSA, DoS, DoD Spying on
You," http://conservativeread.com/police-state-usps-doe-irs-fec-gsa-dea-fbi-nsa-dos-dod
-spying-on-you/.

235 http://www.bodymedia.com/the_interface.html

236 http://www.gizmag.com/facial-blood-vessel-identification/28287/

237 Sharon Gilbert, email to authors.

238 http://ieet.org/index.php/IEET/more/faggella20130731

239 http://www.naturalnews.com/040925_transhumanism_Ray_Kurzweil_cult.html#ixz
z2ajYQEJiK

240 http://www.rationalargumentator.com/index/

241 As quoted by Gennady Stolyarov, "Transhumanism and Mind Uploading Are Not the
Same," *The Rational Argumentator*, July 11, 2013.http://www.rationalargumentator
.com/index/blog/2013/07/transhumanism-uploading-not-same/.

242 Ibid.

243 https://www.youtube.com/watch?v=vG5jQKx-s1A

244 Ibid.

245 "Overview: The Convergence of ICT and Biology," http://www.humanbrainproject.
eu/discover/the-project/overview.

246 http://ec.europa.eu/digital-agenda/en/collective-awareness-platforms

247 Ibid.

248 http://blogs.scientificamerican.com/moral-universe/2013/07/29/empathy-as-a-choice/

249 http://en.memory-alpha.org/wiki/Lore

250 "Nano-scale: Future Materials and Devices," *Digital Agenda for Europe: A Europe 2020 Initiative*, http://ec.europa.eu/digital-agenda/events/cf/ict2013/item-display.cfm?id=10440.

251 http://www.whitehouse.gov/the-press-office/2013/04/02/fact-sheet-brain-initiative

252 https://www.science.org/content/article/brain-project-draws-presidential-interest#:
~:text=A%3A%20In%20September%202011%2C%20George,they%20proposed%
20a%20massive%2C%20coordinated

253 http://turingchurch.com/2013/03/03/the-real-importance-of-brain-mapping-research/

254 http://articles.economictimes.indiatimes.com/2013-08-05/news/41093205_1_memory
-implant-brain-false-memory

255 Script for "Jose Chung's from Outer Space," *X-Files*, as quoted by *Inside the X*, http://
www.insidethex.co.uk/transcrp/scrp320.htm.

256 http://ieet.org/index.php/IEET/more/deane20130805

NOTES

257 Ibid.

258 http://neuroethics.upenn.edu/index.php/penn-neuroethics-briefing/cognitive
-enhancement

259 http://www.welcomehome.org/rainbow/prophecy/hopi1.html

260 http://en.wikipedia.org/wiki/Electromagnetic_pulse

261 https://www.wnd.com/2013/02/sledgehammer-of-cyber-warfare-emp-attack/

262 https://www.dni.gov/files/documents/Global%20Trends_2025%20Global%20
Governance.pdf

263 http://www.npr.org/2011/08/19/139779301/foreign-policy-a-predictable-future-for
-technology

264 http://bits.blogs.nytimes.com/2013/04/28/disruptions-no-words-no-gestures-just
-your-brain-as-a-control-pad/

265 Waclaw Szybalski, *In Vivo and in Vitro Initiation of Transcription*, 405. In A. Kohn and
A. Shatkay (eds.), *Control of Gene Expression*, 23–24, and Discussion 404–405 (Szybalski's Concept of Synthetic Biology), 411–412, 415–417 (New York: Plenum, 1974).

266 "First Self-Replicating Synthetic Bacterial Cell," *J. Craig Venter Institute*, http://www
.jcvi.org/cms/research/projects/first-self-replicating-synthetic-bacterial-cell.

267 Peter E. Nielsen, "Triple Helix: Designing a New Molecule of Life," *Scientific American* (12/08) http://www.scientificamerican.com/article.cfm?id=triple-helix-designing
-a-new-molecule&ec=su_triplehelix.

268 Charles W. Colson, *Human Dignity in the Biotech Century* (Downers Grove, IL: Inter-
Varsity, 2004) 8.

269 C. Christopher Hook, *Human Dignity in the Biotech Century* (Downers Grove, IL:
InterVarsity, 2004) 80–81.

270 https://www.science.org/content/article/chain-reaction-spreads-gene-through-insects

271 Garreau, *Radical Evolution*, 116.

272 *Institute for Responsible Technology*, http://www.responsibletechnology.org/GMFree/
Home/index.cfm.

273 Francis Fukuyama, *Our Posthuman Future: Consequences of the Biotechnology Revolution*
(New York: Picador, 2002) 6.

274 Garreau, 106.

275 Garreau, 113–114.

276 "Carried Away with Convergence," New Atlantis (Summer 2003) 102–105, http://
www.thenewatlantis.com/publications/carried-away-with-convergence.

277 Summer 2003 issue of The New Atlantis, http://www.thenewatlantis.com/publications
/carried-away-with-convergence.

278 Bill Joy, "Why the Future Doesn't Need Us," Wired (April 2000) http://www.wired.com
/wired/archive/8.04/joy.html; emphasis added.

279 Mark Walker, "Ship of Fools: Why Transhumanism Is the Best Bet to Prevent the
Extinction of Civilization," Metanexus Institute (2/5/09), http://www.metanexus.net
/magazine/tabid/68/id/10682/Default.aspx.

280 https://www.christianheadlines.com/columnists/denison-forum/what-mission-impossible
-teaches-us-about-the-battle-for-our-world.html

281 https://www.huffpost.com/entry/stephen-hawking-ai-artificial-intelligence-dangers_n
 _6255338#:~:text=All%20that%20sounds%20impressive%2C%20for,increasing%20
 rate%2C%22%20Hawking%20said.

282 http://www.ict-21.ch/l4d/pg/file/read/895132/can-we-build-ai-without-losing-control
 -over-it-sam-harris-in-tedsummit--june-2016#:~:text=At%20a%20certain%20point%
 2C%20we,could%20get%20away%20from%20us.

283 https://www.npr.org/transcripts/547886482

284 Ibid.

285 George Orwell, *1984* (New York: Harcourt, 1949), 2.

286 Ibid., 156.

287 Paul Sloane, "How Star Trek Inspired an Innovation." Destination Innovation, 2020.
 Accessed November 6, 2020. https://www.destination-innovation.com/how-startrek
 -inspired-an-innovation-your-cell-phone/.

288 Sam Costello, "How the iPod Got its Name." Lifewire. December 10, 2019. Accessed
 November 6, 2020. https://www.lifewire.com/how-did-ipod-get-its-name-1999778.

289 Daniel Engber, "Who Made That Earbud?" *New York Times*. May 16, 2014. Accessed
 November 6, 2020. https://www.nytimes.com/2014/05/18/magazine/who-made-that
 -earbud.html.

290 Luke Westaway, "See the 2015 Tech That 'Back to the Future Part II' Predicted, and
 What It Missed." CNET Online. October 17, 2015. Accessed November 6, 2020.
 https://www.cnet.com/news/heres-the-technology-back-to-the-future-part-ii-predicted
 -and-what-it-missed/.

291 Fritz Lang, director, *Metropolis*. (Babelsberg Studios, Universal Film A.G.; 1927).

292 Alicia Prince, "15 Awesome Things You Didn't Know Siri Can Do For You." Lifehack
 Online. 2020. Accessed November 6, 2020. https://www.lifehack.org/articles/technology
 /15-awesome-things-you-didnt-know-siri-can-for-you.html.

293 Sharon Profis, "10 of the Best Things You Can Do with the Amazon Echo." CNET
 Online. February 13, 2017. Accessed November 6, 2020. https://www.cnet.com/how-to
 /the-best-things-you-can-do-with-amazon-echo/.

294 "9 Ways a Smart Home Can Improve Your Life." SmartThings Online. March 31,
 2015. Accessed November 6, 2020. https://blog.smartthings.com/news/roundups
 /9-ways-a-smart-home-can-improve-your-life/.

295 Ibid.

296 Ibid.

297 "Meet Kodomoroid, Japan's Android Newsreader." *Sydney Morning Herald*. June 25,
 2014. Accessed November 6, 2020. https://www.smh.com.au/technology/meet
 -kodomoroid-japans-android-newsreader-20140625-zskoq.html.

298 Rina Caballar, "What Is the Uncanny Valley?" IEEE Spectrum. November 6, 2019.
 Accessed November 6, 2020. https://spectrum.ieee.org/automaton/robotics/humanoids
 /what-is-the-uncanny-valley.

299 Todd Haselton, "Samsung's Neon 'Artificial Humans' Look Like Super-Realistic Video
 Chatbooks." CNBC Online. January 7, 2020. Accessed November 6, 2020. https://www
 .cnbc.com/2020/01/06/samsung-neon-artificial-human-announced-at-ces-2020.html.

300 John LaFia, "Intersections in Real Time," *Babylon 5*: Season 4, Episode 18. (Burbank, CA: Warner Brothers, 1997). DVD.

301 Ibid.

302 Loren Grush, "NASA Is Opening the Space Station to Commercial Business and More Private Astronauts." The Verge. June 7, 2019. Accessed November 6, 2020. https://www.theverge.com/2019/6/7/18656280/nasa-space-station-private-astronauts -commercial-business.

303 Ibid.

304 Kyle Mizokami, "Russia to Demonstrate Active Camouflage for Soldiers, Tanks." *Popular Mechanics*. August 20, 2018. Accessed November 6, 2020. https://www .popularmechanics.com/military/research/a22777736/russia-to-demonstrate-active -camouflage-for-soldiers-tanks/.

305 Talha Dar, "This Is How Invisibility Cloaks Work to Make You Disappear." Wonderful Engineering. May 13, 2015. November 6, 2020. https://wonderfulengineering.com /this-is-how-invisibility-cloaks-work-to-make-you-disappear/.

306 "Virtual Reality: Another World Within Sight." Iberdrola Online. 2020. Accessed November 6, 2020. https://www.iberdrola.com/innovation/virtual-reality.

307 Donald Cammell, director, *Demon Seed* (US: Metro-Goldwyn-Mayer; 1977). Amazon Prime, 94 min.

308 Scott Adams, "Can Humans and Computers Mate and Have Babies?" Scott Adams Says Online. February, 23, 2018. Accessed November 6, 2020. https://www.scott adamssays.com/2018/02/23/can-humans-computers-mate-babies/.

309 Ibid., Accessed November 20, 2020.

310 Diana Chandler, "Teen Is Youngest Legal Euthanasia Victim in Belgium." *Baptist Press Online*. September 19, 2016. Accessed November 9, 2020. https://www.baptistpress .com/resource-library/news/teen-is-youngest-legal-euthanasia-victim-in-belgium/.

311 John Carpenter, director, *They Live* (US: Alive Films, Larry Franco Productions; 1988). DVD, 94 min.

312 Ibid.

313 Amanda Prestigiacomo, "Abortionist Testifies: 'No Question' Babies Being Born Alive to Harvest Organs." *The Daily Wire Online*. September 26, 2019. Accessed October 8, 2019. https://www.dailywire.com/news/abortionist-testifies-no-question-babies-being -born-alive-to-harvest-organs.

314 Maggie Fox, "Planned Parenthood Video: Why Use Tissue from Aborted Fetuses?" *NBC News Online*. July 17, 2015. Accessed October 9, 2019. https://www.nbcnews.com /health/health-news/planned-parenthood-video-raises-question-why-use-tissue-fetuses -n393431.

315 Prestigiacomo, "Abortionist Testifies."

316 "Use of Aborted Fetal Tissue: Questions and Answers." *Charlotte Lozier Institute*. June 5, 2019. Accessed October 9, 2019. https://lozierinstitute.org/use-of-aborted-fetal-tissue -questions-answers/.

317 Ibid.

318 "Induced Abortion in the United States." *Guttmacher Institute Online*. 2019. Accessed October 2, 2019. https://www.guttmacher.org/fact-sheet/induced-abortion-united-states.

NOTES

319 Michael Bay, director, *The Island* (US: Dreamworks, Warner Bros.; 2005). DVD, 2hrs 16min.

320 Henry Greely, "Human Reproductive Cloning: The Curious Incident of the Dog in the Night-time." Stat News Online. February 21, 2020. Accessed November 6, 2020. https://www.statnews.com/2020/02/21/human-reproductive-cloning-curious-incident -of-the-dog-in-the-night-time/.

321 Robert Zemeckis, director, *Forrest Gump*. (US: Paramount Pictures, 1994). DVD, 2h 22min.

322 ColdFusion. "Deepfakes-Real Consequences." April 28, 2018. YouTube Video, 13:12. Accessed September 6, 2019. https://www.youtube.com/watch?v=dMF2i3A9Lzw.

323 Karl Stephan, "Seeing May Not Be Believing: AI Deepfakes and Trust in Media." *Mercatornet*. October 15, 2018. Accessed September 6, 2019. https://www.mercatornet.com /connecting/view/seeing-may-not-be-believing-ai-deepfakes-and-trust-in-media/21827.

324 Kathy Kiely, "Facebook Refusal to Curb Fake Nancy Pelosi Drunk Video Highlights Need for Responsibility." *USA Today*. May 28, 2019. Accessed September 10, 2019. https://www.usatoday.com/story/opinion/2019/05/28/facebook-fake-video-nancy -pelosi-drunk-responsibility-column/1249830001/.

325 Drew Harwell, "Faked Pelosi Videos, Slowed to Make Her Appear Drunk, Spread across Social Media." May 24, 2019. Accessed September 10, 2019. https://www. washingtonpost.com/technology/2019/05/23/faked-pelosi-videos-slowed-make-her -appear-drunk-spread-across-social-media/.

326 "Why It's Getting Harder to Spot a Deepfake Video." *CNN Online*. Accessed September 7, 2019. https://www.cnn.com/videos/business/2019/06/11/deepfake-videos-2020 -election.cnn.

327 Deepfakes. "Nicholas Cage: Mega Mix Two." February 2, 2019. YouTube: 2:05. Accessed September 10, 2019. https://www.youtube.com/watch?v=_Kuf1DLcXeo.

328 Usersub. "Nick Cage DeepFakes Movie Compilation." January 31, 2018. YouTube: 2:17. Accessed September 10, 2019. https://www.youtube.com/watch?v=BU9YAHigNx8.

329 "What Is a Deepfake?" *The Economist*. August 7, 2019. Accessed September 6, 2019. https://www.economist.com/the-economist-explains/2019/08/07/what-is-a-deepfake.

330 Ibid.

331 ColdFusion. "Deepfakes-Real Consequences." April 28, 2018. YouTube Video, 13:12. Accessed September 6, 2019. https://www.youtube.com/watch?v=dMF2i3A9Lzw.

332 Ibid.

333 Ibid.

334 Ibid.

335 Ibid.

336 Ibid.

337 Ibid.

338 Ibid.

339 Ibid.

340 Usersub. "Nick Cage DeepFakes Movie Compilation." January 31, 2018. YouTube Video: 2:17. Accessed September 10, 2019. https://www.youtube.com/watch?v=BU9 YAHigNx8&t=33s.

341 TheFakening. "Keanu Reeves as Forest Gump Deepfake—It's Breathtaking!" July 24, 2019. YouTube: 3:12. Accessed September 10, 2019. https://www.youtube.com /watch?v=cVljNVV5VPw&t=72s.

342 TheFakening. "President Donald Trump on Alec Baldwin Deepfake." February 19, 2019. YouTube: 0:42. Accessed September 10, 2019. https://www.youtube.com /watch?v=XdBDouKV828.

343 "What Is a deepfake?" *The Economist*.

344 Ibid.

345 Ibid.

346 The *New York Times*. "Deepfakes: Is This Video Even Real? NYT Opinion." August 14, 2019. YouTube Video: 3:38. Accessed September 10, 2019. https://www.youtube .com/watch?v=1OqFY_2JE1c.

347 John LaFia, "Intersections in Real Time." *Babylon 5*: Season 4, Episode 18. 1997; (Burbank, CA: Warner Brothers, 1997). DVD.

348 "What Is a Deepfake?" *The Economist*.

349 Ibid.

350 Ibid.

351 https://www.dailystar.co.uk/news/world-news/deepfake-videos-will-cause-worldwide -20574174

352 Ibid.

353 Karl Stephan, "Seeing May Not Be Believing: AI Deepfakes and Trust in Media." October 15, 2018. Accessed September 10, 2019. https://www.mercatornet.com/mobile /view/seeing-may-not-be-believing-ai-deepfakes-and-trust-in-media/21827.

354 Ibid.

355 Ibid.

356 J. M. Porup, "How and Why Deepfake Videos Work—And What Is at Risk." CSO US Online. April 10, 2019. Accessed September 10, 2019. https://www.csoonline. com /article/3293002/deepfake-videos-how-and-why-they-work.html.

357 Stephan, "Seeing May Not Be Believing."

358 Porup, "How and Why Deepfake Videos Work."

359 Ibid.

360 Victor Tangermann, "Congress Is Officially Freaking Out About Deepfakes." *Futurism Online*. June 13, 2019. Accessed September 10, 2019. https://futurism.com/congress -deepfakes-threat.

361 Ibid.

362 Jack Corrigan, "DARPA Is Taking on the Deepfake Problem." *Nextgov*. August 6, 2019. Accessed September 10, 2019. https://www.nextgov.com/emerging-tech/2019 /08/darpa-taking-deepfake-problem/158980/.

363 CNN Business. "Why It's Getting Harder to Spot Deepfake Videos." June 12, 2019. YouTube: 2:45. Accessed September 10, 2019. https://www.youtube.com/watch?v= wCZSMIwOG-o.

364 Ibid.

365 Corrigan, "DARPA Is Taking On the Deepfake Problem."

NOTES

366 Ibid.

367 Ibid.

368 Ibid.

369 Stephanie Sarkis, "11 Warning Signs of Gaslighting." *Psychology Today.* January 22, 2017. Accessed September 10, 2019. https://www.psychologytoday.com/us/blog/here -there-and-everywhere/201701/11-warning-signs-gaslighting.

370 "Dr. Claire Wardle: Co-Founder and Leader of First Draft." *Cyber Harvard.* September 25, 2018. Accessed September 10, 2019. https://cyber.harvard.edu/people/dr-claire -wardle.

371 The *New York Times.* "Deepfakes: Is This Video Even Real?"

372 Benjamin Powers, "'Deep Fake' Video Can Ruin Reputations. Can Life Logs Prevent That?" *Public Security Today Online.* November 28, 2018. Accessed September 10, 2019. https://publicsecurity.today/deep-fake-video-can-ruin-reputations-can-life-logs -prevent-that/.

373 Ibid.

374 Ibid.

375 Ibid.

376 https://finance.yahoo.com/news/worldcoin-says-allow-companies-governments-1049 48485.html

377 Ibid.

378 Ibid.

379 The *New York Times,* "Deepfakes: Is This Video Even Real?"

380 Ibid.

381 https://en.wikipedia.org/wiki/Year_Zero_(political_notion)

382 https://www.good.is/articles/george-washington-racist-mural

383 https://www.foxnews.com/us/which-confederate-statues-were-removed-a-running-list

384 Gary Lachman, *Politics and the Occult: The Left, the Right, and the Radically Unseen* (Quest Books; 1st Quest Ed edition, November 1, 2008), 97–98.

385 https://www.christianheadlines.com/contributors/mikaela-matthews/california-lawmakers -want-to-control-what-pastors-preach-about-lgbt-beliefs.html

386 Robert, Chesney and Danielle Keats Citron, "Deep Fakes: A Looming Challenge for Privacy, Democracy, and National Security," July 14, 2018, *107 California Law Review 1753 (2019); University of Texas Law; Public Law Research Paper No. 692; University of Maryland Legal Studies Research Paper No. 2018–21,* last revised December 17, 2019, last accessed September 1, 2023, https://papers.ssrn.com/sol3/papers.cfm?abstract_id =3213954.

387 Ibid.

388 Professor John McCarthy, "The Father of Ai. What Is AI?" http://jmc.stanford.edu /artificial-in- telligence/what-is-ai/index.html http://jmc.stanford.edu/artificial -intelligence/what-is-ai/in- dex.html (accessed: 17 April 2018).

389 Vincent James, "Google's AI Is Warming up for World Domination by Killing Inbox Spam," The Verge, July 10, 2015. https://www.theverge.com/2015/7/10/8927573 /google-ai-gmail-spam. Accessed April 23, 2018.

390 https://www.statista.com/statistics/420391/spam-email-traffic-share/

391 Ray Kurzweil, *The Age of Spiritual Machines: When Computers Exceed Human Intelligence* (New York: Penguin, 1998), https://archive.nytimes.com/www.nytimes.com /books/first/ k/kurzweil-machines.html. Accessed April 22, 2018.

392 Gary Stearman, "The Extraterrestrial Question," *Prophecy in the News* (March 2010) 10.

393 Hendrik Poinar, "Recipe for a Resurrection," *National Geographic* (May 2009) http:// ngm.nationalgeographic.com/2009/05/cloned-species/Mueller-text).

394 Chuck Missler and Mark Eastman, *Alien Encounters* (Coeur d'Alene, ID: Koinonia House, 1997) 275.

395 Louis Pauwells and Jacques Bergier. *The Dawn of Magic*, first published in France under the title *Le Matin des Magiciens*, (Paris: Editions Gallimard) 68.

396 Annette Yoshiko Reed, Fallen Angels and the History of Judaism and Christianity: The Reception of Enochic Literature (Cambridge, 2005) 214.

397 Ashlee Vance, "The Lifeboat Foundation: Battling Asteroids, Nanobots and A.I." *New York Times* (7/20/10) http://bits.blogs.nytimes.com/2010/07/20/the-lifeboat-foundation -battling-asteroids-nanobots-and-a-i/.

398 Ian Sample, "Global Disaster: Is Humanity Prepared for the Worst?" *Observer* (7/25/10) http://www.guardian.co.uk/science/2010/jul/25/disaster-risk-assessment -science.

399 Ibid.

400 Rory Cellan-Jones, "First Human 'Infected with Computer Virus,'" *BBC News*, (5/27/10). http://www.bbc.co.uk/news/10158517.

401 Hook, 92.

402 Ibid., 93.

403 Mihail Roco and William Sims Bainbridge, ed. *Converging Technologies for Improving Human Performance* (New York: Kluwer Academic, 2003; emphasis in original).

404 Garreau, 7–8.

405 Robert Jeffress, *The Divine Defense: Six Simple Strategies for Winning Your Greatest Battles* (Colorado Springs, CO: WaterBrook, 2006) 78.

406 John Horgon, "We're Cracking the Neural Code, the Brain's Secret Language," *Adbusters* (1/25/06) https://www.adbusters.org/the_magazine/63/Were_Cracking_the _Neural_Code_the_Brains_Secret_Language.html.

407 "Brain-Computer Interface Allows Person-to-Person Communication Through Power Of Thought," *ScienceDaily* (10/6/09) http://www.sciencedaily.com/releases/2009 /10/091006102637.htm.

408 Charles Ostman, *The Internet as an Organism: Emergent Human / Internet Symbiosis* (Vienna, Austria: Thirteenth European Meeting on Cybernetics and Systems Research at the University of Vienna, April 9–12, 1996) emphasis added.

409 Sue Bradley, email to Thomas Horn.

410 Sounding the Codes, 2007. http://www.thecenteroflight.net.

411 Robert Maguire, Charles J. Doe, *Commentary on John Bunyan's The Holy War* (2009) 11.

412 Ibid., 7.

413 Frank Jordas, "Study on Cell Phone Link to Cancer Inconclusive," *Associated Press* (2010) http://abcnews.go.com/print?id=10668283.

414 "How Technology May Soon 'Read' Your Mind," *CBS 60 Minutes* (June 2009) http://www.cbsnews.com/stories/2008/12/31/60minutes/main4694713.shtm.

415 "Remote Control Brain Sensor," BBC (November 2002) http://news.bbc.co.uk/2/hi/health/2361987.stm.

416 R. Douglas Fields, "Mind Control by Cell Phone," *Scientific American* (May 2008) http://www.scientificamerican.com/article.cfm?id=mind-control-by-cell.

417 Liane Young, Joan Albert Camprodon, et al, "Disruption of the Right Temporo-Parietal Junction with Transcranial Magnetic Stimulation Reduces the Role of Beliefs in Moral Judgments," Proceedings of the National Academy of Sciences (March 2010) http://www.eurekalert.org/pub_releases/2010-03/miot-mjc032510.php.

418 Mark Baard, "EM Field, Behind Right Ear, Suspends Morality," *Sci-Tech Heretic* (March 2009) http://heretic.blastmagazine.com/2010/03/em-field-behind-right-ear-suspends-morality.

419 Stephen King, *Cell* (New York: Simon and Shuster, 2006).

420 Jeremy Hsu, "Video Gamers Can Control Dreams, Study Suggests," *LiveScience* (5/25/10) http://www.livescience.com/culture/video-games-control-dreams-100525.html.

421 Aaron Saenz, "Is the Movie 'Inception' Getting Closer to Reality?" (7/15/10) http://singularityhub.com/2010/07/15/is-the-movie-inception-getting-closer-to-reality-video/.

422 Naomi Darom, "Will Scientists Soon Be Able to Read Our Minds?" Haaretz http://www.haaretz.com/magazine/week-s-end/will-scientists-soon-be-able-to-read-our-minds-1.291310.

423 Sharon Weinberger, "The 'Voice of God' Weapon Returns," *Wired* (12/21/07) http://www.wired.com/dangerroom/2007/12/the-voice-of-go/.

424 Joshua Ramo, "The Big Bank Theory," *Time* (4/27/98) http://www.time.com/time/printout/0,8816,988228,00.html.

425 https://www.rt.com/news/561379-world-economic-forum-implants/

426 Eric Bland, "Part-Human, Part-Machine Transistor Devised," *Discovery News* (6/2/10) http://news.discovery.com/tech/transistor-cell-membrane-machine.html, emphasis added.

427 Ashlee Vance, "Merely Human? That's So Yesterday," *New York Times* (6/11/10) http://www.nytimes.com/2010/06/13/business/13sing.html?_r=1.

428 Wesley J. Smith, "Pitching the New Transhumanism Religion in the NYT," *First Things* (6/14/10) http://www.firstthings.com/blogs/secondhandsmoke/2010/06/14/pitching-the-new-transhumanism-religion-in-the-nyt/.

429 Gregory Jordan, "Apologia for Transhumanist Religion," *Journal of Evolution and Technology, Published by the Institute for Ethics and Emerging Technologies* (2005) http://jetpress.org/volume15/jordan2.html.

430 Brent Waters, "The Future of the Human Species (Part 1)," http://www.cbhd.org/content/future-human-species.

431 As quoted by C. Christopher Hook in "The Techno Sapiens Are Coming," *Christianity Today* (January 2004) http://www.christianitytoday.com/ct/2004/january/1.36.html.

432 Ibid.

433 Rod Dreher, "Vatican Bioethics Document and Competing Moral Visions," *BeliefNet* (12/12/08) http://blog.beliefnet.com/crunchycon/2008/12/vatican-bioethics-document-and.html.

NOTES

434 C. S. Lewis, *The Abolition of Man*, http://www.columbia.edu/cu/augustine/arch/lewis/abolition3.htm.

435 "Ethics of Human Enhancement," *Human Enhancement Ethics Group* http://www.humanenhance.com/category/news-and-events/press-releases/.

436 Book of Enoch 6:1–8, (Oxford: The Clarendon Press) emphasis added.

437 Deborah McComber, "Robert E. Lee," *Berean Bible Heritage Church* http://berean bibleheritage.org/extraordinary/lee_robert.php.

438 "City Upon a Hill," *Wikipedia*, http://en.wikipedia.org/wiki/City_upon_a_Hill.

439 Dr. Albert Mohler Jr., "Moralistic Therapeutic Deism—the New American Religion," Christian Post, (4/18/05). http://www.christianpost.com/article/20050418/moralistic-therapeutic-deism-the-new-american-religion/pageall.html.

440 Gregory A. Boyd, *God at War: The Bible and Spiritual Conflict* (Downer's Grove, IL: InterVarsity, 1997) 19, 55.

Printed in the USA
CPSIA information can be obtained
at www.ICGtesting.com
CBHW030742260224
4587CB00013BA/15